The 1985 Price Guide to Crested China

Sandy Andrews
and
Nicholas Pine

Milestone Publications

Published by Milestone Publications
Goss & Crested China Ltd,
62 Murray Road,
Horndean, Portsmouth, Hants. PO8 9JL.

Design Brian Iles
Photography Michael Edwards Studio
Typeset by Inforum Ltd, Portsmouth
Printed and bound in Great Britain by
R. J. Acford, Industrial Estate, Chichester, Sussex

British Library Cataloguing in Publication Data

Andrews, Sandy
  The 1985 price guide to crested china.
  1. Porcelain—Prices
  I. Title   II. Pine, Nicholas
  388.4'37382   NK4373

ISBN 0 903852 44 6

Contents

Acknowledgements

This catalogue could not appear without several hundred thoughtful collectors taking the trouble to notify us of pieces not listed in **Crested China**, published in 1980, to which this Guide is the sequel.

In particular, we would like to especially thank the Riley family who have tirelessly assisted in so many ways over the years. A large proportion of the new models listed have been provided by Robin and Philip Riley and this book would be sadly lacking without their help.

Jutta and Günter Griebel of Germany were kind enough to supply much new information on German manufacturers of crested china, including pages from original catalogues which have helped us to identify German wares with much more confidence. We would like to say a special thank you to them for their help.

We also wish to thank Len Harris and Brenda and Alf Dixon who have conscientiously forwarded regular lists of new pieces almost on a weekly basis.

The following collectors have all forwarded lists, new information, photographs, further information when asked, and we are extremely grateful to each and every one.

G. Abrey, Mrs P. Atkinson, Mrs J. Barnes, D.H. Bates, J.E. Belger,
C.W. Bell, Mrs P.A. Belton, S.J. Bennett, G. Bishop, H. Bloomfield,
Mrs B. Bowker, R.E.J. Brazier, Mrs M. Briggs, C.H.A. Brown,
Mrs J.M. Brown, Mrs S.N. Brundle, Mr and Mrs J. Bullock, A.O. Carter,
R.J. Carter, B. Cover, Mrs F.L. Cox, P.R. Cox, D.F. Cremer, Mrs J. Dadds,
Mrs E.M. Davies, A. Donnelly, L.J. Dunn, Mr and Mrs M. Elliott,
Miss C.E. Fellows, Mrs D. Ferguson, G. Flett, Mrs Geddes,
Mrs J.M. Gladwell, S.K. Godly, Mrs M. Green, J. Gribben,
D.T.C. Gulliver, J.R. Hampton, R.A. Harvey,
Canon B.H. Hawkins, Mrs B. Hewlett, K. Hill, A.F. Hirons,
Mrs K. Hodgson, B.W. Hollman, T. Hood, Mrs Hunt, D.K. James,
Mrs A.L. Jarman, Ms C. Johns, Mrs P.P. Jones, R. Jones, Ms V. Juniper,
G. Karon, Mrs J.M. Kenton, Miss R. Kingston, M.A. Larkin, D.J. Leach,
Mr and Mrs W. Llewelyn, G.J. Loveday, T. Mabe, Mrs B. Malin,
Mrs W. Maynard, Mrs R. Merrill, Mrs V. Miles, Mrs S. Milroy,
S.P. Molyneux, A.M. Munday, Mrs S. Munday, Mrs J. McGregor,

Mrs P. McLean, P. Owen, Mrs E. Pare, B.S. Pike, Mrs J. Pinder,
E. Pote, W. Pye, Mrs A. Reader, G.M. Du Sautay, M. Shears,
R. Sheridan, Mrs H. Simpson, Mrs J. Sinclair, V. Skitterall, R.H. Slater,
Mrs J. Stonelake, Mrs C. Taggart, T. Usher, B. Waines, Mrs C. Waller,
Mr and Mrs M. Wallington, A.W. Webley, J.P. Whipp, W. Will,
Miss M. Williams, S. Williams, Mrs R.A. Woolford, H.J. Yallop,
Mrs J.D. Yarnall.

Finally a special thank you to Lynda Pine who has toiled tirelessly on the
manuscript. Without the benefit of her researches and knowledge this
book would contain many more inaccuracies than it does.

**Please continue to send details of any new models to
Milestone Publications for inclusion in future editions of 'The Price
Guide to Crested China'.**

Preface

'The Price Guide to Crested China' should be read in conjunction with 'Crested China' by Sandy Andrews, the standard work on the subject. The prices of W. H. Goss china models will be found in 'The 1984 Price Guide to Goss China' by Nicholas Pine, published as the companion volume to this guide.

This price guide is essentially a listing of all the pieces in 'Crested China' without the full descriptions given in that volume, to which have been added some two thousand pieces which have been notified since 1980. The total number of recorded pieces is now 6,300. A number of pieces have been omitted from this edition that are not now believed to exist. It you have accurate information on any piece that cannot be located in this Guide, please inform the publishers in order that it may be included in a future edition. To find the value of any piece first look up the correct manufacturer; this will be found by reference to the mark on the base of the piece in question. All items are listed in the order of the headings given on page 19.

This guide is designed to represent average prices that one would expect to pay from a dealer. Some criticism of the first 1981 edition of this guide was voiced by some who thought some prices on the low side. The reasons for this were that the market was rising strongly when the prices were set, and between preparation and publication, the market continued to rise. This trend continued during 1981 and 1982 until by the end of that year prices in this guide were often looking decidedly low.

As a matter of editorial policy, prices in the previous edition were not set on the high side as it is considered more important that a collector should not pay too much for a piece rather than he miss the odd bargain.

During 1983, some boiling over of prices was noted, particularly for pieces whose increase in value could only be described as meteoric during the previous few years. The market has now been stable for around a year and the prices in this 1985 guide have each been given a good deal of thought.

They represent the current prices charged by Goss and Crested China Ltd. as at April 1984 and are, in our opinion, fair and true values of the current retail selling price, net of any Value Added Tax.

Goss & Crested China Ltd. are the leading dealers in heraldic porcelain and whilst we do not have every piece we do have a constantly changing stock of several thousand pieces to interest the collector. We produce 'Goss & Crested China' an illustrated monthly sales list containing 24 pages of items for sale. This is available by subscription, please enquire for details of this and our range of fifteen different publications on the subject of heraldic china. Visitors are welcome to view our stock at any time, but preferably by prior appointment please.

Full details of all the listed factories, their histories, downfalls and details of their numbering systems, if any, may be found in 'Crested China' and are not repeated here.

Any particular decorations will add value to a piece, i.e. transfer printed scenes, views, birds, animals or floral decorations or indeed some pieces may be found solely coloured in blue, red or yellow. A premium of between £2 and £10 should be added for any piece having an unusual or attractive decoration or verse. Inscriptions have been omitted from the guide unless they are essential in determining the nature of the piece. Some models have military inscriptions, i.e. details of particular engagements during the Great War. For such pieces, usually produced by Savoy, £4–£8 should be added. Matching crests are very few and far between on models produced by factories other than W.H. Goss and may be disregarded. In the case of buildings, monuments and the like a small premium should be paid for the correct arms although most items will be found to display local crests as they were usually sold in those areas.

Much domestic ware was produced, often carrying coats-of-arms as an afterthought as much as by design. Such pieces, including cups and saucers, plates, milk jugs, large pots and vases, are only worth around £1–£2 each but tend to be the most overpriced items at fairs, markets etc. Such ware is not very collectable. Ordinary small vases, jugs, pots, ewers, etc. from any factory are worth 50p–£1.00 and named models £1.50–£2.50.

Many similar pieces carry different factory marks on their bases, for example Arcadian, Swan and Clifton were all made by Arkinstall & Son Ltd. Where the same piece could have been produced with several different marks the reader's attention is drawn in such cases to the names of the factories and chapters under which one should look if the piece cannot be found listed under the factory or mark shown on the base. To aid the reader a table of the principal manufacturers of Crested China and their trademarks, subsidiaries and firms using their products will be found on page 16. Manufacturers were constantly merging, being taken over, ceasing production and selling their designs and moulds to other potters so pieces constantly appear with different marks.

Many items which are normally found coloured can also be found white, either with or without gilding; and sometimes having no factory mark. Such items would normally be worth approximately $^1/_2$ to $^2/_3$ of the value of the coloured version. Likewise, a piece normally found white glazed only would be increased in value by $^1/_2$ to $^3/_4$ should a coloured variety be found.

New items are constantly coming to light but after assuming that a piece is a new model as it is not listed under the appropriate heading in this guide, one must refer to *Crested China* or the table of principal manufacturers on page 16 and check under all other relevant factory headings. Many known models are now being seen with different factory marks, these are all worth the same as identical pieces listed elsewhere.

One point that needs to be clearly made is that pieces from one factory are not worth more than those from another. For example, Savoy is not worth any more than Swan or for that matter Carlton, Grafton or Shelley etc. Over the years one has often been told by amateur dealers and stallholders that Arcadian is worth more than other factories. This is not so. The only reasons for the constant uttering of this myth I would venture are that firstly Arkinstall & Son Ltd. were more prolific than most and that there are hundreds of Arcadian pieces to be found, dealers therefore would usually have a number in stock and these would be preferred to items with no factory mark or a lesser known one – in fact little-known marks are definitely rarer, but, alas they are not worth a premium either. Secondly, this fallacy has been passed on over the years when there were no books or other information available to disprove it and in this vacuum of knowledge, such gems as this have thrived. I am pleased to say that I have heard it little during recent years.

The value of crested china may be determined by three factors: theme, rarity and condition – in that order. The most popular themes are: Great War; Buildings; Animals (including birds); Transport; Memorials; Monuments; Statues; Cartoon/Comedy Characters; Comic/Novelty; Sport; Alcohol and Musical Instruments. This list is by no means exhaustive but it does cover the main spheres of interest among collectors. Rarity is self explanatory; a 'Bomb Thrower' is rarer than a 'Cenotaph' and therefore it is worth more. These two factors may be summed up as 'Collectability', for example a scarce animal would be worth far more than, say, a unique billiken because there is far more demand for the animal from theme collectors. Thus supply and demand play an important part. It should always be borne in mind that even the most attractive and rare crested cup and saucer will never be worth more than a few pounds whereas a rare military piece could command as much as £400.00

Condition is the third factor which affects price. Whilst not as important as with Goss china, it still affects the value of an item considerably and the following remarks should be noted. Crested china produced by other manufacturers was never as fine as that of the Goss factory. William Henry Goss conducted over one thousand experiments which took many years before he perfected the parian body which he used as his medium. The other producers were not interested in the high standards that Goss set himself, they were only concerned with jumping on the crested china bandwagon and producing wares as quickly and as cheaply as possible for the profitable souvenir trade which was rapidly developing. Some factories were better than others and Grafton in particular produced some very detailed and delicate models. Most foreign ware (mainly German or Czechoslovakian) is of poor quality, tending to be rather crude and heavy, therefore worth less as a general rule than English china, although this itself was usually 'pot' or some other similar rather grey coloured material, only occasionally having the same degree of whiteness as Goss.

Having made the point that crested china factories were not that particular about the quality of their products it follows that many pieces were substandard even before leaving the factory. The producers were not usually too concerned about this and many pieces were sold having firing cracks, chips (under the glaze) or other flaws; rubbed, poorly applied or non-existent gilding, imperfect transfers, coats-of-arms and inscriptions as well as having indifferent glazing. This was sometimes incomplete and often heavy and too liberally coated, leading to a green/grey tinge in grooves and internal corners where the glaze has built up. This latter occurrence often leads to minor glazing cracks appearing in such build ups of glaze. These do not affect value. In addition, pieces were often wrongly named on the base.

Minor defects such as those given above are commonplace and do not affect value although naturally a piece completely free of such manufacturers' imperfections would be preferable. Such items however number less than 10% of all crested china produced so to restrict a collection to these pristine items only would be frustrating if not impossible. If one seeks perfection then W.H. Goss is the only factory that can be considered by the serious collector, indeed, many if not most Goss collectors consider other crested china to be 'rubbish' and would not dream of collecting it themselves. It does however have charms other than those of complete perfection to commend it. Pieces with particularly bad factory defects were often sold off without factory mark, crest or inscription, such items are worth around $2/3$ of the price of a normal item.

Damage occuring in the period subsequent to manufacture such as cracks or chips affect value considerably and any piece so damaged would only be worth between $1/4$ to $1/2$ of the perfect price. The same applies with restoration, whilst a restored item looks better than a damaged one it is worth no more and if the restoration is bad then it is worth less. These points should be borne in mind when buying from market stalls, antique fairs and shops where dealers seem to disregard damage when endeavouring to sell their wares. Damaged items are usually overpriced, if indeed the damage has even been noticed by the dealer concerned; it must be fully allowed for in the price when buying. It is only when one comes to sell that the wisdom of this advice will become apparent.

No forecast can be made as to whether prices will rise or fall in the future, that will depend upon economic factors which cannot be discussed here. During the last decade however, prices have multiplied approximately ten times with the rarer items increasing many times faster than the smaller pots and vases and the more common shapes. Over the years crested china has been a very good investment with all the fun of collecting thrown in. The publication of 'Crested China' by Sandy Andrews has substantially increased interest in the subject and this price guide can only further that interest. Three major London auction houses now include crested china in with their sales of Goss and overseas interest is on the increase.

Milestone Publications would be pleased to hear of any pieces or unusual or notable crests or decorations (apart from non-models and domestic ware) that are not mentioned in the listings in this guide or in the main book for inclusion in a future supplement.

Should you wish to sell please note that the prices in this guide are used as a basis for purchasing and that we will pay up to and often above half the listed price. Please send us a list of the pieces that are for sale or exchange stating in each case the factory, height, crest and condition in order to receive our individual offers.

Nicholas Pine

Manufacturers and Trade Marks

The myriad of different manufacturers, wholesalers, retailers, marks and names found on the bases of crested china is confusing even to the authors, who have only in recent years been able to work out with some reasonable degree of accuracy who made what and for whom.

There are perhaps only eight main and a further two medium sized manufacturers. These are followed by some eighty to one hundred very minor firms, which are usually only responsible for the production of a handful of pieces, and often only then as a sideline to their main areas of manufacture.

In order that the original manufacturer of a piece may be ascertained more easily, the following table has been included to aid identification. Under the name of the manufacturer that firm's main trade name has been given in bold in each case. Under this name will be found all known trade marks that can be attributed to that firm.

Therefore, if you have a piece that does not appear in the listings for that particular mark, try looking it up in the following table and check under firstly, the main and then under the subsidiary marks until it is located, you can then note the value of the item. Please do not forget to let the authors know about any models which are not listed under their own factory mark in order that they might be included in future editions.

Table of the principal manufacturers of Crested China and their Trade Marks, Subsidiaries and other firms using their products

Arkinstall & Son
Arcadian China
Albion China
Aldwych China
Amber China
Avon China
Boots
Carmen China
Clifton
Coronet Ware
Fords China
FL
FP & S

The Griffin China
Iceni Crest China
JW
Kensington China
One and All
Palatine China
Queens Crest China
R & L
Robinson & Leadbeater
Raphael China
Snowdon China
Sussex China S.P. Co.
Swan China

Vectis
Victis
Warwick China
Waverley China
Wembley China

Belleek Pottery
Belleek Pottery
Shamrock China

Wiltshaw & Robinson Ltd.
Carlton Ware
Aldwych China
Cambrian China
Caledonia Heraldic China
Craven China
Crown China
Cyclone
Lion China
Mother Shipton
Syren China

Sampson, Hancock & Sons
Corona
Alexandra
Anglo-Heraldic Co.
The Duchess China
Exceller
Granic China
Grosvenor Ware
Heraldic China
Raleigh China
Regency Ware
Sussex China

E. Hughes & Co.
Fenton
E. Hughes & Co.
Royal China

Taylor & Kent
Florentine
Albion China
Atlas Heraldic China
C & SC
Caledonia China
Cascade China
Challenge China
Cyclone
The Dainty Ware
Doric Herald
Filey China
Gladstone China

Ionic Heraldic
Premier
Taylor & Kent

Charles Schmidt & Co.
Gemma
Fairyware
Ness

Alfred B. Jones & Sons Ltd.
Grafton China
C.L. Reis
Diamond China
Herald China
Herald Series
King China
Wil-Wat China

Wm. Kutzscher & Co.
Impero
Princess China
St. George China
W.H.H. and S.
Unmarked
Saxony
Made in Saxony

Edwin Leadbeater
Leadbeater Art China
Marine Art China
Nornesford China
Panorama

James MacIntyre
J. MacIntyre
Argonauta Porcelain
Caledonia China

Max Emanuel & Co.
Mosanic
Maxim China
Unity China
Austria
Czechoslovakia
Foreign
Germany

Nautilus Porcelain Co.
Nautilus Porcelain
Celtic Porcelain

Podmore China Co.
Podmore
Strand China

William Ritchie & Son Ltd.
Porcelle
Empire China
Ivora Ware
Mermaid
W.R. and S.

Robinson & Leadbeater
R & L
Royal Ivory Porcelain
Victoria Porcelain

Birks, Rawlins & Co.
Savoy China
Aldwych China
Birks China
Bow China
Caledonia Heraldic China
Diamond China
Endor China
Niagara Art China
Patriotic China
Queens China
Queens Ware

Wileman & Co.
Shelley China
The Foley China

R.H. & S.L. Plant Ltd.
Tuscan China
Nornesford China
Rowena
Shamrock Crest China

Charles Waine & Co.
Venetia China
CW & Co.
Etruscan China
Kyle Series

James Reeves
Victoria China
Botolph China

English Emporium China
Gothic

Hewitt and Leadbeater
Willow Art China
Abbey China
Alexandra
Balmoral China
Cable China
Caledonia Heraldic China
Clays
Curzon Art
Devonia Art China
Diamond China
Disa Art China
Elite China Series
Famous Henley China
H & L
H & S
JBC
Kingsway Art China
Kingsway Crest China
Lochinvar
Marine Art China
Mayfair
The Milton China
Norfolk Crest China
Oxford Art China
Pearl Arms China
Regis
Roman Bath China
St. Pauls
Star Bazaar Art China
Sussex Ware
Thistle China
Tourist Art China
Towy China
Tudor Arms China
Waterfall Heraldic
Wilco Series
Willow China
W and R
Wy Knot
Wy Not

Introduction to Trademarks and Recorded Models

These have been arranged by marks in alphabetical order, with manufacturer's name, if known, and recorded models after each mark.

The models have been grouped into types of souvenirs and have been arranged for the most part in the order in which they would have been made. The headings are as follows:

Unglazed/Parian
Parian busts are also found under this heading.

Ancient Artefacts
Models of historic interest as produced by W.H. Goss.

Buildings – Coloured

Buildings – White
Including bridges

Monuments (including crosses)

Historical/Folklore

Traditional/National Souvenirs
These have been listed in the following order: British, England, Ireland, Scotland, Wales, other countries.

Seaside Souvenirs
These have been listed in the following order: Bathing Machines, Crafts, Fishermen/Lifeboatmen, Lighthouses, Shells, Luggage, People and Punches.

Countryside

Animals
These listings include animals which are really regional symbols such as the Sussex

Pig. Most collectors would include these in an animal collection.

Birds (including Eggs)
These listings also include regional or national emblems such as the Kiwi.

Great War
These models have been grouped as follows: Personnel, Aeroplanes/Airships/Zeppelins, Ships/Submarines, Armoured Cars/Red Cross Vans/Tanks, Guns/Mortars, Small arms, Shells, Bombs, Grenades, Mines, Torpedoes, Personal Equipment, Memorabilia and Memorials. (Florence Nightingale statues are always included in Great War collections although she died before 1914. Certainly the statue was offered for sale at the same time, so it is listed under this heading).

Home/Nostalgic

Comic/Novelty

Cartoon/Comedy Characters

Alcohol

Sport

Musical Instruments

Transport

'Modern' Equipment
'Modern', that is, at the time it was made.

Miscellaneous

Miniature Domestic

Domestic

Under these headings models are listed alphabetically, if that is possible. All inscriptions and verses are printed in *italics*.

If a model is best described by its inscription this will be placed at the beginning of an entry in *italics*.

Sizes are height unless otherwise stated.

All values are given in £ and p in Sterling currency.

The 1985 Price Guide to Crested China

has been designed and produced as a revision to **Crested China**, the base reference work. This Price Guide contains additional information which has come to light since 1980.

Crested China Manufacturers

Abbey China

For mark see *Crested China*, p. 19.

Trademark used by Hewitt & Leadbeater for fancy goods retailer or wholesaler in Tewkesbury.
Hewitt & Leadbeater usually used the trademarks Willow or Willow Art.
Stock numbers where known as Willow Art.

Seaside Souvenirs
Lighthouse Pepper Pot. 110mm.   2.25
   (There is almost certainly a
   matching Salt Pot.)

Birds
Peewit posy holder. 78mm long.   4.00

Animals
Cat, sitting, one ear down.
   102mm.   7.50

Home/Nostalgic
Grandfather Clock, inscribed:
   *Make use of time let not advantage
   slip. Shakespeare*. No. 149.
   140mm.   8.25

Cartoon/Comedy Characters
Baby with arms outstretched,
   inscribed: *Cheerio*. Some
   colouring on face. 125mm.   8.25

Miscellaneous
Schoolboy's Cap. 62mm long.   10.50

Adderleys

For marks see *Crested China*, p. 19.

Trademark used by Adderleys Ltd., Daisy Bank Pottery, Longton.

Range of 'smalls' to commemorate
   the Great War – inscribed: 1914
   WAR EDITION.   4.00

Alba Pottery

Trademark used by a British Pottery for exported goods. The only model found has an Honduras crest.

Monuments

Iona Cross. 110mm.   4.00

Albion China

For marks see *Crested China*, p. 21.

Trademark used by Robinson and Beresford, Baltimore Works, Longton. Subsequently a branch of J.A. Robinson Ltd.

Ancient Artefacts

Glastonbury Bowl. No. 55. 50mm.   1.75
Lincoln Jack, inscribed *Model of the
    Lincoln Jack from original in
    museum*. No. 50. 63mm.   2.25
*Loving cup originated by Henry of
    Navarre King of France*. 2 or 3
    handled. No. 579. 40mm.   2.50
Newbury Leather Bottle. No. 83.
    65mm.   1.75
Silchester Vase. No. 54. 60mm.   1.75

Historical/Folklore

Ancient coaching hat, model of.
    No. 687. 65mm long.   6.00

Albion China

For marks see *Crested China*, p. 21.

Trademark used on china made for a Scottish
wholesaler by Taylor and Kent (Ltd.),
Florence Works, Longton. (Usual trademark Florentine.)

Ancient Artefacts
Puzzle Jug. 67mm.   3.50

Buildings – White
Blackpool Tower. 120mm.   5.50

Historical/Folklore
Mother Shipton. 72mm.   4.00

Traditional/National Souvenirs
Lancashire Clog. 88mm long.   4.00
Welsh Hat with blue band. 62mm.   3.00

Seaside Souvenirs
Lighthouse on rocky base.
    100mm.   3.00
Portmanteau. 60mm long.   2.25
Yacht. 130mm.   7.50

Animals
Cat, sitting, very furry coat. 90mm.   7.50
Dolphin Jug. 100mm.   3.00
Elephant kneeling. 88mm long.   6.50
Frog Jug. No details of size.   4.00
Hare. 95mm long.   7.50
Pig, standing. 90mm long.   8.25

Birds
Giant Hen, brooding. 91mm long.   6.50
Pelican Jug. 83mm long.   4.00
Swan Posy Holder. 80mm.   2.25

Great War
Monoplane with 4-bladed prop.
    170mm long.   26.00
Shell. 75mm.   2.25
Bury St. Edmunds Bomb.   4.50

Home/Nostalgic
Firebucket. 65mm.   3.00
Old Armchair, The with verse.
    85mm.   5.50
Lamp. 69mm.   2.25
Pillar Box. 76mm.   5.50

Miscellaneous
Carboy. 76mm.   2.25

Miniature Domestic
Coffee pot. 76mm.   3.00
Tea Pot. 60mm.   4.00

Aldwych China

For marks see *Crested China*, p. 23.

Trade name used by the retailer, Samuels, The Strand, London on crested china manufactured by Arkinstall and Son Ltd. (usual trademark Arcadian), Birks, Rawlins and Co. (usual trademark Savoy) and Wiltshaw and Robinson Ltd. (usual trademark Carlton).

Stock numbers where known coincide with those used on other models made by above firms.

Aldwych (A and S) Models

Mark used on wares manufactured by Arcadian. See *Crested China*, pp. 26/27.

Parian/unglazed
Bust of George V. 130mm.   30.00
Bust of Queen Mary. 130mm.   30.00

Monument
Nelson's Column. 169mm.   40.00

Animals
Elephant. 75mm long.   6.50
Tortoise. 72mm long.   4.00

Birds
Cock, standing, inscribed: *Cock o'
the south*. 100mm.   7.50

Great War
Cannon Shell, inscribed: *Jack
Johnson*. 90mm.   4.00
Steel Helmet with EP on side.
70mm long and only 24mm
high.   17.50

Home/Nostalgic
Grandfather clock, inscribed.
108mm.   10.50

Miscellaneous
Horseshoe. 55mm long.   2.00

Aldwych (BR and Co) Models

BR & Co. mark as used by Savoy. See *Crested China*, p. 216.

Most pieces found with this mark are small vases etc. Only one model has been recorded.

Countryside
Acorn, model of. No. 110. 56mm.   2.50

Aldwych (W & R) Models

W & R mark as used by Carlton Ware. See *Crested China*, p. 76.

Monuments
Nelson's Column with four lions
at base. 165mm.   40.00

Great War
Tank inscribed: *HMLS Creme de
Menthe*. 150mm long.   23.00

Alexandra China

For further marks see *Crested China*, p. 23.

Trademark used by a wholesaler, china manufactured by several leading producers of crested china.

Ancient Artefacts
Aberdeen Bronze Pot.	1.75
Bronze Bowl. 50mm.	1.75

Buildings – White
Marble Arch. 75mm.	8.50
Bottle Oven. No. 233. 82mm.	7.50
St. Paul's Cathedral. 2 sizes:	
90mm.	15.00
135mm.	20.00
Tower Bridge. 140mm long.	21.75
Westminster Abbey, West Front.	
3 sizes: 90mm.	13.00
114mm.	13.00
130mm.	17.50

Monuments
Cleopatra's Needle. 130mm.	56.50
Monument, The. 159mm.	56.50
Nelson's Monument, Trafalgar Square. 165mm.	40.00
Peter Pan Statue. 144mm.	47.50

Historical/Folklore
Burns and Highland Mary (also impressed WILLOW). 117mm.	18.50
Man in the Moon. 35mm.	12.50

Traditional/National Souvenirs
Welsh Harp. No. 292. 95mm.	4.00

Seaside Souvenirs
Canoe. 106mm long.	4.00
Shell. No. 56. 83mm long.	2.25

Animals
Black Cat in Boot. 93mm long.	21.75
Cat, sitting, with ruff of fur. 100mm.	7.50
Cat, sitting, very long neck. 68mm.	5.50
Cat, Manx. 75mm long.	13.00
Dog, Bulldog, standing. 63mm.	8.75
Can be found inscribed *'Duggie Haig'* with Union Jack on back. 63mm. If so, add	100.00
Dog, Scottie with glengarry. 88mm.	6.50
Fish. 120mm long.	1.75
Fish Vase. 63mm.	1.75
Monkey holding coconut. 75mm.	6.50
Pig, standing. 80mm long.	8.75
Polar Bear. 185mm long.	30.00
Rabbit, crouching, ears back. 67mm long.	3.50
Shetland Pony. 110mm long.	13.00

Birds
Swan. 51mm.	2.25
Wise Owl with verse. 110mm.	8.75

Great War
Monoplane, with movable prop. 145mm long.	30.00
British Airship on stand. 130mm long.	13.00
Battleship with 2 guns forward and 1 aft. 120mm long.	10.50
Lusitania. 163mm long.	50.00
Submarine, inscribed: *E4*. 110mm long.	8.75
Red Cross Van. 98mm long.	17.50
Tank with inset trailing wheels. 100mm long.	10.50
Renault Tank. 115mm long.	55.00
Field Gun. 130mm long.	11.00
Torpedo. 150mm long.	21.75
Bell Tent. 85mm.	5.50
Flash Light. 88mm.	4.00
Ghurka Knife. 140mm long.	13.00
Ad Astra. RAF Memorial with inscription: *Unveiled by HRH Prince of Wales July 16th 1923*. 170mm.	65.00

Cenotaph, inscribed: *The Glorious
Dead MCMXLV, MCMXLX*,
with green wreaths. 2 sizes:

145mm.	4.75
184mm.	6.50

Edith Cavell Memorial London.

2 sizes: 115mm	9.50
155mm.	12.50

Florence Nightingale Statue.

146mm.	10.50

Home/Nostalgic

Baby, in Bootee. 76mm.	6.50
Chair, high backed. 105mm.	12.00
Desk, with inkwells.	4.00
Grandfather clock. 138mm.	7.50
Sundial with verse. 112mm.	7.50
Tobacco Pouch. 75mm long.	5.50
Watering Can. 70mm.	4.75

Alcohol

Barrel on Stand. 65mm.	2.25
Hand holding a beaker. 50mm.	4.00
Spirit Flask. 89mm.	4.00

Musical Instruments

Upright Piano. 62mm.	8.50

Transport

Petrol Can. No. 249. 66mm.	8.50

Modern Equipment

Gas Cooker, 70mm.	6.50

Miscellaneous

Castle, chess piece. 67mm.	3.00
King chess piece. 110mm.	20.00
Ladies' Button Boot. 65mm.	7.50
Ladies' 18th Century Shoe. 70mm long.	7.50
Ladies' Lace-up Walking Shoe. 114mm long.	7.50
Sabot. 120mm long.	4.00

Miniature Domestic

Cheese Dish, 1 piece.

Two sizes: 70mm long	4.75
82mm long.	4.75

Cheese Dish and Cover. 2 sizes:

50mm	4.00
60mm.	4.00
Coffee pot, with lid. 75mm.	3.00
Tea pot with lid, bagware. 70mm.	4.75

Alexandre

No details of mark available.

Only one Jug, 50mm, with a
London Crest has been found
with this mark.   .75

Amber China

CHINA

Trademark used by a retailer or wholesaler probably in Manchester on china manufactured by Arkinstall & Son Ltd. (usual trademark Arcadian).

Great War
Tank with inset steering wheels.
  110mm long.   10.50

Anglo Heraldic Co

For mark see *Crested China*, p. 26.

Trademark used by Sampson Hancock (& Sons), Bridge Works, Stoke (usual trademark Corona).

Ancient Artefacts
Canterbury Leather Bottle.
  No. 156.   1.75
Glastonbury Bowl. 40mm.   1.75
Puzzle Jug with verse. 70mm.   3.50

Animals
Bear, sitting. 80mm.   6.50
Cheshire Cat always smiling, The.
  95mm.   4.75
Dog. Bulldog, standing. 112mm
  long.   8.75
Pig, standing. 84mm long.   8.25

Home/Nostalgic
Coal Scuttle. 64mm.   2.25
Milk Churn. No. 168. 70mm.   2.25
Shaving Mug. 58mm.   4.00
Watering Can. 70mm.   4.75

Miscellaneous
Ladies' Button Boot. 65mm.   7.50
Ladies' 18th Century Shoe.
  No. 146. 90mm long.   8.25

Miniature Domestic
Cheese Dish and Lid. 50mm.   4.00

Arcadian China

For marks see *Crested China*, pp. 26/27.

Trademark used by Arkinstall & Son Ltd., Arcadian Works, Stoke on Trent, subsequently a branch of J.A. Robinson & Sons, later Cauldon Ltd., and finally Coalport China Co. (John Rose & Co.) Ltd.

Parian/unglazed

Busts

Bust of King Edward VII in military uniform, later models found with inscriptions. On circular glazed base.	
2 sizes: 130mm.	43.50
140mm.	43.50
Bust of King Edward VII wearing trilby, overcoat and suit, on circular glazed base. 125mm.	35.00
Bust of Queen Alexandra, on circular glazed base. 2 sizes:	
120mm	30.00
140mm.	30.00
Smaller size can be found named in blue lettering.	
Bust of King George V, can be found with circular glazed or keyhole base. With inscription. 135mm.	30.00
Bust of Queen Mary, can be found with a glazed circular or keyhole base, with inscription. 135mm.	30.00
Bust of Prince of Wales (later Edward VIII) in midshipman's uniform, inscription in red and blue. On glazed circular base. 135mm.	47.50
(Any of the above can be found with crests on their glazed bases, for which £5.00 may be added).	
Bust of *Burns*, found with poem by Wordsworth. On circular glazed base. 120mm.	10.50

Bust of *Napoleon*, on square glazed base. 120mm.	25.75
Bust of *Nelson*, on square glazed base. 120mm.	25.75
Bust of *John Peel*, with verse. 120mm.	21.50
Bust of *Scott*, on circular glazed base. 120mm.	10.50
Bust of Duke of Wellington on glazed base. 130mm.	25.75
Bust of *King of the Belgians* on square glazed base, sculpted by W.C. Lawton. 2 sizes: 155mm	56.00
175mm.	60.00
Bust of *Sir Douglas Haig* on square glazed base, sculpted by S.R. Sanders. 150mm.	56.00
Bust of *Sir John French* on square glazed base, sculpted by W.C. Lawton. 155mm.	47.50
Bust of *Sir John Jellicoe* on square glazed base, sculpted by W.C. Lawton. 170mm.	56.50
Bust of *General Joffre* on square glazed base, sculpted by W.C. Lawton. 2 sizes: 145mm	43.50
175mm.	47.50
Bust of *Lord Kitchener* on square glazed base, sculpted by W.C. Lawton. 2 sizes: 155mm	47.50
175mm.	56.50
Bust of David Lloyd George on round glazed base. 130mm.	40.00
Bust of Rt. Hon. W.S. Churchill on square glazed base, sculpted by W.C. Lawton. 160mm.	60.00

Ancient Artefacts

Most inscriptions begin *model of,* so this will not be repeated throughout the listing. These models are often found not named and numbered.

Aberdeen Bronze Pot.	1.75
Ancient Bronze British Pot. No. 618. 68mm.	2.25
Ancient Tyg, 1 or 2 handles. No. 58. 70mm.	2.25
Ancient Urn. No. 85. 35mm.	2.25
Ashbourne Bushel, with inscription. No. 99. 67mm dia.	3.25

Butterpot, old, of 17th Century.
45mm. 2.75
Cadogan teapot, working model of. 6.00
Cambridge Roman Jug. No. 67.
2 sizes: 60mm 2.75
75mm. 2.75
Canterbury Roman Ewer. No 23.
60mm. 2.25
Canterbury Roman Vase,
inscribed: *Roman Vase found near*
Canterbury original in Cantrbury
museum. 7 different shapes:
No. 21. 65mm. 2.25
No. 24. 66mm. 2.25
No. 27. 66mm. 2.25
No. 28. 70mm. 2.25
No. 29. 60mm. 2.25
No. 30. 60mm. 2.25
No. 32. 63mm. 2.25
Chester Roman Vase, inscribed:
Roman vase now in Chester
Museum. 2 different shapes:
No. 131. 56mm. 2.25
No. 136. 60mm. 2.25
Chester Roman Vase, inscribed:
Roman vase found at Chester from
original in Museum. No. 263.
58mm. 2.25
Chinese vase, original in Hanley Museum.
No. 127. 38mm. 2.25
Colchester Vase. 1.75
Derby Roman Vase. No. 26.
63mm. 2.25
Devon Oak Pitcher. No. 165.
60mm. 2.25
Dogger Bank Bottle. No. 206.
2 sizes: 50mm 2.25
70mm. 2.25
Dorchester Jug. No. 66. 55mm. 2.25
Dorset Ewer, inscribed: *Roman*
Ewer in Dorset Museum found at
Bath. No. 69. 70mm. 2.25
Eddystone Spanish Jug. No. 585.
60mm. 2.25
Egyptian Urn. No. 130. 2.25
Egyptian vase, ancient, about 230 BC.
No. 155. 45mm. 2.25
Egyptian Water bottle. 60mm. 2.25
Exeter vase from original in Museum.
No. 70. 68mm. 2.25
Fountains Abbey Cup. 50mm. 1.75
Glastonbury Bowl. No. 55.
40mm. 1.75

Glastonbury Bronze Bowl.
No. 74. 40mm. 1.75
Glastonbury Vase. No. 642.
55mm. 1.75
Grecian bronze pot found at Pompeii.
No. 138. 50mm. 2.25
Greek Cauldron, Ancient. 2.25
Hastings Kettle. No. 237. 62mm. 1.75
Hereford Terracotta Kettle. 2.25
Highland Whiskey Jar. No. 679.
72mm. 2.25
Highland quaich or whiskey bowl.
134mm wide. 3.50
Horsham Vase, inscribed:
13th century vase found at
Horsham. No. 201. 2 sizes:
45mm 2.50
75mm. 2.50
Irish bronze pot, Ancient. No. 62.
50mm. 2.25
Irish Kettle. No. 95. 70mm. 2.25
Jersey milk can. Ancient (and lid).
No. 523. 72mm. 3.00
Kendal Jug. No. 9. 75mm. 2.25
Lichfield Jug. No. 60. 70mm. 1.75
Lincoln Jack from original in
museum. No. 50. 62mm. 2.25
Lincoln vase from original in the
museum. No. 80. 66mm. 2.25
Loving cup originated by Henry of
Navarre King of France.
2 or 3 handled. No. 579. 40mm. 2.50
Newbury Leather Bottle,
inscribed: *Leather bottle found on*
battlefield of Newbury 1044 now in
museum. No. 83. 65mm. 1.75
Norwich Cinerary Urn. 50mm. 2.25
Phoenician vase original in Stoke-on-
Trent museum. No. 25. 60mm. 2.25
Pompeian Vessel. No. 208. 55mm. 1.75
Pompeii lamp. No. 603. 90mm long. 2.25
Portland vase now in British
Museum. No. 52. 60mm. 2.25
Puzzle jug original in South
Kensington Museum. No. 147.
70mm. 3.50
Salisbury Jack. 2.25
Salisbury Kettle. No. 90. 107mm. 2.25
Salt Maller. 1.75
Scarborough Jug. No. 82. 52mm. 1.75
Shakespeare's Jug. 60mm. 3.00
Shrewbury Salopian Ewer.
No. 613. 75mm. 1.75

Silchester Vase. No. 54. 55mm.	1.75
Southwold Jar. No. 627. 95mm.	1.75
Toby Jug, inscribed: *This is an exact copy in miniature of the old toby jug*. No. 253. 75mm.	8.00
Tutankhamun's Cup, inscribed: *Kings wishing cup found in King Tutankhamuns tomb at Luxor*. 55mm.	5.50
Upstones Jug. No. 73. 60mm.	2.25
Wedgwood Roman Vase. No. 202. 60mm.	1.75
West Malling Elizabethan jug or stoup. No. 152. 75mm.	2.25
Winchelsea Roman Cup. No. 137. 50mm.	1.75
Winchelsea Vase. 2 sizes:	
No. 68. 55mm.	1.75
No. 87. 75mm.	1.75
Winchester Bushel, blue feet and handle. 83mm dia.	8.75
Winchester Vase.	1.75
Windsor Roman Urn. No. 123. 50mm.	1.75
Wokingham Tankard. No. 88. 78mm.	1.75
York Roman Ewer. No. 57. 60mm.	1.75

Buildings – Coloured

These buildings are not normally found crested.

Bridlington Priory Church, model of. Light brown colour. 68mm long.	45.50
Dean Goodman's Birthplace (rare). 85mm long.	110.00
First and Last House with annexe. 100mm long.	65.00
Guildhall, Thaxted. 83mm (rare).	110.00
Old Blacksmiths shop and marriage room, Gretna Green. 85mm long (late Willow mould).	30.00
Old Star Inn, Alfriston. 80mm (rare).	110.00
Round House, Alton, inscribed: *The Ancient Lock Up*. Light brown colour. 86mm.	40.00
Shakespeare's House. 2 sizes:	
63mm	14.00
127mm long.	30.00
Wells Cathedral. Stone coloured with some colouring on doors and windows. 110mm long.	43.50

Buildings – White

Aberystwyth University. 110mm long.	47.50
Ann Hathaway's Cottage. 83mm long.	6.50
Big Ben, also found inscribed: *City of London*. 3 sizes:	
92mm	10.50
130mm.	13.00
150mm.	16.00
Blackpool Tower. 144mm.	10.50
Blackpool Tower with Buildings. 107mm.	8.75
Blackpool Tower with Buildings on heavy base. 2 sizes:	
135mm	5.50
165mm.	8.75
Boston Stump. 2 sizes:	
89mm long	29.50
110mm long.	29.50
Bunyan's Cottage. 95mm.	16.00
Canterbury Cathedral. West front. 126mm.	19.50
Canterbury. *Westgate*. 93mm.	16.00
Carillon Tower, Loughborough. 162mm.	32.50
Chester Cathedral. 120mm long.	40.00
Chesterfield parish church AD 1037. Model of. 125mm.	24.50
Clifton suspension bridge. 175mm long.	30.00
Cottage. 50mm.	4.00
Cottage on rectangular base usually found with no inscription.	6.00
Can be found inscribed: *Model of Highland cottage* or *Welsh cottage*. 60mm. If so, add	20.00
Ely Cathedral. 140mm long.	40.00
Fair Maid's House, Perth. 84mm.	50.00
First and last refreshment house in England. Often found without 'refreshment' inscription. 73mm long.	8.50
Also found with annexe. 2 sizes:	
100mm long	16.00
138mm long.	19.50
Forth Bridge. 158mm long.	30.00
Gloucester Cathedral. 128mm long.	40.00
Grimsby hydraulic tower. 170mm.	21.75
Hastings Castle ruins. 96mm.	16.00
Hastings, clock tower. 2 sizes:	
135mm	7.50
152mm.	8.75

Hop Kiln. 86mm.	14.50
Houses of Parliament. 73mm long.	26.00
Irish round tower. 106mm.	8.50
King Alfred's tower. 92mm.	26.00
Lantern Hill Church, *Ilfracombe*.	
98mm long.	17.50
Largs Tower. 104mm.	7.50
Launceston Castle. 112mm long.	40.00
Lincoln Stonebow. 88mm long.	19.50
London bridge, Ye olde.	
2 sizes: 88mm	16.00
170mm.	17.50
Marble Arch. 3 sizes: 45mm	8.75
65mm	5.50
80mm.	6.50
Martello tower, with inscription:	
'Erected for Coast Defence	
1804'. 73mm dia.	24.50
Morpeth Clock Tower, not found	
named. 122mm.	10.50
Mundesley-on-Sea Castle Ruins.	
105mm.	43.50
Norwich Cathedral. 105mm long.	40.00
Old curiosity shop. Immortalized	
by Charles Dickens. No. 14,	
Portsmouth Street. 95mm long.	24.50
Old Pete's cottage (near Ramsey).	
75mm long.	23.00
Pegwell Bay, clock tower. 135mm.	16.00
Plymouth, clock tower. 150mm.	10.50
Portsmouth, Guildhall.	
60mm long.	40.00
Queen Mary's dolls house. 3 sizes:	
75mm	15.25
95mm	16.00
118mm.	21.75
Two smaller sizes are often	
found as boxes with loose roof	
lids. (These models can be	
found with the 'Cauldon' mark	
as well as 'Arcadian'.	
Same price.)	
Rochester castle, dating from 1126.	
70mm.	30.00
Rowton Tower, with inscription:	
King Charles 1st stood on this	
tower, Sept. 24th 1645 and saw his	
army defeated on Rowton Moor.	
88mm.	30.00
St. Albans. The clock tower. 125mm.	37.50
St. Nicholas Chapel, Ilfracombe.	
100mm long.	19.50
St. Pauls Cathedral. No. 114.	
3 sizes: 72mm	14.50
95mm	15.25

130mm.	16.00
St. Tudno's Church, Llandudno.	
73mm.	30.00
Salisbury Cathedral.	
120mm long.	40.00
Salisbury Clock Tower, not found	
named. 130mm.	13.00
Shakespeare's House. 3 sizes:	
50mm long	6.50
83mm long	8.50
100mm long.	14.50
Skegness, clock tower. 125mm.	12.50
Smallest house in Great Britain. 2 sizes:	
88mm	13.00
115mm.	16.00
Southampton, the Bargate. 66mm.	15.25
Temple Bar. 2 sizes: 60mm	10.50
95mm.	16.00
Tom Tower, Christchurch, Oxford.	
88mm.	21.75
Tower Bridge. 135mm long.	21.75
Tower of Refuge, Douglas I.O.M.	
68mm.	30.00
Tudor House, L shaped. 80mm.	30.00
Tynwald Hill, Model of, with	
lengthy inscription.	
110mm dia.	60.00
Wembley Stadium. 136mm long.	26.00
Westminster Abbey. 2 sizes:	
70mm	30.00
115mm.	40.00
Westminster abbey, West front.	
118mm.	13.00
Wimborne Minster. 127mm long.	40.00
Windmill with moveable sails.	16.00
Very rarely found inscribed:	
Windmill. Woodhouse. 85mm.	26.00
Windsor Castle. 80mm.	20.00
Windsor, round tower.	
2 sizes: 58mm	12.50
90mm.	14.00
Worcester Cathedral. 2 sizes:	
127mm long	30.00
140mm long.	40.00
York Minster. 105mm.	40.00

Monuments (including Crosses)

Banbury Cross, with nursery	
rhyme: *Ride a cock horse*.	
160mm.	16.00
Bloody corner, Ilfracombe with very	
lengthy inscription of slaying	
of King Hubba on all 3 sides.	
Same mould as Rufus Stone.	
100mm (rare).	60.00

Bunyan Statue. 140mm.   10.50
Caister on Sea Lifeboat Memorial.
   150mm.   14.50
Castleton village cross. 140mm.   30.00
Celtic Cross. 125mm.   12.00
Conway *Seven are we* Grave, with
   inscription: 'The Grave
   immortalised by Wordsworth's
   Poem' and poem 'Two of us in
   the
   churchyard lie'. This is a
   triangular tube shaped tomb
   with seven small towers.
   110mm long (rare).   52.50
Drake Statue. 160mm.   8.75
Douglas Jubilee Clock Tower.
   127mm.   40.00
Ethelfreda Memorial. 150mm.   40.00
Fishermen's Memorial, not
   named but probably Hull.
   160mm.   12.50
(The) Globe, Swanage. Model of.
   80mm.   10.50
Iona Cross. 142mm.   4.00
Irish Monument, not named but
   appears with Irish Crests.
   Circular base with man
   standing on top. 138mm. This
   is the metal man at Tramore
   (rare).   56.50
King Alfred the Great, Statue.
   Winchester. Rd. No. 521701.
   170mm.   30.00
*Maiwand Memorial, Forbury
   Gardens, Reading*. (Lion on
   Base). 100mm.   13.00
Moffat Ram Memorial, ram moun-
   ted on rock. 108mm (rare).   75.00
Margate Surf Boat Memorial.
   125mm.   9.50
Nelson's column. 102mm.   40.00
Nelson Monument, Great
   Yarmouth. 206mm.   60.00
Newton Monument. 165mm.   15.25
Richmond, Yorks, Market Cross.
   125mm.   12.50
*(The Great) Rock of Ages, Burrington
   Coombe, near Cheddar. Som.* with
   three verses of hymn. 83mm.   6.50
Rufus Stone. 100mm.   4.00
Sailor's Stone, Hindhead. 100mm.   8.75
Saxon Lady and Child, both with
   swords, on glazed base. 153mm.   43.50

Series of at least three figures
   standing on a square plinth.
   (These are not easily identifi-
   able and could be statesmen,
   industrialists or literary figures.
   It is thought that one is Joseph
   Chamberlain and another is
   Charles Dickens); inscribed:
   Industry is the parent of success.
   Edged in green. 135mm.   Each   50.00
Toad Rock. 85mm.   12.50
*Tom Hughes Monument, Rugby
   School*. 142mm.   30.00
Victorian lady and gentleman
   figure group on base, inscribed:
   he that is satisfied is rich. Found
   with colour transfer of children.
   115 mm (rare).   50.00
Statue found with York Crest,
   Lion and three Imps or Satyrs
   on a square pedestal. 115mm.   30.00
Weymouth Jubilee Clock. 128mm.   16.00

Historical/Folklore
Archbishop of Canterbury's Chair.
   95mm.   12.50
Coaching Hat, can be found
   inscribed: *Model of ancient coach-
   ing hat*. No. 687. 65 mm long.   6.00
Ducking stool, 2 pieces, hinged
   together. With long details of
   its last employment in
   Leominster in 1809 and 1817.
   120mm long (very rare).   87.50
English Folksong Bride beside
   chest. 93mm.   30.00
Execution block with axe. 50mm
   (very rare).   24.50
Henry V cradle. 78mm.   13.00
Jenny Geddes stool 1637, 3 legged.
   More often found unnamed.   3.00
   40mm, named   10.50
Judge bust, with inscription:
   *Defend the children of the poor and
   punish the wrong doer.*
   2 sizes: 55mm   6.50
              70mm.   10.50
   With inscription add   5.00
Lady Godiva, Coventry, on horse-
   back, circular base. 85mm.   21.75
   with verse. 2 sizes: 76mm   4.00
                        115mm.   7.50

Lady Godiva on heart shaped base. 80mm.	15.25
Miner's Lamp, inscribed: '1836'. 85mm.	10.50
Mother Shipton, can be found with verse. 2 sizes: 76mm	4.00
115mm.	7.50
Peeping Tom, bust. 110mm.	16.00
Man in the Sun. 94mm.	40.00
Man standing in Pillory, can be found inscribed: Time for reflection, AD1600. 190mm.	15.25
Man sitting in Stocks, can be found inscribed as above and very rarely: Berkswell stocks or The stocks, Dartmouth. 88mm.	18.50
	29.50
Shakespeare's desk from the original in the museum, model of. Can be found in lustre. 62mm long.	13.00
Trusty servant on ornate rectangular base, with verse. Fully coloured and without crest. 137mm.	87.50
Trusty servant on small square base, can be found with verse. Fully coloured with crest and unglazed. 130mm.	87.50
Wishing Chair, Giants Causeway. 75mm dia.	41.50
Yorick's Skull, inscribed: Alas poor Yorick. 57mm.	6.50

Traditional/National Souvenirs

John Bull, bust. 3 sizes: 65mm	5.50
85mm	7.50
100mm.	16.00
Largest size found with black hat. Blackpool Big Wheel. 2 sizes:	
60mm	7.50
110mm.	10.50
Cheddar cheese, prime. 60mm.	4.00
Cheddar cheese, prime, with slice out. 60mm.	5.25
Cornish pasty. 98mm long.	8.25
Devonshire dumpling. 45mm.	8.25
Isle of Wight, relief map standing upright on pintray. Coloured. 106mm long.	21.75
Lancashire Clog. 94mm long.	4.00
Lancashire Clog, high narrow type. 2 sizes: 95mm long	4.00
140mm long.	6.50

Lancashireman's Jug with verse. 75mm.	6.00
Lincoln imp. 110mm.	4.00
Lincoln imp, on square stand. 125mm.	5.50
Manx Legs on stand. 101mm.	13.00
Manx Legs on rock. 51mm.	10.50
Mill Lass, bust, shawl draped round head and shoulders. 60mm (rare).	26.00
Sometimes inscribed: Lancashire Lass.	30.00
Yorkshireman's Jug with verse. 83mm.	5.00
Irish Colleen, fully coloured on Ashtray base. 105mm. (One of a series of Ashtrays, see **Comic** section).	27.50
Irish Harp with green shamrocks. 108mm.	4.50
Irish jaunting car, Model of. With horse and driver. 120mm long. (Very rare).	75.00
Irish Lady, bust, inscribed: My simple graceful Nora Criena. 85mm.	24.50
Pat the Irishman, bust. 80mm.	19.50
Bagpipes. 110mm long.	13.00
Gretna Green, Anvil from and verse. 66mm.	4.75
Scotsman, bust of. 65mm.	17.50
Souter Johnny, sitting figure on chair with verse. Some colouring. 130mm.	21.75
Tam O'Shanter (bonnet) inscribed: Tha can sit on the thistle noo. Coloured feather and pom-pom. 95mm dia.	21.75
Thistle Candlestick. 50mm.	2.25
Thistle on stalk base (Candlestick or Vase) inscribed: Tha can sit on the thistle noo. 85mm.	1.75
Thistle Vase, wide necked. 2 sizes: 45mm	1.75
85mm.	2.25
Welsh Harp. 80mm.	4.00
Welsh Hat, Model of. Often unnamed. Can be found with longest Welsh place name round brim, for which add	2.00
2 sizes: 52mm	3.00
72mm	4.00

Welsh Hat, much wider brim.		
49mm.	4.00	
Welsh Lady, bust. Found with		
inscription: *Wales! Wales! My*		
Mother's sweet home ere.		
3 sizes: 65mm	7.50	
80mm	8.25	
100mm.	10.50	
Larger sizes found coloured.	14.00	
Welsh Leek, can be found with		
inscription: *King Henry V. The*		
Welshmen did goot servace (at		
Crecy) in a garden where Leeks did		
grow. Shakespeare. 2 sizes: 76mm	2.25	
98mm.	2.50	
Welsh Tea Party, 3 Welsh ladies		
taking tea, can be found with		
hats and cloaks coloured.		
2 sizes: 50mm	30.00	
95mm.	40.00	
Welsh Tea Party, as above, on Ash-		
tray base. 50mm.	30.00	

Seaside Souvenirs

Bathing Machine. 3 sizes: 50mm	4.00
65mm	4.75
85mm	6.50
Lifebelt. 80mm dia.	7.50
Lifeboat, can be found inscribed	
with any of the following names:	
Bob Newson; Charles Susanna	
Stephens; The Charlie and Adrian;	
James Stevens No. 5; Nancy Lucy;	
Charles Arkcoll; Richard Coleman;	
Elizabeth Simpson; Kentwell; Mark	
Lane; Co-operator No. 2 and	
Charles Medland. 118mm long.	4.75
If named add	7.00
Rowing Boat. 83mm long.	4.00
Yacht. 125mm long.	8.25
Lifeboatman, bust. 85mm.	12.50
Fishing Basket, found inscribed:	
A good catch. 50mm.	3.50
Fisherman's Creel, with separate	
lid. 60mm.	3.25
Beachy Head Lighthouse, with black	
band. 2 sizes: 102mm	4.00
140mm.	5.50
Bell Rock, Lighthouse. No. 14.	
108mm.	12.50
Cove Sea Lighthouse. 136mm.	20.50
Eddystone Lighthouse, often found	
unnamed. 3 sizes: 70mm	2.25

105mm	3.00
140mm.	4.75
Manghold Head Lighthouse.	60.00
Pharos Lighthouse, Fleetwood,	
Model of. No. 255.	
2 sizes: 100mm	5.50
140mm.	3.50
Smaller sized (fully inscribed)	
has been found as a pepper	
pot.	
Spurn head Lighthouse. 110mm.	8.50
Withernsea Lighthouse. 105mm.	6.50
Crab, very detailed. No. 6 or 9.	
85mm long.	7.50
Crab Ashtray. 90mm long.	6.75
Oyster Shell dish. 72mm dia.	1.75
Nautilus shell on three legs.	
80mm long.	7.00
Scallop Shell 2 sizes: 70mm	2.00
92mm dia.	2.00
Scallop Shell dish, very ornate.	
83mm dia.	3.50
Scallop Shell on rock, *Menu*	
holder. 58mm.	6.50
Shell Ink Well, one open shell	
inverted on another, usually	
inscribed: *We are always glad to*	
hear from you. Can also be found	
inscribed: *We're aye prood to hear*	
fae ye or *pins.* 105mm.	6.00
Whelk Shell, can be found	
inscribed: *listen to the sea* or *We*	
are always glad to hear from you.	
Size varies from 80mm–100mm	
long.	2.50
Gladstone bag. 82mm long.	6.50
Bathing Belle on trinket box.	
110mm.	14.00
Can also be found in coloured	
lustre finish.	
Punch and Judy show. Rd. No.	
37083? 90 mm (moderately rare).	26.00
Judy, bust, some colouring. 90mm.	18.00
Punch, bust, some colouring.	
2 sizes: 65mm	8.75
80mm.	13.00

Countryside

Acorn. 55mm.	3.00
Beehive on table. 78mm.	4.00
Hay Stack, circular. 58mm.	3.50
Hay Stack, rectangular. 50mm.	4.00
Pinecone, curved. 88mm long.	3.00
Tree Trunk Vase. 70mm.	3.50

Arcadian. Hand holding beer labels

Arcadian. Table

Arcadian. Wishing Chair

Arcadian. Gramophone in Cabinet

Arcadian. Ball of String

Arcadian. Trench Mortar

Arcadian. Twisted fish

Arcadian. Wiltshire Pig

Arcadian. Hampshire Hog

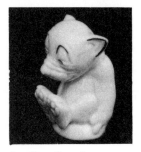

Arcadian. 'Bonzo'

Arcadian. Henry V Cradle

Arcadian. Teapot

Animals

Small models of 'pets' were obviously made in great numbers for many years so the moulds do vary. Large, more exotic animals were much more expensive at the time and so are consequently much more rare.

Bear with Ragged staff. 80mm.	16.00
Bull, Highland. 130mm long (rare).	40.00
Calf, inscribed: *Why the Natives are called Isle of Wight Calves.* 100mm long.	10.50
Camel, 2 humps – Bactrian. 70mm.	17.50
Cat, angry, standing with arched back and green eyes, inscribed: *My word if you're not off.* 63mm long, no colouring	8.75
with colouring.	10.50
Cat, climbing into boot, which has a mouse peeping out of its toe. 100mm long.	13.0
Cat, Cheshire. No bow round neck, inscribed: *Keep smiling.* 90mm.	4.75
Cat, The Cheshire. With orange or red bow round neck, inscribed: *The smile that wont come off.* 95mm.	10.50
Cat, long necked and sitting, inscribed: *My word if youre not off.* 108mm.	6.50
Cat, Manx with coloured face. 70mm long, no colouring	13.00
with colouring.	21.75
Cat, playing flute. 75mm.	17.00
Cat with bow, sitting on plinth. Bow sometimes coloured blue. 123mm.	17.00
Cat sitting with tail curled round feet, red bow and green eyes. No. 77. 67mm.	9.50
Cat sitting and smiling (grotesque, rather similar to Cheshire Cat), bow round neck, sometimes coloured orange. 75mm.	5.50
Cat sitting with bow round neck. 56mm.	7.50

Arcadian Black Cat Registered Series

No. 1. Black Cat on Jug. 60mm.	35.00
No. 2. Black Cat on vertical horse-shoe 76mm.	30.00
No. 3. Black Cat on pillar box posting letter. 56mm. This cat has also been found in cobalt blue instead of black.	35.00
No. 4. Black Cat on telephone. 65mm.	35.00
No. 5. Black Cat in canoe. 80mm long.	47.50
No. 6. Black Cat on wall. 70mm.	30.00
No. 6. Black Manx Cat on wall, cat without tail. The model has a matching Douglas Crest. (A different mould to the above.)	47.50
No. 7. Black Cat in boot. 61mm.	35.00
No. 8. Black Cat with bottle, bottle can have solid or cork top, can be inscribed: *Cheerio from . . .* (can be found in lustre). 70mm.	30.00
No. 9. Black Cat on milk churn. *New milk* moulded on churn. 70mm.	30.00
No. 10. Three Black Cats in bed (quite rare).	47.50
No. 11. Black Cat on swing. 63mm (quite rare).	47.50
No. 12. Black Cat in well. (Can be found in lustre.) 63mm.	35.00
No. 13. Black Cat operating radio. 63mm.	30.00
No. 14. Black Cat in Pram. 70mm (very rare).	56.50
No. 15. Three Black Cats in basket, and one on top. 70mm (rare).	47.50
No. 16. Black Cat on scooter. (Can be found in lustre.) 70mm (rare).	75.00
No. 17. Black Cat with umbrella. 65mm (very rare).	75.00
No. 18. Black Cat on bicycle. 80mm long (rare).	75.00
No. 19. Black Cat in yacht. 96mm long.	56.50
No. 20. Black Cat playing double bass. 70mm (very rare).	80.00
No. 21. Black Cat on seesaw. 85mm long (very rare).	75.00
No. 22. 5 Black Cats on a house, their rails spell: *Good luck.* 65mm (rare)	56.50
No. 23. Black Cats on sledge (very rare).	75.00
No. 24. Black Cat playing piano. 52mm (very rare).	75.00

There are also very similar black
cats that are not part of the
Registered Series:
Black Cat, wearing kilt and
glengarry, playing golf
standing on golf ball. 70mm.   56.50
(This is from a Willow mould.)
Black Cat, standing alongside
Welsh Leek. 60mm.   60.00

Sitting Black Cats
Can be found on the following bases:
Armchair 2 sizes: 55mm   21.50
     90mm.   19.50
Ashtray, horseshoe shaped.
93mm long.   14.00
Pouffe, inscribed: *Good luck*.
2 sizes: 80mm   20.00
     95mm.   20.00
Trinket box, horseshoe shaped.
70mm.   27.50
(All of these cats have blue/
green eyes and usually red
bows, but yellow bows are
sometimes found.)

Chimpanzee, sitting. 70mm (rare).   22.00
Cougar (or panther). 102mm long
(rare).   40.00
Cow, Jersey. 125mm long (quite
rare).   30.00
Crocodile (or alligator).
125mm long.   40.00
(Can be found with blue lustre
finish.)
Bill Sykes dog, Model of, sitting.
Sometimes inscribed: *My word
if youre not off*. No. 300. 103mm.   12.50
Bill Sykes dog, Model of, standing.
Sometimes inscribed: *My word
if youre not off*.
3 sizes: 88mm   8.75
     102mm   10.50
     118mm long.   10.50
Bulldog, black, emerging from
kennel inscribed: *The Black
Watch*. 2 sizes: 56mm & 96mm.   9.00
Bulldog, sitting, very thin face.
57mm.   10.00
Bulldog, standing, sometimes
inscribed: *Who said Germans*.
No. 301. 2 sizes: 115mm   10.50
     130mm long.   10.50
     If inscribed add   8.50

Dog, Collie, lying down. 78mm
long.   7.50
Dog, Collie, standing. Sometimes
inscribed: *Shetland collie*.
2 sizes: 60mm   7.50
     95mm long.   8.25
Dog, Dachshund. 90mm long.   35.00
Dog, King Charles Spaniel,
begging on cushion.
2 sizes: 68mm   5.50
     95mm.   11.00
Dog (Pup), sitting with one ear
raised. 68mm.   4.50
Dog, Scottie, standing. 60mm.   5.50
Dog, Scottie wearing Tam
O'Shanter. Hat can be found
coloured blue. 85mm.   4.50
Dog, Scottish Terrier, can be
found inscribed: *Scotch terrier* or
*As old Mrs Terrier said to her pup,
in all life's adventures keep your
tail up*. 66mm.   6.50
Dog, standing, facing sideways,
curly tail and blue collar.
80mm long.   8.25
Dog, Staffordshire bullterrier,
sitting, sometimes inscribed:
*Daddy wouldn't buy me a bow
wow*. 72mm.   7.50
           Inscribed   12.00
Dog, walking, blue collar. With
Old Mrs Terrier inscription.
90mm long.   7.50
Dog Posy Holder, some
colouring. 103mm.   4.00
Donkey. 2 sizes: 80mm   15.50
     120mm long.   16.00
Smaller size has saddle. Large
size can have inscription: *Hee-
haw*.
Elephant, trunk attached to
body. 55mm.   6.50
Elephant, trunk modelled free
from body, sometimes inscribed:
Baby Jumbo. 50mm.   6.50
Fawn. 50mm.   26.00
Fish, fat. 98mm long.   2.50
Fish, open mouthed.
2 sizes: 80mm   1.75
     108mm.   2.25
Fish, curved body. 110mm long.   6.50
Fish ashtray in shape of plaice,
usually inscribed: *A pla(i)ce for
ashes*, but can be inscribed:
Caught at . . . 125mm long.   4.00

Fish dish in shape of plaice,
inscribed: *A pla(i)ce for every-*
thing. 125mm long.   4.00
Fox. 102mm long.   40.00
Fox on square plinth. 114mm.   40.00
Frog, closed mouth. 45mm.   10.50
Frog, open mouthed and green
eyes, inscribed: *Always croaking*.
3 sizes: 60mm – no inscription   4.75
           80mm   5.50
           100mm long.   6.50
Goat. 82mm long.   32.50
Hare. 73mm long.   7.50
Kangaroo. 75mm (rare).   40.00
Hippopotamus. 88mm long
(very rare).   45.00
Lion, roaring. 85mm long.   22.00
Lion, walking. 3 sizes:
    85mm   8.75
    116mm   8.75
    140mm long.   10.50
Smallest size can be found
inscribed: *King of the forest*, for
which add: 2.00
Monkey, sitting hand to mouth.
65mm.   10.50
Monkey, sitting, holding
coconut. No. 34. 85mm.   22.00
Monkey, wearing coat. 75mm.   5.50
Mouse, holding acorn. 60mm.   10.50
Otter, holding fish in mouth.
120mm long.   40.00
Pig, smiling and sitting. 63mm
long.   6.50
Pig, short and standing, inscribed:
I won't be druv. 70mm. 63mm
long.   7.50
Pig, tall and standing, inscribed:
You can push or you can shuv but
I'm hanged if I'll be druv. 78mm.
63mm long.   10.50
Hampshire hog, Model of, sitting.
No. 148C. 70mm long.   10.50
Hampshire Hog, Model of, standing
inscribed: *Wunt be druv* and
verse No. 145. 105mm long.   12.00
Sussex pig, Model of, sitting,
inscribed: *Won't be druv*.
No. 148. 88mm long.   10.50
Sussex pig, Model of, standing fat
pig, can be found inscribed:
Mochyn bad with Welsh Crest.
No. 148. 80mm long, if named   19.50
Sussex pig, Model of, standing thin
pig, inscribed: *You can push or*

you can shuv but I'm hanged if I'll
be druv or *Won't be druv*. No.
148. 78mm long.   14.00
Wiltshire pig, Model of, sitting up
on haunches, alert ears. No.
148. 60mm.   12.50
Wiltshire pig, Model of, standing fat
pig with double chin, inscribed:
Wunt be druv. No. 148. 85mm.   10.50
Piglet, kneeling. 70mm long.   7.50
Polar Bear, 2 sizes: 100mm long   40.00
                     135mm long.   47.50
Pony, New Forest, can be found
unnamed. 100mm long.   19.50
Pony, Shetland, often found
unnamed. 2 sizes: 105mm   19.50
                  120mm long.   21.50
Rabbit, ears lying along back.
Found numbered 22 and 23.
Sizes vary between 65–80mm
long.   4.00
Rabbit, sitting, ears apart. No. 13.
Sizes vary between 50–68mm.   4.00
Rhinoceros. 90mm long (very rare).   45.00
Russian bear, inscribed: *War edition*
and carries Russian Imperial
Crest. 70mm.   45.00
Seal. 102mm long.   10.00
Squirrel, holding nut, on base.
65mm.   10.50
Squirrel Jug. 80mm.   10.00
Teddy bear, sitting. 90mm.   9.00
Smaller size, 68mm, not found
inscribed.   7.00
Terrapin, walking, erect head.
74mm long.   8.75
Tortoise. 72mm long.   4.00
Tortoise, standing upright,
wearing blue helmet. 75mm.   30.00
Welsh goat, Model of, inscribed: *Yr*
Afr Cymreig. 100mm long.   40.00
Wembley Lion. 100mm long
(stylised symbol of the B.E.E.).   13.00
3 Wise Monkeys on wall inscribed:
I see no evil, I speak no evil, I hear
no evil. 76mm.   8.75
Isn't this rabbit a duck. On its base a
rabbit, turned on its side a duck.
(Can be found in lustre.) 75mm.   17.00

Birds (including Eggs)
Chick, breaking out of egg. Can be
found inscribed: *Just out*.
2 sizes: 63mm   4.00
         86mm long.   5.50

Larger size can be found
inscribed: *Easter egg*, for which
add   2.00
Chick in Egg Pepper pot. 58mm.
Chick, very tiny and completely
yellow, sitting on a white egg,
inscribed: *Every little helps
mother will be pleased*. 50mm
long.   12.50
Egg salt and pepper pots.
58mm.   Each   1.00
Eggshell, broken open. 39mm.   2.75
Egg with flat base, can be found
inscribed: *Sparrows egg*. 44mm.   8.50
Cock, standing, legs modelled
separately, inscribed: *Cock o' th'
North* or *Cock o' th' South*. Some
colouring to head. 100mm.   8.25
Cock, standing, legs modelled
together. Some colouring to
head. 85mm.   10.50
Hen, standing, some colouring.
62mm (matches above).   10.50
Hen, roosting. 54mm.   3.00
Heron, on circular base. 83mm.   19.00
Bird perched on circular base.
(Reputedly a blackbird). 68mm.   16.00
Bird, perched on tree, wings
extended. 125mm
(very impressive).   36.00
Bird salt and pepper pots.
70mm.   Each   2.25
Dove, Fantail on square base.
70mm.   13.50
Duck. 86mm.   5.50
Norwich warbler. Canary. 100mm.   13.00
Coloured yellow.
Norwich warbler. Canary on rock,
with whistle and bubble blower
base. Often found unnamed.
126mm.   21.50
Owl, baby. 40mm.   5.25
Owl, Barn. 63mm.   4.75
Owl, Horned (long eared). 74mm.   5.50
Owl (Wise), one eye closed, with
verse. 98mm.   7.50
Parakeet. 60mm.   4.75
Parrot, sometimes inscribed:
Pretty Polly. No. 751. 75mm.   6.50
Peacock, yellow beak and coloured
plume. Rd. 115mm (rare).   23.00
Peacock on ashtray. (Can be
found in lustre.) 80mm long.   8.75
Pelican, with details of its stomach
capacity. 70mm.   21.75

Penguin. No details of size (rare).   37.50
Seagull. 76mm (rare).   30.00
Seagull, colouring to tip of wings
and yellow beak. 100mm.   24.50
Stork. 80mm.   15.00
Swan. 3 sizes: 50mm   2.50
                70mm   3.00
                85mm   5.00
        (detailed plumage).
Swan Posy Bowl. 88mm.   2.25
Turkey, on round base. 60mm.   10.50
Turkey, on square base. 76mm.   13.00

Great War
Many of these models are found with the
inscription *War Edition AD1914* and a
crest of 'one of the allied countries', (add
£4.50 for this).
Some of the soldiers, although sold
separately, were based on the same
design idea and form a set. They are
therefore grouped together in the listings.
British soldier, Model of, more often
than not unnamed. 135mm.   75.00
Colonial soldier, Model of. 135mm.   110.00
French soldier, Model of. 135mm.   87.50
Scots soldier, Model of. 135mm.   87.50
Bugler boy, Model of. 135mm.   115.00
Drummer boy, Model of. 135mm.   115.00
(All these figures are standing
to attention on an oval domed
base.)

British cavalry soldier, Model of, on
horseback. 122mm.   117.50
Russian Cossack, Model of, on horseback. 122mm.   117.50
Belgian Soldier, bust, usually
found with Belgian Crest.
80mm (rare).   87.50
Despatch rider, Model of, on motor-
bike. (Can be found in lustre).
120mm long.   40.00
*Nurse and wounded Tommy, Model
of*. 108mm long.   75.00
Nurse, inscribed: *Soldier's friend*.
Red cross on chest. 132mm.   40.00
Sailor, bust, found with hatband
impressed: *HMS Lion* or *HMS
Queen Elizabeth*. Inscribed: *The
Handyman, HMS Dreadnought*.   19.50

With verse: 25.75
Can be found with hat coloured
blue or model coloured. 92mm.
Sailor, standing with hands on hips.
2 sizes: 95mm 65.00
132mm. 56.50
Sailor winding capstan, Model of.
105mm. 75.00
Soldier, bust, inscribed: *Tommy
Atkins* or *Territorial*, either
found with verse 'Its the
Soldiers of the King my lads'. 21.75
Some colouring. 90mm.
with verse 26.00
Soldier with respirator, bust,
inscribed: *Model of new gas mask.*
95mm. 170.00
*Tommy driving a steam roller over
the Kaiser*, inscribed: *To Berlin.*
120mm (very rare). 400.00
Tommy in bayonet attack, Model of.
130mm. 95.00
*Tommy and his machine gun, Model
of.* 72mm. 26.00
Tommy on sentry duty, Model of, in
sentry box. 110mm. 40.00
*Tommy throwing his grenade, Model
of.* 130mm. 87.50
New aeroplane, Model of. Biplane
with fixed prop, and roundels
in relief. 120mm long. 75.00
New aeroplane, Model of. Monoplane with revolving propeller.
153mm long. 30.00
Monoplane, V winged, with fixed
prop. Propeller can be found
with 2 or 3 blades.
2 sizes: 118mm & 140mm long. 40.00
(This model has a circular por-
tion added for no other reason
than to carry the crest.)
Aeroplane Propeller.
150mm long. 13.00
Rarely factory marked.
British airship, Model of, with sus-
pended engine. 120mm long. 40.00
British Airship on stand. 128mm
long. 13.00
*Observer or Sausage balloon, Model
of.* 84mm. 30.00
Super Zeppelin, Model of.
127mm long. 17.50
N.B. The captions for the
Super Zeppelin and the
British airship have been trans-

posed on page 58 of *Crested
China.*
Battleship, the larger only
inscribed: *HMS Queen Elizabeth.*
2 sizes: 115mm 10.50
160mm long. 19.50
Battleship, 3 funnels and tiny
gun fore and aft.
3 sizes: 100mm 10.50
120mm 13.00
165mm long. 19.50
Minesweeper, not found named.
126mm long. 13.00
RMS Lusitania. 182mm long. 50.00
Torpedo boat destroyer, Model of.
108mm long. 16.00
Submarine, inscribed: *E4.*
95mm long. 8.75
New submarine, Model of,
inscribed: *E5.* 126mm long. 13.00
Airfield tractor, Model of.
80mm long (rare). 75.00
Armoured car, Model of.
95mm 22.50
Red Cross Van, red cross on each
side rear. 'EH 139' printed on
radiator. 3 sizes: 78mm 17.50
85mm 17.50
160mm long. 220.00
(The large size is extremely rare).
Staff car, 'EH 139' printed on
front and rear. 115mm long. 30.00
Tank, Model of.
5 sizes: 100mm long 80.00
115mm long 8.75
160mm long 19.50
180mm long 21.75
325mm long. 350.00
The smallest size is quite rare
and largest size is very rare,
being so enormous that it must
have been made for shop display. It has also been seen in
lustre.
Tank, Model of, with inset wheels.
This model has an exhaust
pipe which looks like a gun on
the top turret. 115mm long. 10.50
Can be found inscribed:
Original made in Lincoln. 25.00
Tank, Model of, with trailing steering wheels. Also has an exhaust
pipe in turret. 144mm long. 13.00
Tank, with trailing steering
wheels, no exhaust pipe in
turret. 138mm long. 13.00

Tank, Model of, exactly as above
but with one trailing wheel.
144mm long (rare). 350.00
Tank, Model of, exactly as above
but with a second wheel
attached to the one-wheeled
tank. 45.00
Whippet Tank, large hexagonal
gun turret at rear. 172mm long
(rare). 220.00
Field Gun. 2 sizes: 120mm 11.00
140mm long. 11.00
New field gun with screen, Model of.
105mm long. 13.00
German howitzer, Model of.
2 sizes: 115mm long 10.50
150mm long. 13.00
Trench mortar, Model of. Can be
found inscribed: *Roaring Meg.*
70mm long. 8.75
Mortar on square base. (Krupp).
70mm. 10.50
Revolver, Model of. 83mm long. 40.00
Anti-aircraft shell, Model of. 98mm. 8.75
Cannon Shell. 3 sizes: 70mm 2.25
90mm 3.00
135mm. 11.00
The 90mm and 135mm sizes are
often inscribed: *Jack Johnson* and
sometimes: *Hartlepool's
Bombardment Dec 16th 1914,*
for which £5.00 should be
added.
Cannon Shell Salt and Pepper
pots. 70mm. Each 1.75
Clip of bullets, Model of. 57mm. 10.50
Trench flying pig, Model of. (Flying
pig is a nickname for a type of
Stokes bomb.) 95mm long.
(very rare). 110.00
(N.B. At least 3 flying pigs
reported.)
*Bomb dropped from Zeppelin, Model
of.* Inscription sometimes
reads: *German Zeppelin* or *on
Bury St. Edmunds.* 75mm. 4.75
If inscribed 5.50
*Bomb dropped from Zeppelin upon
Sheringham during first raid on
England 8.30 Jany, 18th 1915,
Model of.* With movable three
bladed propeller. 115mm. 65.00

Also found with the following
inscription: *First bomb dropped
from Zeppelin at Loftus Sept 8th
1915 at 9.30* or 82.50
*Model of first bomb dropped from
Zeppelin on Skinningrove
Ironworks Sept. 8th 1915 at
9.30p.m.* 75mm. 90.00
British aerial bomb, Model of.
75mm. 21.75
Canister bomb, Model of. 60mm. 8.75
Plum pudding bomb, Model of.
Often found unnamed.
72mm (rare). 75.00
German hand grenade, Model of.
92mm (very rare). 82.50
Hairbrush grenade, Model of.
104mm long (rare). 130.00
Mills hand grenade, Model of. 62mm. 8.75
British aerial torpedo, Model of.
102mm long. 21.75
German aerial torpedo, Model of.
88mm long. 21.75
Bandsman's Drum. No. 226.
53mm. 4.50
(Probably made originally for
the S. African War.)
Bell Tent, inscribed: *Camping out.* 5.50
64mm dia. If named 7.50
Capstan. 56mm. 4.00
Ghurka knife, Model of. 110mm long. 13.00
Pair of field glasses, Model of. Often
found not named. 78mm long. 10.00
Sandbag, Model of. 73mm long. 8.75
Tommy's hut, Model of. 105mm long. 40.00
Trench dagger, Model of.
102mm long. 40.00
Trench lamp, Model of. 70mm. 8.75
Water bottle, Model of. 65mm. 8.75
Colonial hat, Model of, found
inscribed: *Anzacs.* 88mm wide. 5.50
Inscribed 7.50
Glengarry. 90mm long. 11.25
New Zealand Hat. 71mm dia. 17.50
Officer's peaked cap, white or
more usually with coloured
badge and hatband. Can be
found inscribed: *Territorials cap.*
65mm dia. 8.75
Solar Topee (Pith helmet). 60mm. 10.50
Steel helmet. 65mm dia. 17.50
Anti-Zeppelin Candle Holder.
65mm. 8.75
Fireplace, inscribed: *We've kept the
home fires burning.*
2 sizes: 90mm 8.75
115mm. 10.50

Angel with raised arms, found
with R.A.F. Crest (not named
but must be a R.A.F. Memorial.
No details of size (very rare).   65.00
Bishop's Stortford *War Memorial*.
132mm (rare).   65.00
Brora War Memorial. 155mm (rare).   65.00
Burford War Memorial, with
inscription. 128mm (rare).   65.00
Burnham on Crouch *War
Memorial*. 146mm (rare).   65.00
Cavell Memorial, inscribed: *Nurse
Cavell*. 2 sizes: 147mm   11.50
160mm   14.50
Cavell *Memorial statue, Norwich,*
inscribed: *Edith Cavell – Nurse,
Patriot and Martyr*. 175mm.   17.00
Cenotaph, Model of, with green
wreaths. 4 sizes: 80mm   4.00
100mm   3.00
140mm   4.00
180mm   7.50
Three larger sizes with inscrip-
tion.
Cheltenham War Memorial.
2 sizes: 150mm   40.00
185mm.   47.50
Chesham *War Memorial*. 159mm.   65.00
Dover Patrol Memorial. 130mm.   21.75
Dover *War Memorial*. 140mm.   56.50
Dovercourt War Memorial. 137mm.   65.00
East Dereham War Memorial,
with inscription (rare).   65.00
Florence Nightingale statue,
inscribed: *The Lady of the Lamp*.
170mm.   13.50
147mm smaller version from
different mould.   10.50
Folkestone War Memorial
inscribed: *May their deeds be held
in reverence*.
2 sizes: 97mm long   56.50
156mm long.   56.50
Fryatt Memorial, with inscription
(rare).   65.00
Great Yarmouth *War Memorial*,
with inscription. 146mm.   21.75
Invergordon *War Memorial*.
148mm (rare).   65.00
Killin War Memorial. 150mm.   65.00
*Earl Kitchener Memorial, drowned
off Marwick Head, Orkney, 5th
June 1916*. 110mm.   65.00

Loughborough War Memorial.
155mm.   40.00
Margate *War Memorial*. 160mm.   40.00
March War Memorial. 160mm.   65.00
Newhaven Mercantile Memorial,
with inscription.   56.50
Norwich *War Memorial*.
134mm (rare).   65.00
Plymouth Naval *War Memorial*,
with inscription.
3 sizes: 125mm   40.00
156mm   41.50
178mm   47.50
Plymouth Royal Naval Memorial,
on octagonal stepped base.
144mm.   65.00
Sheringham War Memorial, with
inscription. 165mm.   47.50
Southsea Naval War Memorial.
2 sizes: 140mm   40.00
162mm   41.50
Stowmarket Memorial Gates.
110mm long.   65.00
Woodhouse Eaves, War Memorial
with inscription. 130mm (rare).   65.00

Most War Memorials are rela-
tively rare, possibly because
they were ordered in small
numbers by local shops, and
were only made for a short
time.

Home/Nostalgic
Anvil on tree trunk base, horse-
shoe, tongs etc. against base.
70mm.   4.75
Armchair. 65mm.   7.50
Armchair, inscribed: *The old arm-
chair*, with verse. 90mm.   5.50
Basket with twisted handle.
73mm long.   1.75
If inscribed: *Fruit Basket*   5.00
Bellows. 95mm long.   5.00
Chair, highbacked. 90mm.   5.50
Child in long nightdress, for use
as candlesnuffer. Some
colouring. 100mm.   10.00
Coal Scuttle. 65mm.   2.75
Coal Scuttle, sometimes found
inscribed: *Coal scuttle*. 80mm.   3.75
Cradle. 48mm.   4.00
Dressing Table, swing mirror,
with drawer. 50mm.   5.50
Dust pan. 95mm long.   5.25

Firebucket. 55mm. — 3.00

Fireplace, with teapot, cat, etc. in bold relief. Inscribed: *There's no place like home*. Some colouring.
2 sizes: 90mm — 8.75
112mm. — 11.00

Fireplace, with cauldron, teapot, etc. moulded in slight relief. Inscribed: *There's no place like home*. Some colouring. 65mm. — 13.00

Frying Pan. 120mm. — 5.50

Grandfather clock, Model of. Usually inscribed: *Make use of time let not advantage slip. Shakespeare*. Can be found inscribed: *Top o' the morn*. No. 209. 108mm (two moulds). — 10.50

Grandmother Clock. 103mm. — 10.50

Jardinere. 95mm. — 2.75

Kennel, can be found inscribed: *Beware of the dog*. 50mm. — 4.25

Lantern. 2 sizes: 70mm — 3.50
90mm. — 3.75

Lantern, horn, not found named but sometimes inscribed: *Watchman what of the night*. 85mm. — 4.75

Lantern, with open side. 125mm. — 11.00

Milk Churn. 63mm. — 3.00

Pillar Box, with inscription: *If you haven't time to post a line here's the pillar box*. Found marked G.R.V. 63mm. — 8.25

Shaving mug. 60mm. — 4.00

Spinning Wheel. 84mm. — 11.50

Sundial, inscribed: *Life's but a walking shadow*. 2 sizes: 86mm — 4.00
115mm. — 7.50

Table, four legs. 40mm. — 3.50

Thimble. 41mm. — 8.75

Umbrella, open. 50mm dia. (Usually not marked.) — 7.50

Village Pump with trough. 90mm. — 5.50

Old warming pan, Model of, inscribed: *Polly warm the bed*. No. 254. 125mm. — 6.00

Old Warming Pan, Model of, with ornate handle. No. 251. 120mm. — 6.00

Wheelbarrow. 100mm long. — 6.00

Comic/Novelty

Alarm Clock, inscribed: *Many are called but few get up!*
2 sizes: 40mm. — 19.50
60mm. — 21.50

Basket of Milk, six bottles, tops can be gold or brown. 65mm. — 9.50

Billiken, often found not named. 63mm. — 3.00

Bookmaker with greyhound and hare on ashtray base. Some colouring. 90mm long. — 45.00

Boy Scout, inscribed: *Be prepared*. 105mm. — 25.00

Clown, bust. No inscription or colouring. 65mm. — 7.50

Clown, bust, inscribed: *Put me amongst the girls*. Some colouring. 80mm. — 16.50

Clown standing, hands on hips, wearing baggy suit. 104mm. — 20.00

Couple in Bed, inscribed: *John is everything shut up for the night – All but you darling*. 70mm long. — 35.00

Couple in bed, man sitting up, woman with all the blankets, inscribed: *They don't need many clothes in the daytime but they want 'em all at night*. 70mm long. — 47.50

Fat lady on weighing scales, scale registers 20 stone. Inscribed: *Adding weight*. Blue bonnet. 90mm. — 27.75

Japanese Girl, with fan and parasol. No. 250. 64mm. — 27.75

Jester, double faced bust, happy and sad and eyes open and closed. Can be found inscribed: *Ye Jester awake. Ye Jester asleep*. Some colouring.
2 sizes: 65mm. — 4.00
90mm. — 11.00

Judge in his box reading a book. 82mm. — 34.50

Lavatory Pan with brown seat, inscribed: *Ashes*. Not found crested. 60mm (rare). — 9.50

Mister Gollywog, Now children when I've tucked you safely in, just say Mr Gollywog good-night. 118mm. — 50.00

Negro Minstrel, bust, verse by Eugene Stratton. Some colouring. 100mm (rare). — 21.50

Negro, standing with hands in pockets as vase. 105mm. — 47.00

Policeman, smiling, with arms behind back. 100mm. — 16.00

Policeman, fat and jovial, with raised hand. Inscribed (on hand): *Stop*. 94mm.   16.00

Policeman on duty, with verse. 148mm.   16.00

Policeman, jovial holding large truncheon. Uniform and helmet blue. 106mm (rare).   60.00

Petrol Pump Attendant, body is pump. Inscribed: *Petrol Sir*. Some colouring. 95mm.   40.00

Robinson Crusoe. 122mm.   40.00

Pierrot, standing. 100mm.   24.50

Sailor, standing, cap can be found impressed: *Lion*. Blue cap and coloured face. 95mm.   35.00

Sailor toby jug, blue hat and coat.
   60mm.   47.50
   65mm.   65.00
   108mm.   65.00

Suffragette double sided bust, front sour old lady, inscribed: *Votes for women*, back pretty young girl, inscribed: *This one shall have the vote*. Much colouring. 98mm.   19.50

A smaller version exists with no colouring or inscriptions. 72mm.   8.50

Suffragette candle snuffer, double faced as above. 72mm.   8.75

Suffragette hand bell, double faced as above, with same inscription and colouring. 110mm.   21.50

(All the suffragette items must be considered scarce).

Teapot with eyes, mouth and nose as spout. Some colouring.   12.00

A truck of coal from .....Wagon of black coal. 80mm long.   10.50

Comic Ashtrays: Coloured figures on white trays. (All are quite rare).

Flapper, sitting on bench on heart shaped tray, yellow hat and dress. 105mm.   50.00

(This flapper can also be found on her bench on an oval ashtray)

Hare and Greyhound.   45.00

Irish Colleen – see National section.

Jester, sitting on heart shaped tray, other card symbols are on tray. 65mm (rare).   100.00

Scotsman, really grotesque, sitting on bench on round tray. 95mm.   50.00

Comic Cruet Sets: Only odd items have been sold in sets. They are all fully coloured.

Policeman Salt Pot. 80mm.   40.00

Regimental Sergeant Major Pepper Pot. 80mm.   30.00

Naval Petty Officer pepper pot. 80mm.   26.00

Sailor, comic figure with green parrot on shoulder with white mustard barrel with lid. 63mm.   36.50

Little birds: these are fully coloured heads popping out of white eggs. They do not seem to match any other series of models, the black boy's face is much more carefully detailed than the black boy's listed below.

Flapper's head hatching from egg, inscribed: *A little bird from* .... 50mm long.   12.50

Black boy's head hatching from egg, inscribed: *A blackbird from* .... 50mm long.   21.75

Black Boys – often found marked Rd. No. applied for. All the boys are fully coloured but sit on white boxes, baths and so on. Later models are very brightly and carefully coloured and lightly glazed. These are marked as late in the listing below. All of these models, with the exception of *A little study in black and fright*, are uncommon.

Black Boy standing with hands in pocket, also found as salt pot. 94mm (late).   47.00

Black Girl, standing with hands on hips, also found as Pepper Pot. (Pair with above). 94mm.   56.50

Black Boy playing banjo, boy can be wearing red, yellow or blue striped pyjamas. 85mm.   85.00

Black Boy in bath of ink, towel
hanging at side, inscribed: *How
ink is made* 110mm. (Probably
Willow are mould). 65.00
Black Boy in hip bath holding
yellow soap. 90mm (late). 82.50
Black Boy in bed with spider, inscribed: *A little study in black and
fright*. Boy can have red or blue
striped pyjamas. 70mm long. 40.00
Black Boy being chased up a tree
by a crocodile. 80mm. 100.00
Black Boy eating slice of Melon,
sitting on a soapbox.
80mm (late). 75.00
Black Boy eating melon slice,
standing on corner of diamond
shaped ashtray inscribed: *I'se
not melon-choly!* Rare. 88mm. 105.00
Black Boy sitting at table eating a
boiled egg which has chicken
popping out. 70mm. 75.00
Two Black Boys heads popping
out of box, inscribed: *Box of
chocolates*. 60mm. 30.00
Also found in white only. 13.00
Two black children, boy and girl
sitting on a tree trunk.
80mm (late) 56.50
Black Boy holding container for
cigarettes. 100mm (late). 56.50
Black Boy holding container for
matches. 100mm (late). 56.50
Black Boy peering out of shower
(rare) 67mm. 105.00
Black Boy Toby Jug. 66mm. 45.00
Children: very late models,
beautifully coloured and
detailed children on white arm-
chairs, baths etc. Usually found
marked Rd. No. applied for.
They are particularly appealing and unfortunately rare.
Deduct £20 if not coloured.
Girl and boy sitting in armchair.
Girl is wearing a frilly dress and
has a large bow on her head;
boy is dressed in top hat and
tails. 60mm. 56.50
Girl and boy as above sitting on
tree trunk. 87mm long. 43.50
Boy riding a pig. Boy wearing a
coloured coat. 85.00
Girl standing by hip bath,
wearing towel. 75mm. 85.00

Girl standing naked, red bow in
hair, beside circular bath.
Yellow (face) sponge attached.
62mm. 85.00
Baby in bath with a coloured
transfer of an insect (variously
described as a wasp or a fly).
80mm long. 31.50

Cartoon/Comedy Characters
Ally Sloper, bust, with inscription.
85mm. 25.75
Bonzo, name impressed on collar.
68mm. 37.00
Bonzo, sitting on feeding bowl.
65mm. 29.50
Bonzo and Felix sitting on bench,
coloured and not named.
76mm. 60.00
Harry Lauder, bust. Inscribed: *Stop
ye're tickling Jock*. Often found
not named. Some colouring 9.50
83mm, named 15.25
Mrs. Gummidge, standing figure
with inscription: *A lone lorn
creetur & everything goes contrairy with her*. 112mm (rare). 19.50
Winkie the glad-eyed bird, not
named but can be found
inscribed: *Glad eyes*. 60mm. 7.50

Alcohol
Series of late models of a fully
coloured comic man (looks
rather like Mr. Pickwick, bald
with spectacles, but probably
was a comedian or comic
character associated with heavy
drinking) on white models.
Man, as above, drinking beer
from tankard. Can be in white,
or with silver tankard and
coloured face or   white 25.25
fully coloured. 92mm. coloured 34.75
Man, as above, holding tankard
on horseshoe ashtray, with
inscription: *The more we are
together the merrier we'll be*. 33.00
Man, as above, clinging to neck of
bottle. Fully coloured, white
bottle. 2 sizes: 80mm. 29.50
95mm. 29.50
Man, as above, climbing into large
beaker. 75mm. 34.50

Beaker, fluted, with inscription:
*They speak o' my drinking, but
they dinna consider my drouth*. or
*Ye never ken the worth o' water till
the well not is dry*. 78mm.   4.50
Beer Barrel on stand, inscribed:
XXX on each end of barrel.
55mm   3.00
Beer Bottle and tankard on
horseshoe ashtray, with
inscription: *The more we are
together the merrier we'll be*.   12.50
Bottle. 63mm.   4.00
Bottle with cork. 76mm.   4.50
Drunk leaning against a statue on
an ashtray. Inscribed: *How cold
you are tonight dear*. Coloured
figure on white tray. 100mm.   50.00
Monk, jovial, and holding glass
with verse: *A jovial monk am I
contented with my lot. The world
without this gate, I flout nor care
for it one jot*. 2 sizes: 70mm.   8.75
                          112mm.   10.50
A Nap Hand, hand holding
coloured beer labels on heart
shaped dish. 62mm long.   45.00
Silver Tankard. 85mm long.   11.00
Soda Syphon. 100mm.   7.50
Tankard, foaming, with verse:
'The more we are together'.
50mm.   4.00
Thistle vase, with verse: 'Just a
wee doech-an doris'. 70mm.   2.50
Toby Jug, sometimes found with
verse:*No tongue can tell, No heart
can think, Oh how I love a drop of
drink*. 3 sizes:
45mm. Smallest size, can
              be found coloured
white   4.50
coloured   12.00
65mm. Middle size, is exactly
              the same as Old Toby
              Jug.   5.25
85mm.   7.50
Whiskey Bottle, can have solid or
cork top, inscribed: *One special
Scotch*. 100mm.   4.50
Whiskey Bottle and Soda Syphon
on tray, inscribed: *Scotch and
Soda*. 88mm dia.   12.50
Whiskey Quaich (or bowl)
inscribed: *Scuab As'l*.
134mm long.   6.00

Sport

Billiard Table, cue and three balls.
100mm long.   56.50
Cricket Bag. 80mm long.   6.50
Cricket Bat. 115mm long.   21.50
Curling Stone. 63mm dia.   13.00
Football. 50mm dia.   4.50
The F.A. Cup. 100mm.   10.00
Golf Ball, often inscribed: *The
game of golf was first played in the
year 1448*. 42mm.   4.75
Golf Club Head. 94mm long.   7.50
Golf Bag and Clubs. 105mm.   13.00
Golfer, with Clubs standing on
golf ball. 76mm.   21.75
Golfer's Caddie holding golf bag.
Figure coloured.
110mm (late model)   65.00
Golfer's Caddie, very tiny, hold-
ing huge bag of clubs. 88mm.   40.00
Jockey on racehorse, oval base,
some colouring, horse
unglazed. 115mm.   65.00
Tennis Racquet. 90mm long.   5.50

Musical Instruments

Banjo. 2 sizes: 125mm &
150mm long.   4.75
Double Bass. 153mm long.   25.75
Guitar. 153mm long.   ·   6.50
Piano, Upright. 70mm long.   8.25
Tambourine. 50mm dia.   7.50
Violin with bow. 125mm long.   21.75

Transport

Car, open tourer (2 seater)
inscribed: *EH 139*; can be found
also inscribed: *HELL*.
110mm long.   21.75
Car, saloon, inscribed: *EH 139*.
76mm long.   21.75
Car, open 2 seater showing ex-
haust pipes etc. 105mm long.   40.00
Charabanc, 18 seater, inscribed:
*7734 which upside down reads
HELL*. 138mm long.   19.50
Can of Petrol, impressed: *Motor
Spirit*. 55mm.   8.75
Omnibus, Double decker bus with
stairs outside.
130mm long (rare)   117.50

'Modern' Equipment

Camera, folding. 60mm.   19.50
Gramophone in cabinet.
80mm long.   30.00
Horn Gramophone. 112mm.   18.00

Hats

Boy Scout's Hat. 73mm dia.	12.00
Luton Boater with coloured band. 100mm long.	8.25
Mitre. No. 19. 84mm long.	4.00
Straw Hat. 75mm long.	5.50
Top Hat. 40mm.	3.00

Shoes

Highboot. 85mm.	10.50
High backed narrow shoe. 2 sizes: 90mm.	7.50
130mm long.	10.50
Hobnail Boot. 2 sizes: 65mm.	4.00
80mm long.	5.50
Ladies Ankle Boot. 70mm long.	4.75
Dutch Clog. 102mm long.	4.50
Sabot, pointed toe. 60mm long.	4.75
Oriental Shoe. 2 sizes: 85mm	4.00
105mm long.	6.50
Shoe posy holder. 100mm long.	3.75
Slipper. 100mm long.	7.00

Miscellaneous

Ball of String match holder and striker. 55mm.	5.50
Chess Set. Complete sets can be found but these are very rare. It is extremely difficult to collect a set with matching crests. Individual pieces are often found however, the rook being the most common; the pawn, strangely, is quite rare.	
King. 88mm.	20.00
Queen. 84mm.	20.00
Knight. 63mm.	7.50
Bishop. 60mm.	16.50
Rook. 55mm.	3.00
Pawn. 52mm.	16.50
Flower Bud Vase. 40mm.	3.00
Handbell, no clapper. 53mm.	2.25
Horse's Hoof as inkwell. Inscribed *We're aye prood tae hear frae ye*. 90mm.	5.50
Horse's Hoof on base. No. 151. 30mm.	2.25
Horseshoe. 55mm long.	2.50

Miniature Domestic

These models can be found with crests, views, black cats and other transfer decorations.

Beaker. 40mm.	1.25
Chamberpot. 38mm.	1.25
Cheese dish, one piece. 50mm.	4.75
Cheese dish with cover. 50mm.	7.50
Teacup and saucer. 40mm.	4.00
Teapot and lid. 60mm.	5.50

Domestic

This is listed as it was made specifically to carry crests. Pieces can also be found with 'Lucky Black Cat', 'Lucky White Heather' and other transfer decorations, but not usually views. Late pieces are found with the black cat *Arcadian* mark. Lettering is usually in blue.

Ashtrays, can be found inscribed: *Ashtray*. Various shapes:	
Clovershapes.	1.75
Club, diamond, heart and spade shaped with crinkle edges.	2.25
Club shaped tray with match box stand.	3.00
Heart shaped bowl.	1.25
Horseshoe.	2.50
Octagonal.	1.25
Round tray with match holder.	2.50
Bulb bowl, hexagonal.	2.50
Candle Snuffer, cone.	2.50
Candlesticks, various shapes:	
Column with ornate moulding.	1.75
Octagonal, fluted.	1.75
Short on oblong base with handle.	1.75
Short on fluted oblong base with handle.	1.75
Short on fluted leaf shaped base with handle.	1.75
Fern pots, fluted. 3 sizes.	2.25
Hexagonal. 3 sizes.	2.25
Flower bowl, octagonal.	2.25
Hair pin box, can be found inscribed: *Hairpins*. Fluted oblong or round.	3.00
Hair Tidy, can be found inscribed: *Hair tidy*. Various shapes:	
Hexagonal.	3.00
Octagonal with ornate moulding and blue bow.	4.00
Square, fluted.	3.00

Hat Pin Holder, can be found
inscribed: *Hat pins* Various
shapes:
Octagonal.   5.50
Square fluted. 121mm.   6.50
Square with ornate moulding.
Fluted. 128mm.   7.50
Inkstand.   5.50
Inkstand, with pen holder base.   6.50
Match Holder, can be found
inscribed: *Matches*. Various
shapes:
Hexagonal.   2.25
Round.   2.25
Round on base.   2.50
Pin Tray, can be found inscribed:
Pins. Fluted round or oblong.   2.25
Pot Pourri, 2 shapes:
Round vase shaped, lid with
knob.   2.75
Round with domed lid (rather
like a ginger jar).   3.50
Powder bowl, round.   3.75
Preserve Jar and lid, round or tub
shaped.   4.25
Puff Box, can be found inscribed:
Puff box, hexagonal or round.
2 sizes.   3.50
Ring Stand.   6.00
Rose Bowl, fluted with brass
fittings.   3.50
Tableware: Cups and saucers, coffee cans
and saucers, and plates are all found in
classic and simple shapes.
Also the following:
Beakers, plain and fluted.   1.25
Butter Tub.   2.50
Cream Jugs and Sugar bowls
(matching) in various shapes:
Hexagonal   1.25
Octagonal   1.25
Round, plain.   1.25
Round, fluted.   1.25
These can occasionally be found
inscribed: *Help yourself to the
crame/sugar* or *Be aisy wid the
crame/sugar*. Add £2.00 with
these inscriptions.
Egg Cup.   2.25
Jugs, in a variety of sizes, also
bagware.   1.75
Mugs. 2 sizes.   1.75
Mustard Pots. Various shapes:
Round with pointed lid.   2.00

Round, fluted and ornate.   2.25
Round with silver lid.   4.50
Round, tall, with silver lid.   4.75
Pepper & Salt Pots, various
shapes:
Cone shaped, small.   1.75
Cone shaped, tall with silver
lids.   4.50
Hexagonal.   1.75
Round, fluted and ornate.   1.75
Round, with silver lids.   4.50
Plate, with thistles and leeks
moulded in relief.   2.00
Sugar Basin on Stand.   1.25
Sugar Caster.   1.75
Sweet Dishes, various shapes:
Octagonal.   1.50
Round, crinkle edges. 2 sizes.   1.50
Round, fluted, 2 sizes.   1.50
Teapots. 1, 2 & 3 cup sizes.   5.50
Tobacco Jar, inscribed: *Tobacco*. 6.00
Trinket Boxes, can be found
inscribed: *Trinkets*. Various
shapes:
Heart shaped. 4 sizes.   4.00
Hexagonal.   2.50
Horseshoe shaped.   2.50
Oblong.   2.75
Oval.   2.50
Round. 2 sizes.   2.00
Square.   2.00
Square with bevelled corners.   2.00
Square, fluted.   2.00

Argonauta Porcelain

Argosy China

For mark see *Crested China*, p. 64.

For mark see *Crested China*, p. 65.

Trademark used by James Macintyre & Co Ltd, Washinton China Works, Burslem.

Trademark used by Grafton possibly using a retailer's mark. (Usual trademark Grafton).

Many rather heavy smalls found with this mark.

Ancient Artefacts
Mug, 1 handled. No. 17. 35mm.   2.25

Miscellaneous
Club shaped dish. 75mm long.   2.00

Seaside
Bathing Machine with large
wooden wheels, and panelled
body. 55mm.   6.00

Animals
Elephant, comic, standing with
sandwich boards. 115mm.   24.50

Great War
Colonial Hat. 25mm.   7.50

Miscellaneous
Boot with laces.
No. 234. 80mm long.   7.50

Miniature Domestic
Teapot. 90mm long.   6.50

Asbury

For mark see *Crested China*, p. 65.

Trademark used by Edward Asbury and Co., Prince of Wales' Works, Longton.

Animals
Lion walking. 115mm long.   8.75

Birds
Duck Posy Bowl. 70mm long.   6.50
Swan. 65mm long.   2.75

Great War
Tank. 85mm long.   8.75

Novelty
Billiken, flat grotesque type.
68mm.   3.00

Miscellaneous
Sabot. 80mm long.   4.00
Top Hat. 40mm.   3.00
Tree trunk flower holder. 80mm.   3.50

Atlas Heraldic China

For mark see *Crested China*, p. 65.

Trademark thought to have been used by Taylor and Kent, Florence Works, Longton, for a wholesaler in Scotland. (Usual trademark Florentine).

Ancient/Artefacts
Salisbury Kettle, not named.
100mm.   1.25

Monuments
Iona Cross. 108mm.   4.00

National Souvenirs
Welsh Hat with blue cord and
embossed tassels. 56mm.   3.00

Seaside Souvenirs
Whelk Shell. 100mm.   2.50
Suitcase with gilded straps.
80mm long.   2.25

Birds
Kingfisher. 80mm.   10.50
Pelican Cream Jug. 83mm long.   4.00

Home/Nostalgic
Baby in hip bath. 100mm long.   6.50
Sofa. 82mm long.   5.50
Napkin ring. 38mm.   2.50
The Old Armchair, with verse.
85mm.   5.50

Miscellaneous
Carboy. 76mm.   2.25
Oriental shoe with turned up toe.
95mm long.   4.00
Shoe, Ladies' 18th century.
95mm long.   7.50
Thimble. 40mm.   8.75

Miniature Domestic
Cheese Dish and cover. 55mm.   4.00
Coffee Pot and lid. 63mm.   3.00
Teapot. 70mm.   4.00

Avon China

Aynsley

For mark see *Crested China*, p. 67.

For mark see *Crested China*, p. 67.

Trademark used by Arkinstall & Son Ltd, Arcadian Works, Stoke-on-Trent. (Usual trademark Arcadian).

Many small pots and jugs etc. are found with this mark, probably an early Arkinstall's mark.

Traditional/National Souvenirs
John Bull, bust of. 85mm.   7.50

Comic/Novelty
Suffragette bust, double faced.
  89mm.   20.00

Sport
Golf Ball. 43mm.   4.00

Trademark used on china with military crests by John Aynsley and Sons, Portland Works, Longton.

Aynsley models therefore almost always appear bearing military badges.

South African War
Hand Grenade, with flames
  coming from the top. 88mm.   30.00
Cannon Shell. 104mm.   23.00
Empty Shell Case.   40.00
Bandsman's Drum. 55mm.   13.00
High boot. 118mm.   13.00
Tent, with open flaps. 75mm.   15.50
Waterbottle. 80mm.   17.50
Colonial Soldier's Hat.
  80mm long.   13.00
Forage Cap. 85mm long.   15.50
Glengarry. 90mm long.   15.50
Pickelhaube. 69mm long.   17.00
Pith Helmet.   16.00

Miscellaneous
Boot. 60mm.   13.00
Horse's Hoof.   17.50
Horseshoe. 85mm long.   13.00
Circular plaque.   8.00
Circular plaque with silver rim.   13.00
Ladies Shoe. 92mm long.   13.00

B

Balmoral China

For mark see *Crested China*, p. 68.

For mark see *Crested China*, p. 69.

Trademark used by Blairs and Beaconfield Pottery, Longton.

Animals

Pig, standing. 80mm long.   10.50

Miniature Domestic

Cheesedish, one piece. 50mm.   4.50

Trademark used by Redfern and Drakeford (Ltd), Balmoral Works, Longton.

Mark only found on one piece of china with a British Empire Exhibition badge, which has also been seen with a WILLOW ART mark.

Bird

Goose, standing and very fat, with long slender neck. 155mm.   40.00

Bell China

Belleek

W W
L

This mark found on one piece of domestic ware with an EPNS top, evidently made for a Llandudno retailer. Taylor and Kent specialised in producing china for manufacturers to add metal lids etc. as did many other potteries.

Domestic
Sugar Sifter with EPNS top.
(Llandudno Crest). 160mm.   1.25

For mark see *Crested China*, p. 69.

Trademark used by Belleek Pottery (David McBirney and Co.), Belleek, Co. Fermanagh, N. Ireland.

National Souvenirs
Shamrock shaped loving cup. 3
  handles. 50mm.   9.50

Animal
Pig, sitting.   13.00
Terrier, standing. 88mm.   14.00

Alcohol
Barrel. 57mm.   9.50

Many very fine 'smalls' were
  produced by this Pottery often
  with the characteristic Belleek
  Lustre finish. These are valued
  at £8.00–£10.00.

Birks China

Blairs China

For mark see *Crested China*, p. 69.

For mark see *Crested China*, p. 71.

Trademark used by Birks, Rawlins & Co. (Ltd.), Vine Pottery, Stoke, previously L.A. Birks & Co., established in 1885. (Usual trademark Savoy).

Great War
Battleship with 3 funnels,
  inscribed: *HMS Tiger*.
  116mm long.   56.50

Home/Nostalgic
Basket. 48mm.   2.25
Handbag. 88mm.   6.00

Novelty
Biscuit, impressed: *Huntley &*
  Palmers. On stand.
  Impressed 399. 85mm.   30.00
  With holes for hatpins.

Trademark used by Blairs Ltd, Beaconsfield Pottery, Longton.

This trademark had only been found on a range of 'smalls' with Great War inscriptions or commemorative prints.

Boots

Botolph China

For additional mark see *Crested China*, p. 71.

Trademark used for Boots The Chemist by Arkinstall & Son Ltd, Arcadian Works, Stoke-on-Trent. (Usual trademark Arcadian).

Ancient Artefacts
Glastonbury Abbot's Cup, not
   named. No. 238. 48mm.   1.25

Animal
Pig, standing, inscribed: *Wunt be*
   druv. 85mm long.   9.50

Many 'smalls' also produced not of very good quality. These often have Great War inscriptions.

For additional marks see *Crested China*, p. 71.

Trademark probably used by J. Wilson and Sons, Park Works, Fenton.

Buildings – White
Big Ben.

Two sizes:	92mm	11.50
	130mm.	13.00
Blackpool Tower. 117mm.		4.00

Marble Arch, Model of.

2 sizes: 60mm.		5.50
	80mm.	6.50
Old London Bridge, Ye. 86mm.		16.00

St. Paul's Cathedral.

2 sizes:	76mm.	14.50
	127mm.	16.00
Temple Bar. 96mm.		16.00

Tower Bridge.

133mm long	20.00

Wembley Sports Stadium.

134mm long.	26.00

Westminster Abbey, West Front.

2 sizes: 80mm		13.00
	116mm.	14.50

Historic/Folklore

Man standing in Pillory. 105mm.	13.00
Mother Shipton. 73mm.	4.00

Traditional/National Souvenirs

Yarmouth Bloater. 100mm long.	2.25
Irish Harp. 106mm.	4.50

Seaside Souvenirs

Bathing Machine with bather wearing towel in the doorway. 75mm.	8.50
Houseboat. 90mm long.	3.00
Yacht. 125mm long.	8.25
Life Belt. 85mm dia.	7.00
Fisherman's creel, fixed lid. 60mm.	2.25
Lighthouse. 95mm.	3.50
Suitcase. 58mm.	2.25
Whelk Shell. 98mm long.	2.50

Countryside

Haystack, rectangular. 56mm long.	4.00

Animals

Cat, arched back, coloured features. 82mm.	10.50
Cat, long neck. 106mm.	6.50
Dog, Bulldog. 57mm.	10.00
Dog, Labrador puppy with curly tail, sitting. 90mm.	7.50
Dogs, King Charles Spaniels, two in Top Hat. 78mm.	12.00
Dolphin vase. 110mm.	4.00
Pig, standing. 55mm.	7.50
Rabbit. 70mm long.	4.00
Tortoise. 70mm long.	4.00

Birds

Chicken in egg. 63mm long.	4.00
Hen, roosting. 52mm.	3.00
Kingfisher. 76mm.	10.50
Owl, baby. 70mm.	6.00
Swan. 63mm.	3.00
Swan Posy Holder. 90mm long.	3.00

Great War

Nurse, inscribed: *A Soldier's Friend*. 125mm.	75.00
Sailor, bust of. 83mm.	18.50
Monoplane, with movable prop. 175mm long.	30.00
Observer Sausage Balloon. 80mm.	30.00
Zeppelin on stand. 130mm.	13.00
Battleship, 2 sizes: 115mm.	13.00
165mm long.	19.50
Larger size found with inscription: *Great War 1914–18. The*	

German Fleet surrendered 74 warships Nov 21st 1918. Torpedo Boat Destroyer.

110mm long.	16.00
Submarine, inscribed: *E4*. 95mm long.	8.75
Submarine, inscribed: *E5*. 127mm long.	13.00
Red Cross Van. *EH 139*, with 3 red crosses. 88mm long.	17.50
Tank, Model of. 155mm long.	19.50
Tank with small integral steering wheels. 105mm long.	10.50
Field Gun. 120mm long.	11.00
Howitzer. 135mm long.	13.00
Trench Mortar. 70mm.	8.75
Cannon Shell, inscribed: *Jack Johnson*. 94mm.	4.00
Clip of Bullets. 85mm.	10.50
Revolver. 83mm long.	40.00
Bandsman's Drum. 58mm dia.	4.50
New Zealand Hat. 73mm long.	17.50
Fireplace, inscribed: *We've kept the fires burning*. 110mm.	11.50
Cenotaph, Whitehall London, Model of. With green wreaths and inscription. 3 sizes: 80mm.	4.00
120mm.	3.50
145mm.	4.00
Cavell Memorial Statue, London, inscribed: *Nurse Cavell*. 2 sizes: 115mm.	8.25
160mm.	11.50

Home/Nostalgic

Armchair, inscribed: *The Old Armchair* and verse. 90mm.	4.00
Baby in hip bath. 103mm long.	6.50
Boy on scooter. 103mm.	13.00
Coal Scuttle. 60mm.	3.00
Edwardian Boy and Girl cruet set. 90mm. Each	10.50
Garden Roller. 85mm long.	4.75
Lantern. 70mm.	3.50
Sofa. 80mm long.	4.00
Watering Can. 70mm.	4.00

Comic/Novelty

Bust of smiling boy, Spill Holder. 71mm.	3.50
Jack in the Box. 95mm.	10.50
Screw, inscribed: *A big fat screw*. 75mm.	13.00

Pierrot, sitting, planying banjo.
Some colouring on hands and
face. 120mm.   20.00

Sport
Cricket Bag. 110mm long.   6.50
Golf Club Head. 2 sizes:
   75mm.   7.00
   95mm.   7.50
Snooker Table on 6 legs. With 3
   balls and cue resting on top.
   100mm long.   56.50

Musical Instruments
Grand Piano. 85mm.   12.50

Transport
Car Horn, inscribed: *Pip Pip*.
   90mm long.   13.00
Omnibus, double decker bus with
   stairs outside. 130mm long.   117.50
Saloon car, always found gilded
   on one side only. 86mm long.   30.00

Miscellaneous
Bishop's Mitre. 55mm.   4.00
Boater, hat. 75mm long.   5.50
Oriental Shoe with pointed
   turned up toe. 98mm long.   4.00
Shoe, ladies', 18th century.
   93mm long.   7.50
Thigh Boot, with scalloped rim.
   100mm.   10.50
Toby Jug. 65mm.   5.25

Bow China

For mark see *Crested China*, p. 73.

Trademark used by Birks, Rawlins & Co
(Ltd.), Vine Pottery, Stoke (Usual trademark Savoy).

Ancient Artefacts
Celtic Vase in British Museum,
   Model of. No. 25. 45mm.   2.25
Greek Vase, inscribed: *Model of*
   Greek Vase from the collection of
   Sir Henry Englefield. No. 66.
   72mm.   2.25
Lincoln Jack from original in
   museum, Model of.
   No. 39. 60mm.   2.25

Animals
Elephant and Howdah.
   70mm (rare).   20.00

Great War
Battleship found inscribed with
   one of the following: *HMS Lion*   50.00
   or *HMS Ramilies*.   56.50
   No. 524. 168mm long.   56.50
Submarine, inscribed: *E1*, usually
   found with inscription.
   150mm long.   35.00
Howitzer. 170mm long.   24.50

Miscellaneous
Top Hat. No. 339. 44mm.   3.00

Bramwell China

Trademark used by an unknown manufacturer for a retailer probably in Sheffield. Only one model known with Sheffield Crest.

Ancient Artefacts
Leather Jack, not named. No. 751.
  62mm.   1.25
(This number does not occur for a model like this in other ranges – possibly the Stock No. should be 75 or 51. The other numeral being a paintresses mark).

Cable China

Trademark used by a branch of J.A. Robinson & Sons, probably Willow Potteries Ltd. (Usual trademark Willow).

Novelty
Minstrel, bust, no colouring.
  90mm.   11.00

Miscellaneous
Shoe. 113mm long.   10.50
Tulip in hand. 81mm.   2.25

C and SC

Cambrian China

For mark see *Crested China*, p. 74.

For mark see *Crested China*, p. 74.

Trademark used by Taylor & Kent Ltd. (Usual trademark Florentine).

Seaside Souvenirs
Yacht in full sail. 127mm long.   8.25

Great War
Cannon Shell. 75mm.   4.00
Anti-Zeppelin Candle Holder,
    handle at back. 80mm.   8.25

Trademark used for a Welsh retailer by Wilt-shaw and Robinson Ltd, Carlton Works, Stoke-on-Trent. (Usual trademark Carlton).

National Souvenir
Welsh Hat, Model of, with largest
    Welsh place round brim.
    No. 283. 56mm.   5.50

Caledonia China

For mark see *Crested China*, p. 74.

Trademark used by Taylor and Kent (Ltd), Florence Works, Longton for the Glasgow wholesaler CR and Co. (Usual trademark Florentine). (See also Atlas Heraldic China).

Seaside Souvenirs
Yacht in full sail. 127mm long.	8.25

Animals
Camel, kneeling. 95mm long.	10.50
Manx Cat, wiry. 53mm.	15.00
Pig, standing. 80mm long.	7.50
Rabbit. 105mm long.	7.50

Great War
Monoplane. 127mm long.	35.00
Liner converted to troop ship, inscribed: *HMS Lion*.	87.50
Glengarry. 90mm long.	13.00

Home/Nostalgic
Kennel, inscribed: *Beware of the Dog*. 62mm long.	4.00
Sofa. 82mm long.	5.50

Comic/Novelty
Policeman, standing, hands behind back, appears to be holding shears. 105mm.	18.00

Alcohol
Barrel inscribed: *Real Scotch*. No. 405. 55mm.	4.50

Miniature Domestic
Cheese Dish and cover. 2 pieces. 55mm.	4.50
Shaving Mug. 55mm.	4.00

Caledonia China

For mark see *Crested China*, p. 75.

Trademark used by James Macintyre and Co Ltd, Washington China Works, Burslem, for sale in Scotland.

Traditional/National
Welsh Hat. 56mm.	3.00

Animals
King Charles Spaniel begging on cushion. 70mm.	6.00
Two King Charles Spaniels sitting in top hat. 75mm.	13.00
Polar Bear, inscribed: *Sam*. 88mm long.	30.00

Birds
Hen, roosting. 51mm.	3.00

Great War
Red Cross Van. 87mm long.	17.50
Cenotaph inscribed: *The blood of heroes is the seed of freedom*. 140mm.	4.75

Caledonia Heraldic China

For mark see *Crested China*, p. 75.

Trademark used by a Scottish wholesaler on crested china manufactured by leading arms ware firms including Birks, Rawlins and Co. (Savoy), Hewitt and Leadbeater (Willow Art) and Wiltshaw and Robinson Ltd. (Carlton).

Parian/Unglazed

Burns at the plough, standing on rectangular base with a red flower on ground. Inscribed: *Wee, modest, crimson tipped flower thou's met me in an evil hour*. 105mm.	52.50
Bust of Burns on square glazed base. 160mm.	11.00
Bust of Scott on square glazed base. 160mm.	10.00

Buildings – Coloured

Model of House in Edinburgh where John Knox the Scottish Reformer died 24 Nov 1573. 93mm (Willow).	110.00

Buildings – White

Burns cottage, Model of. 105mm long.	12.50
Carnegie's Birthplace. 70mm long.	20.50
Cottage, thatched. 60mm long.	4.00
Cottage, inscribed: *Tigh-na-gaat centre of Scotland*. 85mm.	20.50
First and last house in England. 83mm long.	7.50
John Knox's House. 112mm.	30.00
Old town house Dunbar, The. 135mm.	28.50

Monuments

The Black Watch Memorial, Edinburgh. 127mm.	65.00

Historical/Folklore

James V Chair. Stirling Castle. 100mm.	6.50
Mons Meg, Edinburgh Castle. 130mm long.	7.50

Traditional/National Souvenirs

Welsh Hat. 54mm.	4.00

Seaside

Bathing Machine. 80mm.	4.75
Grace Darlings boat, Model of. Fully coloured boat on brown rocks. 108mm long, unglazed.	21.50
Longship's Lighthouse, *Lands End*. 118mm.	10.50
Lighthouse on rocky base. 115mm.	4.00

Animals

Dog, Bulldog, standing with verse: *Be Briton Still to Britain true, Among ourselves united. For never but by British hands, Maun British wrongs be righted. Burns*. 130mm long.	17.00
Fish. 130mm long.	2.50
Pig, lying down. 80mm long.	7.50
Rabbit. 60mm long (Carlton).	4.00

Great War

Scottish soldier on circular base. 160mm.	75.00
Monoplane with revolving prop. 178mm long.	34.50
Liner converted to a troop carrier inscribed: *HMS Lion*. 140mm long.	100.00
Battleship inscribed: *HMS Lion*. 140mm long.	56.50
Torpedo boat destroyer, Model of, 140mm long.	87.50
Red Cross Van. 87mm long.	17.50
Armoured Car (Reputedly a Talbot, but not named). 125mm long.	42.00
British motor searchlight, Model of. 103mm long.	70.00
Tank with trailing steering wheels, inscribed: *HMS Donner Blitzen* and *515* on side. 140mm long.	30.00

Tank, no steering wheels.
Inscription exactly the same as
above. 135mm long.   30.00
Field gun, Model of. 150mm long.   13.00
Shell, inscribed: Iron rations for
Fritz. 160mm.   4.00
French trench helmet. 82mm long.   40.00
Glengarry. 87mm long.   13.00

Alcohol
Pot with inscription: A wee deoch
an doris. 44mm.   2.25

Musical Instruments
Upright Piano. 83mm long.   7.50

Miscellanous
Top Hat. 44mm.   3.00

Miniature Domestic
Cheese Dish. 2 pieces. 50mm.   5.00
Cheese Dish. 1 piece. 40mm.   4.00

Carlton China

For mark see Crested China, p. 76.

Trademark used by Wiltshaw and Robinson
Ltd, Carlton Works, Stoke-on-Trent.

Parian/Unglazed
Unglazed models are mostly
busts which are on circular
glazed bases, normally carrying
crests.

Busts
Bust of King Edward VII, later
    models inscribed. 135mm.   30.00
Bust of Queen Alexandra.
    135mm.   30.00
Bust of King George V. 135mm.   30.00
Bust of Queen Mary. 135mm.   30.00
Bust of Burns, with verse by
    Wordsworth. 120mm.   10.50
Bust of Sir Edward Carson KC, MP
    on round glazed base with
    inscription: Ulster will fight and
    Ulster will be right. Edward
    Carson. 130mm.   50.00
Bust of Joseph Chamberlain.
    115mm.   29.50
Bust of Lord Kitchener. 135mm.   30.00
Bust of Ruskin. 135mm.   30.00
Bust of Shakespeare. 120mm.   8.50
Bust of Sydney, inscribed: Sir
    Philip Sydney. Thy necessity is
    greater than mine. 135mm.   30.00
Bust of Wordsworth, no base.
    77mm.   8.50
Bust of Wordsworth, on glazed
    base, impressed: Wordsworth.
    3 sizes: 115mm.   10.50
            125mm.   12.00
            135mm.   12.50

Monuments
Cavell Memorial Statue. 165mm.   10.00
Captain Cook Statue on glazed
    square base. 140mm.   30.00
Captain Cook's Monument. An
    obelisk. 135mm.   28.00

Globe, Swanage, on square
glazed base. 55mm dia. 86mm. 10.50
Florence Nightingale on square
glazed base, inscribed. 10.50
(John) Ruskin Memorial on
square glazed base. 172mm. 20.00

Ancient Artefacts
These models are often found not
named, named models usually
have a printed number and this
is given where known. Most
inscriptions begin: Model of so
this will not be repeated
throughout the list.
Ancient Lampfeeder found at
St Mary's in a marsh near Hythe.
2 sizes: No. 330. 46mm. 2.25
No. 829. 67mm. 2.25
Ancient Tyg, 1 handle.
No. 184. 66mm. 2.25
Ancient Tyg, 2 handles.
No. 245. 66mm. 2.25
Ancient Vase 1st Century AD,
original in Wedgwood Museum,
Burslem. No. 375. 60mm. 2.25
Cambridge Jug. No. 332. 60mm. 2.25
Chester Ancient Vase. 2.25
Chester Roman Jug. No. 261.
70mm. 1.75
Chester Roman Vase. Found
numbered 154 and 286. 60mm. 1.75
Christchurch Harvest Vase
inscribed: Ancient Harvest Vase
found at Christchurch,
Hampshire. No. 407. 44mm. 2.25
Cobham Bottle. No details of size. 3.00
Colchester Ancient Vases,
4 models: No. 349. 50mm. 1.75
No. 351. 66mm. 1.75
No. 352. 55mm. 1.75
No. 353. 68mm. 1.75
Colchester Famous Vase.
No. 80. 50mm. 2.25
Dogger Bank Bottle.
No. 251. 65mm. 2.25
Dorchester Jug, inscribed: Old Jug
found in North Square,
Dorchester. No. 177. 52mm. 2.25
Dorset Roman Jug found in Bath.
70mm. 1.75
Eddystone Jug. No. 180. 58mm. 1.75
Elizabeth Jug or Stoup.
No. 360. 90mm. 3.00

Etruscan Vase, inscribed: Model of
4th Century Etruscan Vase.
2 models: No. 262. 55mm. 2.25
No. 277. 42mm. 2.25
Fountains Abbey Cup.
No. 238. 50mm. 1.75
Glastonbury Bowl.
No. 172. 39mm. 1.75
Grecian Vase. No. 257. 78mm. 2.25
Grecian Water Vessel, Ancient.
No. 264. 85mm. 2.25
Hampshire Roman Vase.
No. 247. 65mm. 1.75
Hanley Chinese Vase.
No. 263. 62mm. 2.25
Hanley Cyprus Vase.
No. 374. 45mm. 2.25
Hanley Egyptian Vase.
2 different models:
No. 367. 64mm (2 large handles
from neck to body). 2.25
No. 368. 63mm. (2 tiny handles
on body only). 2.25
Hanley Roman Jug.
No. 370. 55mm. 2.25
Hanley Roman Vase. 2 vases:
No. 372. 63mm. 2.25
No. 373. 50mm. 2.25
Hastings Kettle. No. 166. 60mm. 1.75
Hull Suffolk Palace Jug. No 276. 2.50
(Ancient) Irish bronze pot.
No. 183. 45mm. 2.25
Irish Kettle. No. 346. 65mm. 3.00
Jersey milk can, with lid.
No. 242. 70mm. 3.00
Lichfield Jug. No. 181. 60mm. 2.25
Lincoln Jack (from original in
museum). No. 156. 60mm. 2.25
Loving Cup. 2 handled. Not
named. No. 97. 38mm & 47mm. 2.50
Loving Cup. 3 handled. Not
named. 53mm. 2.50
Merthyr Tydfil Roman Pottery.
2 models: No. 382. 50mm. 2.25
No. 383. 52mm. 2.25
Newbury Leather Bottle.
No. 229. 65mm. 1.75
Old bronze porridge pot. No. 221. 2.25
Penmaenmawr Urn.
No. 213. 50mm. 2.25
Phoenician vase (originally in Hanley
Museum). No. 174. 70mm. 2.25
Pompeian Vessel, not named.
60mm. 1.75

Carlton. Dellar's Cafe

Carlton. Tower and Bigwheel Blackpool Ashtray

Carlton. Martello Tower

Carlton. Toad Rock

Carlton. Irish Cabin

Carlton. Irish Cabin. Note the different decoration

Carlton. 'Time for Reflection'

Carlton. Caveman

Carlton. 'Beaver'

Carlton. Red Riding Hood

Carlton. Cricketer on Base

Carlton. Baby

Portland vase (now in British Museum), often found not named. No. 89. 58mm.	1.75
Puzzle Jug, not named. 2 sizes:	
68mm.	3.50
90mm.	4.00
Larger size carries verse.	
Puzzle Teapot with verse. 60mm.	8.25
Roman Pottery. 2 models:	
No. 376. 65mm.	2.25
No. 377. 70mm	2.25
Roman Urn found at Milborne Port.	
No. 265. 44mm.	2.25
St. David's Vase. No. 249. 62mm.	2.25
Salisbury Kettle, 2 models:	
No. 188. 100mm.	2.25
No. 281. 77mm.	2.25
Salopian Ewer. No. 75. 76mm.	2.25
Shakespeare's Jug. 70mm.	2.50
Silchester Urn. No. 193. 54mm.	2.25
Silchester Vase, inscribed: *Vase from Silchester in Reading Museum*. No. 171. 50mm.	2.25
Southampton Pipkin.	
No. 204. 54mm.	1.75
Spilsby Jug.	2.25
(Old) Swedish kettle.	
No. 344. 70mm	3.00
Winchelsea Vase. No. 87. 77mm.	2.25
Winchester Bushel. No. 323.	
80mm dia. and 112mm dia.	8.75
Windsor Urn. No. 284. 50mm.	2.25
Wokingham Tankard.	
No. 217. 78mm.	3.00
York Roman Ewer. No. 178. 57mm.	2.25

Buildings – Coloured

Dove Cottage, the early home of Wordsworth, Model of. 50mm.	130.00
Grasmere Church, Model of. 90mm.	75.00
(The) Transport and General Workers Union Convalescent Home, Littleport. 112mm long.	175.00

Buildings – White

Arundel Castle, The Keep. 120mm long.	30.00
Bandstand, inscribed: *O listen to the band* 85mm.	10.50
Beach House, Canvey-on-Sea. 65mm.	35.00
Blackpool Tower. 125mm.	10.50
Blackpool Tower. 140mm.	9.50
Blackpool Tower with base.	

2 sizes: 100mm.		7.50
164mm.		10.50
Blackpool Tower and Big Wheel on ashtray, inscribed: *Good old Blackpool*. 2 sizes:		
108mm.		7.50
130mm.		8.50
Burns Cottage, Ayr. 70mm long.		10.50
Cairn on Culloden Battlefield, 1746.		
65mm.		26.00
Carnarvon Castle, Eagle Tower. 100mm.		40.00
Conway Castle. 130mm long.		45.00
Cottage. 50mm (very delicate).		4.00
Cottage with coloured doors, hedges and windows with a removable roof lid, and inscribed: *Ours is a nice house ours is,* or with verse *A little wife well willed, A little farm well tilled, A little mouse well filled and I am satisfied.* 70mm.		16.00
Dellar's Cafe, Paignton. 62mm.		52.50
Douglas Jubilee Clock. 127mm.		40.00
Douglas Tower of Refuge. 73mm.		30.00
Dropping Well, Knaresborough, coloured details and water. 77mm.		27.50
Dutch Cottage, Canvey Island, dated 1621. 75mm (scarce).		35.00
Fair Maid's House, Perth. 92mm.		40.00
Farnham Castle, pearl lustre. 98mm.		20.00
Fire Engine House, Leatherhead. 115mm (uncommon).		40.00
Forth Bridge. 166mm long.		26.00
Grasmere Church. 65mm.		45.00
Grimsby Hydraulic Tower, with details. 165mm.		21.75
Harrogate *Pump House.* 75mm. Inscribed: *A nip and a smell from the old sulphur well.*		26.00
Hastings Castle Ruins. 88mm.		22.00
Hastings Clock Tower. 127mm.		10.50
Hop kiln with coloured transfer of hop. 96mm.		14.50
Irish Cabin, coloured shamrock round base. 75mm long.		20.00
Irish Cabin, with woman and spinning wheel outside, some colouring. 82mm.		29.50
Irish round tower. No. 520. 126mm.		7.50
Keswick Town Hall and Clock Tower.		35.00

King Charles Tower, Chester. 85mm.	26.00
Laxey Wheel. 92mm (not often found).	30.00
Lincoln Cathedral. No. 156. 60mm.	30.00
Marble Arch. 127mm long.	8.50
Martello Tower, inscribed: *The Wish Tower, Martello Tower erected in 1804, the date of Napoleons threatened invasion and verse*. 67mm dia.	20.50
Martello Tower, as above as a trinket box and lid. 67mm dia.	24.00
Moot Hall, Keswick. 102mm.	35.00
Old Bishops Tower, Paignton. 82mm (rare).	40.00
Oldest chemyste shop in England, Ye. Knaresborough. Coloured roof and door. 100mm long.	60.00
Old Town House, Dunbar. 130mm.	40.00
Old Welsh Cottage, Model of. No. 400. 75mm long.	20.50
Parade, Chester, inscribed: *Gods providence is mine inheritance*. 108mm.	22.00
Pithead, Model of. 110mm (rare).	40.00
Rochester Castle Keep. 80mm.	26.00
Scarton Church. 90mm long.	40.00
St. Leonards Tower, Newtonabbey. 123mm.	40.00
St. Nicholas Church, Lantern Hill, Ilfracombe. 98mm.	19.50
St. Pauls Cathedral. 112mm.	15.25
Scarborough Castle, Model of. 80mm.	30.00
Skegness Clock Tower. 124mm.	7.50
Smallest house in Wales. 115mm.	16.00
Tintern Abbey, with green moss on walls. 105mm long.	42.50
Tom Tower, Christchurch, Oxford. 127mm.	21.50
Torquay Clock Tower. Inscribed: *Model of Mallock Memorial, Torquay*. 168mm.	17.50
Trinity Castle Clock Gate. 90mm.	34.50
Upleatham Old Church, the smallest church in England. 80mm.	22.50
Wallace Tower. 140mm.	21.50
Wembley Exhibition, British Hall. 88mm long.	30.00
Wembley Stadium, inscribed: *Model of British Stadium Wembley* and details of cost and size. 110mm long.	36.00

Windmill with revolving sails, can be found inscribed: *The Sussex Windmill*. 103mm.	16.00
A Window in Thrums. 55mm.	22.50
Windsor Round Tower. 95mm.	14.00
York, Bootham Bar. 114mm.	16.00
York Cathedral, West Front. 112mm.	22.00
York, Micklegate Bar. 112mm.	17.00
York, Walmgate Bar. 95mm long.	19.50

Monuments (including crosses)

Barrow Memorial, Ulverston. 135mm.	40.00
The Beacon, Alderley Edge 1799, with verse. 102mm.	35.00
Burns Statue, Burns holding a crimson tipped daisy, with verse. 160mm (not often found).	30.00
Caister-on-Sea, Lifeboat Memorial. 160mm.	14.50
Captain Cook's Monument on square glazed base. 135mm.	30.00
Celtic Cross. 142mm.	5.50
Colne Market Cross 1822–1902. 125mm. (rare).	55.00
Feltwell Cross. 142mm.	14.00
Flora Macdonald. Statue. 160mm (not common).	30.00
Garstang Market Cross, inscribed: *Model of Market Cross*. 135mm.	30.00
Globe, Swanage. (Model of the). 86mm.	10.50
Hull, Fishermans Memorial, with inscription. 170mm.	14.50
Hull South African War Memorial. 170mm.	18.50
Irish Cross. No. 519. 2 sizes: 115mm. and 136mm.	7.50
Locke Tower, inscribed: *This tower was erected in memory of the donor of Locke Park by P. Locke, Joseph Locke MP, AD 1877*. 135mm.	30.00
Mallock Memorial, Torquay. See Torquay Clock Tower. 165mm.	
Morecombe Clock Tower. 172mm.	28.00
Nelson's Column, not found named. 163mm.	40.00
Queen Eleanor's Memorial Cross, Northampton. 138mm (scarce).	46.50
Ripon Market Cross. 115mm.	13.00

Rufus Stone. 96mm.	4.00
Ruskin Cross, Model of, unglazed cross on glazed base. 170mm.	13.50
(John) Ruskin Statue. 120mm.	15.25
172mm.	18.50
Selby Market Cross. 130mm.	52.50
Toad Rock, Tunbridge Wells. 78mm.	15.00
Toad Rock, Near Hathersage, Model of. 100mm long.	21.75
Sir William Wallace Statue, Stirling, with long inscription. 130mm.	30.00
Wilberforce Statue, Hull. 155mm.	20.50

Historical/Folklore

Biddenden Maids, inscribed: *The Biddenden Maids were born joined together at hips and shoulders in year 1100 and a 34Y in 1100.* 105mm.	40.00
Bonnie Prince Charles Chair 1745. 110mm	16.00
Caveman, standing figure holding club. Brown hair and club. Can have inscription: *Billie Bus, the man who called for the empties BC umpteen.* 113mm.	65.00
Font, not named. 133mm.	7.00
Fox's chair, inscribed: *Model of chair of George Fox the Quaker, original at Swarthmoor Hall Ulverston.* 96mm	17.00
Grace Darling's boat, Model of, and description. Boat in blue and white or brown rocks. 108mm long.	21.50
Great Peter, handbell with clapper. 40mm.	5.25
John Waterson's Clog. 100mm long.	13.00
Judge, bust, inscribed: *Defend the children of the poor, Punish the wrongdoer (inscription on new Bailey Courts London).* 70mm.	10.50
with inscription	15.50
Mary Queen of Scots Bed, inscribed: *The Bed of Mary Queen of Scots, Holyrood Palace, Edinburgh.* 90mm long.	60.00
Man in Pillory with some colouring, can have inscription: *Ample Time for Reflection.* 100mm.	20.00
Red Riding Hood. 95mm.	50.00

Sanctuary Knocker, Durham, on vase or wall socket.	5.50
Scarborough Ducking Chair formerly fixed on the Pier for the purpose of ducking scolding women!! Last used on Mrs Gamble. Now in Museum. Period 1795. Chair 95mm.	40.00
Sedan Chair, inscribed: *Model of 17th century Sedan chair.* 70mm.	22.00
Thomas A'Becket Shoe. 105mm long.	10.50
Ulphus Horn (York) on base. 115mm long (quite rare).	15.00
(The) Wallace Sword, inscribed: *The sword that seem'd fit for the Archangel to wield was light in his terrible hand.* 105mm long.	25.75
Watchman's Lamp, inscribed: *Model of 16th century watchman's lamp* and *Watchman what of the night.* 2 sizes: 80mm and 115mm.	5.50
Witch's Cauldron with Macbeth verse *Double, double, toyle and trouble, fyer burns and cauldron bubble.* 45mm.	4.00
Witch's cauldron on Tripod (rustic). 115mm.	5.50
Xit, The historical dwarf with inscription. 137mm.	35.00

Traditional/National Souvenirs

John Bull, bust. 100mm.	16.00
John Bull with Bulldog, standing figure on oval base. Union Jack waistcoat and black hat, dog has red, white and blue collar. 125mm.	50.00
Blackpool Big Wheel. Can be found in pearl lustre. 2 sizes: 80mm.	7.50
100mm.	10.50
Bolton Trotter. 105mm long.	4.75
Bolton Trotter, hand holding a trotter inscribed: *A good hold on a Bolton Trotter.* 110mm long.	5.25
Cheddar Cheese, inscribed: *Prime Cheddar Cheese.* Can be found brown coloured and with slice out. 50mm.	4.00
	8.25
Cotton Shuttle, Model of. 93mm long.	35.00

Lancashire clog with verse: *There's many a factory lass wi' clogs on her feet*. 100mm long.	5.50
Lincoln Imp moulded in relief on Lincoln Jack, inscribed: *The Imp, Lincoln Cathedral*. No. 156. 60mm.	6.50
Kelly from the Isle of Man. 3 legged man, holding Manx Kipper in hand, fully coloured. 110mm.	55.00
Manx Legs on base. 95mm.	13.00
(The) *Ripon Horn* on square base, inscribed. 2 sizes: 80mm.	8.25
120mm.	10.50
(The) Sheffield grinding stone. 80mm long (rare).	32.50
York Minster, The Fiddler of. 132mm.	35.00
Yorkshireman, standing figure holding tankard – often found not named. Found with inscription: *Take hod and sup lad* and verses. 126mm.	15.25
Irish cabin trunk, more often found without this inscription. 58mm long.	8.75
Irish Colleen, on circular base. Can have some colouring. 125mm.	50.00
Irish Harp, with green shamrocks. 90mm.	5.75
Irish Harp, Model of surmounted by crown. Decorated with shamrocks. 105mm.	7.50
Irish Jaunting car, with horse and driver, some colouring. 130mm long (This is quite rare).	75.00
Irish spinning wheel. Irish lady sitting by spinning wheel. 95mm.	50.00
Saint Patrick's Mitre. 70mm.	14.00
Bagpipes. 114mm.	13.00
Crown of Scotland, inscribed: 'The Crown of Scotland. Robert Bruce Crowned 1300, Buried Dunfermline 1329'. 68mm.	20.00
Gretna Green, Model of blacksmiths anvil. This anvil is often found without inscription or verse. 70mm.	4.75
Scotch fisher girl at work, coloured fish in barrel. 118mm.	40.00
Scotsman, standing figure, blue tam o'shanter with red bobble and brown walking stick. With	

verse *Just a wee deoch and doris*. 130mm. Harry Lauder.	30.00
Tam O'Shanter (bonnet) with coloured sprig of heather. 80mm dia.	7.00
Thistle Hat Pin Holder. 80mm.	5.50
Thistle moulded teapot with coloured thistle handle, can be lustre. 85mm.	8.00
Thistle Vase. 76mm.	2.25
Jenny Jones, Welsh lady, standing figure with black hat, brown basket and red and green shawl. 147mm. Two varieties.	21.50
Prince of Wales Feathers. 95mm.	13.00
Pat's Hat and dudeen, green ribbon and black dudeen. With *Tipperary* inscription on reverse. 45mm.	20.00
Welsh hat, Model of, can be found with longest Welsh place name round brim. No. 283. 56mm.	6.00
Welsh Hat, with orange band. Can be found in lustre with a coloured transfer 'Welsh Teaparty'. 44mm.	3.50
Welsh leek, Model of, leaves coloured green. 93mm.	3.50
Welsh spinning wheel, two Welsh ladies with spinning wheel, coloured hats and shawls. 95mm.	30.00
Welsh tea party, three Welsh ladies taking tea, coloured hats and shawls, etc. 90mm.	30.00
Bermuda sailing ship, can be found with Bermuda crest. 127mm long.	14.00
Gondola. 127mm long.	9.50

Seaside Souvenirs

Bathing Machine, found inscribed: *Morning dip*. Sizes vary from 55mm.	4.00
to 70mm.	4.75
Lifebelt. 105mm dia.	7.50
Lifeboat. Can be found inscribed: *Queensbury* for which £7.00 should be added. 113mm long.	4.75
Motor Boat on waves. 120mm long.	10.50
Motor Boat with Driver on waves. 102mm long.	16.00
Punt with two women, some	

colouring. 113mm long.	75.00
Rowing Boat. Can be found inscribed: *Model of Grace Darling's Boat*, for which £10.50 should be added. 108mm long.	4.75
Trawler, inscribed on sail: *SM*. 115mm long.	13.00
Yacht with billowing sail, some colouring. 120mm long.	10.50
Yacht, in full sail, found inscribed: *Saucy Sue*. 115mm long.	16.00
Fisherman on Rock, holding brown net, inscribed: *Son of the sea*. 117mm.	19.50
Lifeboatman, bust with colouring on face. 80mm.	11.00
Lifeboatman in boat on sea, black clothing. Lustre. 100mm.	22.50
Lighthouse inscribed: *Sailor Beware*. 140mm.	5.50
Barness Lighthouse, Dunbar. 116mm.	35.00
Beachy Head Lighthouse. 148mm (no named example found).	6.50
Douglas Lighthouse. 128mm.	40.00
Eddystone Lighthouse, Model of, with black band, found inscribed: *Landing of Prince of Orange 1688*. 138mm.	10.00
Flamborough Lighthouse, Model of. Can be found as a hatpin holder. 115mm.	25.75
Flamborough Head Fog Siren Building 87mm long.	28.00
Mumbles Lighthouse and telegraph office. 127mm.	35.00
Pharos Lighthouse Fleetwood, Model of. No. 409. 100mm (Identical model, so named and with same stock number can be found as a pepper pot – same price).	4.00
Scarborough Lighthouse. 135mm.	40.00
Scarborough Lighthouse, Model of, with rectangular building showing shell holes from Great War. 98mm (rare).	66.50
Withernsea Lighthouse. 134mm.	8.50
Limpet shell with 2 feet. 23mm.	2.25
Oyster shell, found inscribed: *A Whitstable native* (when it becomes a traditional souvenir). 70mm.	2.50
Shell Inkwell, inscribed: *We are*	

always glad to hear from you. 95mm.	6.00
Whelk Shell, inscribed: *Listen to the sea*. 100mm long.	2.50
Luggage trolley inscribed: *Luggage in Advance* and/or *LMS Railway to Timbuctoo*. Can be found in lustre. 76mm long.	30.00
Valise (or travelling case) with two straps. 2 sizes: 55mm and 70mm long.	6.00
Bathing Beauty, seated figure with green or blue cap. 110mm long.	40.00
Bathing Beauty lying on edge of lustre shell dish, bathing costume in several colours. Inscribed: *Washed up by the tide*. 110mm.	37.00
Boy on Donkey, can be found inscribed: *Gee up Neddy* or more occasionally: *This beats going to school*. Can be found without base. 98mm long.	30.00
Mr. Punch, bust. 82mm.	13.00
Punch and Judy Booth, with coloured Punch and Judy. Inscribed: *Good Morning Mr Punch* 133mm (A much sought after model).	30.00

Countryside

Beehive on square stand, with coloured transfer bee. 64mm.	7.50
Beehive with squat feet. 63mm.	5.50
Campfire, cauldron inside three upright poles on triangular base. 122mm.	15.25
Pinecone, upright, closed. 79mm.	3.00
Tree Trunk Candleholder. 113mm.	3.00
Tree Trunk Vase, the Great Oak in Sherwood Forest, Nottingham. 115mm.	10.00

Animals

Ape (Orang Outang) holding orange, brown face. 58mm.	13.00
Bear, looks like a Polar Bear, inscribed: *Russian Bear*. 130mm long.	40.00
Bear and Ragged staff. 85mm.	13.00
Bear wearing hat sitting on base. 104mm.	25.00

Bull, inscribed: *King of the heard*, or much more rarely: *The ox of Oxford*. 103mm long. — 40.00

Cat, angry, with back up, inscribed: *My word if you're not off* or *The Midnight Rambler*. 80mm. — 10.50

Cat, Cheshire, inscribed: *The Cheshire cat*, and *The smile that won't come off*. 90mm. — 4.75

Cat, crouching. 81mm. — 14.00

Cat doing hand stand on oblong base, back legs up in the air. Inscribed: *Well what about it*. 115mm (rare). — 56.50

Cat, Manx. 75mm. — 13.00

Cat, long necked, inscribed: *My word* etc. 110mm. — 5.50

Cat sitting, chubby and kittenish. 63mm. — 7.50

Cat sitting on square cushion, impressed: *Good Luck*. 80mm. — 7.50

Cat sitting, with red bow, pepper pot. 70mm. — 10.50

Cat sitting, wearing black topper with shamrock, bow tie can be found coloured red or green. Also found in lustre. 88mm. — 9.50

Cat sitting, with blue bow (bow sometimes left uncoloured) 56mm. — 6.50

Cat sitting, with Swastika round neck. 59mm. — 6.50

This cat can also be found on a pouffe and inscribed: *Good Luck*. 85mm. — 8.00

Black Cat, small, can be found with accompanying model coloured red, for which £20.00 should be added.
Found on the following:
Armchair (upholstered) with green swastika and red horseshoe on arms, inscribed: *Jolly good luck*. Chair can be found all red. 75mm. — 15.00

(Old) Armchair with solid arms. 90mm. — 18.00

Ashtray, circular, can be found with transfer cigarette, inscribed: *Who burnt the cloth*. 110mm dia. — 20.00

Ashtray, club shaped, lustre. 90mm long. — 15.25

Ashtray, diamond shaped, lustre. 95mm long (It seems very likely that small black cats will be found on heart and spade shaped ashtrays as well and that all four were made in white and lustre. — 15.25

Chair. 90mm. — 13.00

Horseshoe Ashtray, inscribed: *Jolly good luck*. — 11.25

Piano. 95mm. — 19.50

Pillar Box. Can be found painted red for which £10.00 should be added. Inscribed: *Good luck*. 110mm. — 24.50

Rocking chair, lustre. 100mm. — 17.00

Sofa, can also be found painted red, for which £10.00 should be added. Inscribed: *Jolly good luck*. 80mm. — 17.00

Trinket box, inscribed: *Trinkets*. 93mm long. — 10.50

Black Cat, large, found on the following:
Oval base with coloured Swastika and horseshoe. Inscribed: *Good luck*. Base can be found in mother-of-pearl or blue lustre. 85mm. — 16.00

Pouffe, the cat's bow is found blue instead of usual red. Inscribed: *Good luck*. 90mm. — 16.00

Black cat and kitten on ashtray with match holder. Inscribed: *Don't scratch me, scratch mother*. Can be in maroon lustre. 70mm. — 21.50

Doe on oval stand. 118mm. — 56.50

Bulldog, sitting, inscribed: *Bill Sykes dog*. 95mm. — 10.50

Bulldog, sitting, thin faced. Inscribed: *Model of Bill Sykes dog* and sometimes found also inscribed: *My word if youre not off*. 51mm. — 10.50

Bulldog, standing, inscribed: *My word if youre not off*; can be found inscribed: *Slow to start, but what a hold*. 120mm long. — 10.50

Dog (French Bulldog), sitting with pricked-up ears and blue eyes. 57mm. — 6.50

Dog playing banjo, inscribed: *Some Band*. 83mm. — 21.75

Dog looking out of kennel, inscribed: *The Blackwatch*. Dog's head is coloured black. 85mm. 8.25

Dog (Puppy) in slipper. Puppy coloured brown. 100mm long. 30.00

Dog (Puppy) sitting with one ear raised. Can be found painted blue. 83mm. 5.50

With painted spots. 8.25

This puppy can be found on a hand mirror (silvered) inscribed: *Me twice*. 105mm long. 24.50

Dog, Scottie, begging, pink ears and red collar. Can be found coloured red. 74mm. 10.50

Dog, Scottie, begging, wearing a glengarry, some colouring. 105mm. 8.75

Dog, Scottie, sitting, wearing a tartan tam o'shanter with red bobble. Also found in lustre. 2 sizes: 60mm. 6.00
80mm. 8.75

Dog, Scottish Terrier, standing with tail in the air. Found inscribed: *As old Mrs Terrier said to her pup in all lifes adversaries keep your tail up*. 100mm long. 7.50

Dog, standing, impressed on collar: *Caesar* and inscribed: *I am the Kings dog*. Some colouring. 106mm long. 25.75

Donkey, inscribed: *Gee up Neddy*. 110mm long. 20.00

Elephant, walking. 51mm. 6.50

Elephant with raised trunk. 51mm. 6.50

Fawn. 70mm. 17.50

Field Mouse, on base. 54mm. 13.00

Fish (Salmon), 112mm long. 2.50

Fish Ashtray, inscribed: *A plaice for the ashes*. 120mm long. 4.00

Flamborough donkey, with orange and blue rosettes. 88mm (rare). 55.00

Monkey, sitting hands to mouth. 90mm. 7.00

Pig sitting on haunches, inscribed: *Wont be druv* or *You can push, you can shuv but I'm hanged if I'll be druv*. 60mm. 10.50

Pig, standing, found inscribed: *Wont be druv*. Also found entirely coloured blue. 65mm long. 8.25

Pig, fat and standing, found inscribed: *Wont be druv*. 80mm long. 10.50

Pig, standing, fat, found inscribed: *You can push* etc. or *I'm the fellow who pays the rent*. 94mm long. 12.50

Pig, sitting, wearing coloured German pickelhaube and with Iron Cross on left breast. Pepper Pot. Reg. No. 642626. 90mm. Very rare. 150.00

Piglet, standing. 70mm long. 8.25

Rabbit, crouching with pricked ears. 65mm long. 4.00

Shetland pony. 138mm long. 14.00

Stag with large antlers on oval stand. 146mm. Probably sold as a pair with doe, but less of them around, possibly because the antlers are easily broken off. 65.00

Terrapin (turtle, tortoise?). 75mm. 5.50

Three Wise Monkeys on wall. Inscribed: *Speak no evil, see no evil, hear no evil*. Can be found coloured brown with red faces on white wall (add £4.00). 90mm long. 5.50

These monkeys coloured brown can be found on an ashtray base with the same inscription. 90mm long. 7.00

Welsh Goat on rocky base, inscribed: *Yafr gymreig* (The Welsh Goat). No. 391. 96mm. 40.00

Wembley Lion on ashtray base, some colouring. 60mm (This was stylised lion symbol of British Empire Exhibition and is usually found with BEE crest). 12.50

Birds (including eggs)

Hen roosting. 60mm long. 3.75

Hen and Cock, salt, pepper and mustard pots, some colouring. 70mm. each 8.25

Chicken hatching from egg. 64mm long. 3.00

Egg cracked open, lying on side. 74mm long. 2.50

Owl. 66mm. 5.50

Owl, wearing black mortarboard with red tassel. (Models with Irish crests can be found with red mortar boards). 75mm.	8.25
Owl cream jug. 88mm.	4.00
Parrot, inscribed: *Pretty Polly*. 74mm.	8.00
Peacock. Can be found coloured blue. 63mm.	10.50
Stork with pink beak, standing on one leg. 110mm.	13.00
Swan. 3 sizes: 55mm.	2.50
63mm.	3.00
76mm long.	3.50
Smallest can be found coloured red (add £5.00).	
Swan pepper pot. 53mm.	2.75
Swan Posy Holder. 78mm.	3.00
Woodpecker, comic, some colouring on wings, beak and feet. 60mm.	30.00

Carlton made a series of 5 birds on green bases and these are listed below:

Cock standing on green base, some colouring to head. 85mm long.	16.00
Duck standing on green base, yellow beak. 72mm.	14.50
Duck standing up, rather comic, on green base. 102mm.	21.75
Duck airing wings, green base, yellow beak. 80mm.	16.50
Turkey on green base, coloured beak and feet. Can also be found in lustre. 70mm.	12.50

Great War
Many Great War models are found with the following Victory inscriptions: *The Victory of Justice, Armistice of the Great War signed Nov 11th 1918* and *Victory of Justice. Peace signed at Versailles June 28th 1919*. These add interest but not value.

Munitions Worker, inscribed: *Doing her bit* and *Shells and more shells*, some colouring. 140mm.	75.00
Nurse with red cross, inscribed: *A friend in need*. 150mm.	34.50
Old Bill, standing figure of Bruce Bairnsfather's cartoon	

character. Inscribed: *Yours to a cinder*. Can be found coloured.	57.50
138mm. coloured	75.00
Sailor, bust. Inscribed: *The Handy Man* and *HMS Dreadnought*. 85mm.	19.50
Sailor, crouching and holding a submarine, inscribed: *We've got U well in hand*.	40.00
70mm. coloured	56.50
Sailor standing to attention with blue trim. Inscribed: *Handy man*. 135mm.	43.50
Scottish Soldier, some colouring. 148mm.	75.00
Scottish Soldier, wearing bearskin (busby). Not glengarry. Some colouring. 153mm.	100.00
Soldier standing to attention, inscribed: *Are we downhearted No!* and with verse *Its a long way to Tipperary*. 153mm.	40.00
Soldier standing to attention with ammunition belt worn over shoulder. 125mm (quite rare).	70.00
Biplane with movable prop. 135mm long.	75.00
Biplane, coloured roundels and tailplane with movable prop. 2 sizes: 140mm	95.00
165mm long.	105.00
Monoplane, rounded fuselage and movable prop. 134mm long.	30.00
Zeppelin or Airship with moulded Iron Cross on side; can be found with cross painted black, or left white and RAF roundels on nose. 118mm long (2 models for the price of one mould).	30.00
with roundels	35.00
British mine sweeper whose splendid work will live forever in the annals of British history. Can be found inscribed: *HMMS Gowan Lea*, *HMS Peggy* or *HMS Minesweeper*.	40.00
115mm long. named	56.50
Battleship, 2 funnels, 4 guns fore, 4 guns aft. 160mm. Named: *HMS Canada*, *HMS Australia*, *HMS Marlborough*	56.50

Battleship, 3 funnels, 4 guns fore,
2 guns aft. 160mm. Named:
HMS *Renown*, HMS *Iron Duke*,
HMS *Princess Royal*,
HMS *Warspite*, HMS *Inflexible*. 56.50
Battleship, 4 funnels, 2 guns fore,
4 guns aft. 160mm. Named:
HMS *Lion*, HMS *Tiger*. 56.50
Battleship, 3 funnels, 4 guns fore,
2 guns midships, 2 guns aft.
Named: HMS *Lion*, HMS *Queen
Elizabeth*. 56.50
All the above can be found with
the following Victory
inscription only: *Great War
1914–18. The German Fleet
surrendered 74 warships Nov 21st
1918*.
Battleship with high prow,
usually inscribed: *Dreadnought*
but can also be found inscribed:
HMS *Humber, Model of British
Monitor*. Has also been found
with same Victory inscription
as above and not named. 30.00
140mm long. named 56.50
Battleship with high prow,
slightly different to above,
inscribed: HMS *Humber, Model
of British Monitor*. 140mm long. 56.50
HM *Hospital Ship Anglia, Model of*
with 2 funnels, often found
with further detailed inscription: *Model of British Hospital
Ship whose voyage was disregarded on three occasions by the
German Submarines*.
165mm long. (Has been found
wrongly inscribed as HMS *Tiger*
and as RMS *Lusitania*). 55.00
RMS *Lusitania*, 4 funnels. Found
with details of sinking: *The
Lusitania was sunk by a German Submarine May 7th 1915.
Lives lost 1198*, or the numeri-
cally incorrect inscription: *Sunk
by German Submarine off the Irish
Coast, May 7th 1915. Lives lost
1275, Saved 703*. 168mm long. 56.50
British submarine, Model of, blunt
nosed, often found without this
inscription but with E9 on side.
Submarines found unnamed
are found with the following

inscription: *Great War 1914–18.
150 German U Boats surrendered
Nov 20th 1918*. 140mm long. 24.50
British submarine, Model of, half-
submerged, inscribed: *E9*.
124mm long. 40.00
Submarine, pointed nose and fish
tail, inscribed: *E9*. 146mm long.
(Much rarer than blunt nosed
model). 30.00
Ambulance with 3 red crosses and
WD on radiator. 100mm long. 19.50
Armoured car with Rolls-Royce
type front. 120mm long. 145.00
Armoured car with 3 guns on
turret, inscribed: *RNAS*.
116mm long. 82.50
British anti-aircraft motor, Model of,
inscribed: *RNAS*. 121mm long. 75.00
Tank with trailing steering
wheels, inscribed: *HMLS Creme
de Menthe*. 2 sizes: 130mm 18.00
160mm long. 23.00
130mm size found with Victory
inscription: *The British Tank
successfully used against the
Germans Combles, Sept 1916*. 23.50
Tank with no steering wheels,
4 sizes: 80mm 110.00
100mm 60.00
134mm 13.00
156mm long. 19.50
Tank Bank, as largest size of tank
above but with slot for coins.
Inscribed: *Buy War Bonds*, and
can be found with *Combles*
inscription.156mm long. 30.00
HM *Whippet tank*. 121mm long. 82.50
Italian Fiat Tank, not named.
100mm long. (rare) 125.00
Vickers Tank, not named. 126mm
long (very rare). The latest
model manufactured, approx.
1928–32. 195.00
British machine gun, Model of, MG
in green wreaths on barrel.
2 moulds, one with open
stand. 100mm long. 25.75
Machine gun, Model of (Vickers),
2 pieces on swivelling tripod.
150mm long. 110.00
British naval gun, Model of.
88mm long (very rare). 175.00

British trench mortar, Model of.
Mounted on steps and barrel at
an angle. 66mm.   8.25
Trench Mortar, not named, with
horizontal barrel. 60mm.   8.25
Field Gun, found inscribed:
French 75. 2 sizes: 11.00
130mm & 148mm long. named   13.00
Field Gun with screen and sight-
hold, inscribed: French 75.
145mm long.   19.50
British 15" shell, Model of. 90mm.   5.50
Cannon shell, Model of. No. 606.
75mm.   4.00
German incendiary bomb, Model of.
75mm.   19.50
British hand grenade. 83mm.   10.50
Floating mine, Model of. 83mm.   21.75
British searchlight, Model of. Some-
times found inscribed: The   21.75
Zeppelin Finder. 68mm. inscribed   26.00
Dockside capstan, Model of, with
brown rope. 70mm.   7.50
Australian Hat, inscribed: Anzacs
for ever. 75mm long.   16.00
Colonial hat, often found un-
named. Also found inscribed:
Anzacs for ever.   8.70
95mm dia.   inscribed   10.50
Forage Cap. 80mm long.   13.00
Glengarry with coloured thistle.
78mm long.   13.00
Kitbag, open neck, with verse.
72mm.   10.50
Kitbag, closed neck, with verse.
72mm.   10.50
Highboot. 63mm.   7.50
Officer's Peaked Cap, coloured
band. 78mm long.   6.50
Royal Flying Corps Cap. 78mm
long.   13.00
Bell Tent. 66mm.   5.50
Territorials hat, coloured hat band.
85mm dia.   8.75
Tommies bungalow. Circular Bell
Tent. 70mm.   10.50
Blighty. Map of England and
Wales, with verse Take me back
to dear Old Blighty. 115mm.   40.00
Kitchen Range, with black kettle
but no teapot. Inscribed: Keep
the home fires burning till the boys
come home. 70mm.   8.75
Kitchen Range, with black kettle

and brown teapot. Inscribed:
We've kept the home fires burning
till the boys came home. 70mm.   13.75
Shrapnel Villa, Tommies dugout
somewhere in France. (From
Bruce Bairnsfather's cartoons).
83mm long.   26.00
Brighton War Memorial. 105mm.
(Building, not a statue).   56.00
Cenotaph, inscribed: The Glorious
Dead with 2 green wreaths.
2 sizes: 105mm.   3.50
146mm.   4.75
Clacton-on-sea War Memorial.
148mm.   16.00
Cranbrook War Memorial. 130mm
(scarce)   65.00
Douglas War Memorial. 160mm.   65.00
Dunbar War Memorial. 123mm.   65.00
Edith Cavell, statue, inscribed:
Brussels dawn October 12th 1915.
Sacrifice. Humanity.
2 sizes: 140mm.   7.50
163mm.   10.50
Elgin War Memorial. 165mm.   65.00
Feltwell War Memorial. 140mm.   65.00
Florence Nightingale, 1820–1910
The Lady of the Lamp. 175mm.   12.50
Northallerton War Memorial.
115mm.   65.00
Ripon War Memorial, found with
Ripon Hornblower inscrip-
tion. 115mm.   32.50
Tunbridge Wells War Memorial,
soldier unglazed on glazed
plinth carrying a rifle with
fixed bayonet. With inscrip-
tion: Our Glorious Dead 1914–18.
Honour, Gratitude, Praise.
170mm.   56.50
Ulverston War Memorial. 140mm.   65.00

Home/Nostalgic
Anvil on tree stump base. 76mm.   4.75
Baby lying on side holding mug.
Sometimes inscribed: Mothers
Darling. Some colouring.
140mm long.   55.00
Basket of fruit, fruit coloured.
88mm (Almost Art Deco).   8.75
Bellows. 95mm.   4.00
Book with lock. 66mm.   3.00
Coal scuttle. 60mm.   3.00
Dog Kennel. 62mm.   4.00

Dust Pan, inscribed: *Who said dust.*
94mm long.   7.00
Fireplace, with a kettle and tea-
pot in the hearth, and dogs and
clock on the mantelpiece.
Found inscribed: *By my Ain fire-*
side or *East, West, Home is best.*
85mm.   13.00
Fireplace with clock and dogs on
mantelpiece, cauldron on fire
and black cat by side. Inscribed
as above. 80mm.   15.25
Flat Iron, can be found in lustre.
60mm.   4.75
Frying Pan. 110mm long.   5.50
Grandfather clock, Model of.
No. 389.
2 sizes: 105mm.   8.00
         135mm.   10.50
Large size found inscribed.
Grandmother clock, inscribed:
Guide morn. 105mm.   13.00
Kettle, fixed lid, inscribed: *Polly*
put the kettle on, we'll have some
tea. 80mm.   7.50
Lantern, inscribed *Watchman what*
of the night? 83mm.   4.75
Miner's lamp. 110mm.   12.50
(The) Old armchair, solid arms,
with verse or inscribed: *Jolly*
Good Luck. 88mm.   5.50
(The) Old armchair, open 'barley
twist' arms, with verse.
120mm.   7.50
Pillar Box GVR, found inscribed:
If you haven't time to post a line
here's the pillar box.   5.50
72mm.   inscribed   8.50
Pillar Box *E VII R.* 72mm.   5.50
Rocking Chair. 98mm.   13.00
Saucepan with lid. 100mm long.   4.75
Shaving Mug. 58mm.   4.75
Spinning Wheel, found in-
scribed: *Model of ye olde spinning*
wheel or more rarely: *The exact*
model of 14th Century spinning
wheel. 74mm.   10.50
Stool, three-legged. 40mm.   4.00
Sundial, round, inscribed: *Model*
of ye olde English sundial, and
What' o'clock: lifes but a walking
shadow. No. 525.
2 sizes: 80mm   8.00
         120mm.   11.00

Sundial, square. Inscribed: *Let*
others tell of storms & showers, I'll
only count the sunny hours.
86mm.   8.00
Time glass. 60mm.   7.50
Thimble. 40mm.   8.75
Trug. 75mm.   1.75
Village Water Pump, round or
square. 76mm.   5.00
Warming Pan, inscribed: *Sally*
warm the bed. No. 392.
127mm long.   6.00

Comic/Novelty
Altar Inkwell with two orange
and black candle holders and
Buddha-like figure as cover for
inkwell. Rare complete,
inscribed: *Sox Kik the god of luck*
and cheerfulness. 90mm long.   40.00
Baby Girl Handbell, with metal
clapper. 100mm.   8.75
Beaver, man with very long beard
on base, some colouring.
120mm.   45.00
Billiken, flat faced grotesque
type. 63mm.   3.00
Billiken sitting on high backed
chair with thumbs raised,
inscribed: *Thumbs up.* 84mm.   4.75
Black girl in hip bath, inscribed:
I'se making ink. Can be lustre.
80mm long.   29.50
Black girl in hip bath (different
from above) same inscription.
85mm long.   29.50
Choir Boy Handbell. 88mm.   8.25
Cigarettes, matches and ash, con-
tainer with cigarette on lid.
85mm long.   6.00
Clown, Bust, inscribed: *Put me*
amongst the girls. Some
colouring. 75mm.   15.25
Girl, toddler with outstretched
arms on circular plinth,
inscribed: *Diddle'ums.* Some
colouring to face and bonnet.
125mm.   22.00
Humpty Dumpty: see sports.
Man in Pillory with red nose,
inscribed: *Ample time for reflec-*
tion. 113mm.   25.00

I'm forever blowing bubbles. Pears advert blue boy blowing bubbles. Clothes blue, bubble and bowl lustre. 110mm.	30.00
Jester, inscribed: *Put me amongst the girls*. Some colouring. 72mm.	13.00
Jester awake, jester asleep, double faced bust. 70mm.	10.50
John Citizen, man carrying sack inscribed: *Housing, unemployment, taxes*. Hat and face coloured. 95mm.	70.00
Negro minstrel, bust, verse by Eugene Stratton. Much colouring. 85mm	
white	16.00
coloured	35.00
Oval Rich Tea, brown biscuit on white base.	25.75
Policeman hailing: *From* .... 138mm.	16.00
Policeman with raised hand, inscribed: *A policemans lot is not a happy one*. 140mm.	16.00
Sack of meal with mouse peeping out. 75mm.	8.75
Suffragette handbell inscribed: *Votes for Women* and *She shall have Votes*. 100mm.	35.00
Truck of Coal, *Black diamonds from* .... Can be found in lustre. 95mm long.	11.00
Weighing Machine inscribed: *Try your weight*. 120mm.	21.75
Yes we have no bananas, oval dish with yellow bananas. 115mm. Can be found in lustre.	13.00

Cartoon/Comedy Characters

Jackie Coogan, coloured figure of boy film star, attached to white tree trunk, ink well with lid. 73mm.	21.75
Harry Lauder, bust, with red bobble on hat and coloured thistle. 80mm.	18.50
Ally Sloper, bust, inscribed: *Vote for Sloper etc*. Some colouring. 85mm.	16.00
Bonzo Dog, standing upright, not named. Red tongue. 110mm.	27.50

Bonzo Dog, with fly on his tail. Inscribed: *When yor're on a good thing stick to it*. Can be found unnamed.	35.00
Felix the Cat, on oval base, inscribed: *Felix kept on walking*. Coloured Felix and swastika and horseshoe on base. 75mm.	50.00
Felix the Cat on lustre Armchair, with Felix inscription. Coloured Felix. 75mm.	50.00
Felix the Cat on ashtrays (various shapes).	42.50
Felix the Cat on lustre pillar box, with Felix inscription. Coloured Felix. 115mm.	50.00
Felix the Cat on lustre sofa, with Felix inscription. Coloured Felix. 90mm.	50.00
Felix the Cat on *Hatpins* box and lid. 80mm long.	45.00
Felix the Cat on Trinket box, with Felix inscription. Coloured Felix. 93mm long.	45.00
Felix the Cat on rectangular base, a much larger and well modelled Felix than the above, with Felix inscription. 82mm (very rare).	110.00
Winkie the gladeye bird, some colouring. 68mm.	11.00
Woody Woodpecker, fully coloured. 63mm.	40.00

Alcohol

Beer barrel on stilts. XXX in red on sides. 57mm.	4.00
Bottle with solid top. 92mm.	4.00
Bottle with cork. 70mm.	4.50
Can be found with Bass sign on reverse and *Bass & Co.'s. Pale Ale*.	6.00
Drunkard leaning on lamp-post, fully coloured on orange lustre ashtray. Inscribed: *Show me the way to go home* and *Swat a night Boys Hic, Snow Usse Hic*. 112mm.	56.50
Gin bottle, inscribed: *Have a drop of gin old dear*. 95mm.	8.00
Hand holding beaker, inscribed: *Good health*. 88mm.	4.75
Man sitting with beer barrel and glass, some colouring.	

Inscribed: *Beer Hic Beer Hic*
Glorious Beer Hic. 70mm.   25.00
Monk holding beaker with verse:
A Jolly Monk am I. 113mm.   9.50
Mr. Pussyfoot, holding umbrella
with one foot on bottle of
Scotch, inscribed: *No home in*
Scotland. 135mm.   20.50
(Mr. Pussyfoot was an
American Prohibitionist).
Toby Jug, with verse: *No tongue*
can tell. No heart can sing How I
love a drop of drink. Can be found
inscribed: *This jug is an exact*
copy in miniature of the old
Toby jug (when it should really
be in the artefacts section). No.
413. 70mm.   5.25
Can be found coloured.   16.00

Sport
Five pieces have been found
labelled British Sports Series.
The Ashtrays labelled in this
way have been listed
separately.

British Sports Series
Games spinner and match holder
on shield ashtray, inscribed:
Put and take: yer ash: a match.
90mm long.   55.00
Goal with keeper and ball on
ashtray, inscribed: *League*
Football first played 1888. Some
colouring. 100mm long.   85.00
Golfer standing with club on
ashtray. Some colouring.
94mm.   80.00
Humpty, Dumpty sat on a wall.
Humpty on wall on ashtray,
some colouring. 97mm. Can be
found with an inkwell inset.   75.00
Tennis player holding racquet
aloft in front of net. Inscribed:
40 Love. Some colouring.
83mm.   70.00

Other Sporting Items
Cricket Bag. 105mm long.   6.50
Cricketer carrying bat, flag
figurine on green base. Some
colouring. 115mm (rare).   72.50

Curling stone, inscribed: *Soop-up.*
61mm dia.   14.50
F.A. Cup. 100mm.   11.00
Footballer with football, arms
outstretched, some colouring.
110mm.   80.00
Golf Ball, can be found inscribed:
The ancient game of golf was first
played in 1448. 50mm.   5.00
Golf Club, can be found inscribed:
Fore, or as above. 95mm.   7.50
Jockey standing on base, silks can
be yellow/blue, red/black,
or orange/black. 121mm.   75.00
Jockey on Racehorse, silks can be
blue/green, blue/brown,
green/yellow or red/yellow.
Very occasionally the horse is
found painted black. Can also
be found with inscription: for
example: *Ala Baculia: St Leger*
first run 1876. 110mm long.   75.00
Jockey on Racehorse with real
hair tail (often missing) on
ashtray base, some colouring.
Inscribed: *Horsey keep your tail*
up. 102mm.   20.50
Racehorse on base. 2 sizes:
                        118mm long.   56.00
                        140mm long.   60.00
Roller Skate. 120mm long.   40.00
Tennis Racquet. 140mm long.   5.50
Trophy. 130mm.   8.00

Musical Instruments
Upright Piano, 2 sizes: 64mm.   8.75
                        90mm.   10.50

Transport
Charabanc, inscribed: *Over the*
hills and far away. 'DN999' on
radiator. 148mm long. Found in
lustre.   19.50
Double Decker Bus, with driver
and outside staircase,
impressed: *Putney—Charing*
Cross: Globe Theatre John Bull
Thursday: General. 'DN999' on
radiator. 126mm long.   82.50
Motorbike and sidecar with rider.
112mm long.   55.00
Motorscooter on rectangular
base. 110mm long.   21.75

Open Sports Car, 'DN999' on
radiator. 106mm long.   30.00
Saloon Car, 'DN999' on radiator.
130mm long.   56.50
Stephenson Locomotive, with
detailed inscription: *I
Locomotion 1825. This Engine was
built by Geo. Stephenson and Son,
and was used at the opening of the
S. and D. Rly. Sept 27th 1825.*
88mm.   82.50

'Modern' Equipment
Gramophone in Cabinet, black
record on turntable, inscribed:
Music hath charms. Found in
lustre. 92mm. Can be found
coloured blue.   30.00
Gramophone, square with Horn,
inscribed: *HMV* or *His Masters
Voice*, with transfer of 'HMV'
dog and notes of music. 96mm.   19.50

Gramophone with dog listening
to horn, on oval base. Inscribed:
His Masters Voice. Some
colouring. 88mm long (a much
sought after model). Very
rarely found in lustre.   40.00
National cash register with '£.s.d.'
Found unnamed but with
'£.s.d.' in lustre. 70mm (not
very common).   22.50
Radio Operator, inscribed:
Listening in. Some colouring.
85mm.   39.50
Radio Operator with
microphone, inscribed:
Listening in. Some colouring.
85mm.   39.50
Radio Operator with horn,
inscribed: *Listening in*. Some
colouring. 85mm.   39.50
Telephone, stick type, inscribed:
Hello, Hello and *All alone by the
telephone*. 115mm.   11.00
Treadle sewing machine, found
inscribed: *Singer*. 80mm.   16.50

Miscellaneous
Boot. 2 sizes: 50mm.   4.75
              72mm long.   4.00
Boot Pin Box.   6.50
Candleholder. 118mm.   3.00

Sabot. 100mm long.   4.50
Slipper Wall Pocket.
105mm long.   7.50
Bishop's Mitre. 70mm.   4.00
Boater hat. 104mm long.   7.50
Boy Scouts Hat. 95mm dia.   10.50
Top Hat. 40mm.   3.00
Dice Pin Box. 50mm square.   10.50
Hand holding crinkle topped
flower vase (not a tulip as
usually found). 85mm.   2.75
Hatpin Holder Lighthouse, in-
scribed: *Sailor Beware*. 136mm.   7.00
Hatpin Holder in shape of a
Thistle on leaves. 80mm.   7.00
Hatpin Holder, square. 97mm.   6.50
Horseshoe. 115mm.   2.00
Horses Hoof Pin Box and lid.
98mm long.   3.00

Miniature Domestic
Cheese Dish (one piece). 45mm.   4.75
Cheese Dish with cover. 50mm.   7.50
Cheese Dish, fluted with cover.
50mm.   7.50
Coffee Pot with separate lid. No.
271. 78mm.   3.00
Kettle. 60mm.   4.00
Photograph Frame, horseshoe
shape inscribed: *The Best of
Luck*. 125mm long.   10.50
Teapot with separate lid. 50mm.   5.00

Carlton also made a whole range
of pin or ashtrays, pill boxes
and trinket boxes in club,
diamond, heart and spade
shapes. They can be found
with crest or transfer views.
Very few articles for domestic
use, plates, cups etc. have
been found but this is probably
because they were used and
broken. A 108mm long teapot
has been found with elaborate
moulding and a miniature
swan projecting from lid, and
objects like this which are
obviously decorative are likely
to have survived. Price range:
                                       1.75 to 8.00

Carmen China

Cascade China

For mark see *Crested China*, p. 105.

Trademark used for E. A. Green, Rugby by J. A. Robinson & Sons Ltd, Arcadian Works, Stoke-on-Trent (Usual trademark: Arcadian)

Ancient Artefacts
Model of vase found near Winchelsea.
75mm.   2.25

Monuments
Tom Hughes Monument, Rugby
School. 135mm.   30.00

Seaside Souvenirs
Eddystone Lighthouse. 125mm.   3.50

Animals
Dog, Scottish Terrier. 66mm long.   6.50
Tortoise. 69mm long.   4.00

Birds/Eggs
Egg with flat base. 44mm.   2.25
Hen roosting. 54mm.   3.00

Great War
Model of Tommy on Sentry Duty.
105mm.   40.00
Battleship, 3 funnels and tiny
    gun fore and aft. 100mm long.   10.50
Torpedo Boat Destroyer, not
    named. 108mm long.   16.00
Jack Johnson. Shell. 90mm.   3.00
Tommy's Hut. 104mm long.   40.00
Bomb dropped from Zeppelin.
80mm.   4.75
Bandsman's Drum. 53mm.   4.50
Officers peaked cap with
    coloured badge and hatband.
65mm dia.   8.75

Comic/Novelty
Clown, bust, inscribed: *Put me*
    amongst the girls. 85mm.   15.25

Trademark used for a retailer on china manufactured probably by Taylor & Kent Ltd. Florence Works, Longton (Usual trademark Florentine)

Miscellaneous
Book. No. 72. 57mm.   3.00

Cauldon China

For mark see *Crested China*, p. 105.

Trademark used by Cauldon Ltd, Stoke-on-Trent.

Buildings – White
Queen's Doll's House, found
both glazed and unglazed.
3 sizes: 95mm.　　16.00
　　　118mm.　　21.75
　　　146mm.　　21.75
Queen's Doll's House with
removable 'roof' lid. 2 sizes:
75mm & 95mm. Both can be
found with inscription.　　16.00

Celtic Porcelain

For mark see *Crested China*, p. 106.

Trademark used by the Nautilus Porcelain
Co., Possil Pottery, Glasgow.

Countryside
Log Vase. 32mm.　　4.50

Miscellaneous
Carboy.　　4.25

　　Many 'smalls' have also now been found.

Ceramic China

Challenge China

For mark see *Crested China*, p. 106.

Trademark thought to have been used by a German manufacturer for china imported into England.

One 'small' with a St Andrews
  crest known.

Trademark used by an unknown manufacturer (But probably Taylor & Kent Ltd) for a retailer probably in the Birmingham area.

One piece known – jug. 83mm
  with Birmingham crest.

Chelson China

For mark see *Crested China*, p. 106.

Trademark used by New Chelsea Porcelain Co. (Ltd), Bagnall Street, Longton.

Range of Great War
  commemoratives on 'smalls'
  were produced. Value around
  £5.00 each.

Civic

For mark see *Crested China*, p. 107.

Trademark used by an unknown pottery manufacturer during the Great War.

Animals
Cat sitting with long neck.
  105mm. (This is a model of a
  Destroyer's Ship's mascot
  which became popular during
  the Great War).   5.50
Manx Cat. 90mm.   8.75

Great War
Bandsman's Drum. 55mm dia.   4.75

Sport
Cricket Bag. 110mm long.   6.50

Clarence Crest China

For mark see *Crested China*, p. 107.

Trademark used by Beresford Bros., Clarence Works, High Street, Longton. The models either bear a close resemblence to H & L (Willow Art) models or are the same. There must have been some connection between these two firms, both working in Longton.

Ancient Artefacts
Loving cup, 3 handled. 40mm.   2.25

Buildings – white
Windmill. 85mm.   16.00

Monuments
Baron Burton statue. 130mm.   16.00

Animals
Cat, sitting. 78mm.   7.50
Dog, Dachsund, sitting.
   75mm long.   40.00
Elephant, standing. 78mm long.   6.50

Birds
Swan. 57mm.   2.50

Great War
Nurse, inscribed: *A friend in need.*
   130mm.   25.75
Monoplane with revolving
   prop. 150mm long.   30.00
Field gun with screen.
   114mm long.   13.00
Bandsman's Drum. 58mm.   4.75
Kit Bag, with inscription *Pack up
your troubles in your old kit bag*.
   70mm.   10.50
Tommy's Steel Helmet.
   76mm long.   16.00
Kitchen Range, with pot on fire
   inscribed: *Keep the home fires
burning*. No. 199. 78mm long.   9.50

Miscellaneous
Trump indicator ashtray. 110mm
   dia.   8.00

A small range of domestic china was produced bearing colour transfers of good quality.

Clays

Clifton

For mark see *Crested China*, p. 108.

For mark see *Crested China*, p. 108.

Trademark used on crested china manufactured by Hewitt Bros. (Usual trademark Willow Art).

Trademark used by a branch of J.A. Robinson Ltd, Stoke-on-Trent. Subsequently Cauldon Ltd. (Usual mark Arcadian).

Historical/Folklore
Bell inscribed: *Curfew must not ring tonight*. 72mm.   5.00

Animals
Elephant, walking. 70mm long.   6.50
Pig, standing. 96mm long.   8.50

Birds
Wise Owl, with verse. 98mm.   7.50

Great War
Soldier, with rifle, inscribed: *Our brave defender*. 132mm.   21.75
Battleship, impressed:
HMS Lion. 140mm long.   13.00
British Tank, Model of, with 2 front steering wheels. No. 107.
125mm long.   10.50
Officers peaked cap. No. 100.
75mm dia.   5.50

Cartoon/Comedy Characters
Baby, with arms outstretched, inscribed: *Cheerio*. Some colouring on face. 125mm. (Great War cartoon character, could be 'Pooksie'.)   12.50

Parian/Unglazed
Bust of King George V, glazed circular base, with inscription:
King George V born June 3rd 1865, ascended the throne May 6th 1910.
135mm.   30.00
Bust of Queen Mary, glazed circular base, with inscription:
Queen Mary born May 26th 1867.
135mm.   30.00

Ancient Artefacts
Most inscriptions begin: *Model of*, so this will not be repeated throughout the list.
Ancient Tyg. No. 58. 70mm.   2.25
Ashbourne Bushel, inscribed: *His Majesty King Charles 2nd's Royal Standard Bushel fastened to the Market Cross in the year 1677.*
95mm dia.   3.25
British Bronze Pot, Ancient. 71mm.   2.25
Canterbury Roman Vase,
2 shapes: No. 22. 63mm (with handle); No. 29. 60mm (no handle).   2.25
Carlisle Salt Pot. No. 110. 40mm.   2.25
Chester Roman Vase. No. 131.
60mm.   2.25
Chinese vase originally in Hanley Museum. 58mm.   2.25
Derby Roman Vase, inscribed:
Roman Vase found at Little Chester, Derby. No. 26. 63mm.   2.25
Dorchester Jug, inscribed: *Old Jug found in North Street, Dorchester.*
No. 17. 55mm.   2.25
Egyptian Vase, ancient, about 230BC. No. 155. 45mm.   2.25

Fountains Abbey Cup. No. 94. 50mm.	1.75
Glastonbury Bowl. No. 65. 40mm.	1.75
Glastonbury Vase. No. 642. 55mm.	1.75
Hastings Kettle. No. 237. 62mm.	1.75
Loving cup originated by Henry of Navarre King of France. 3 handled. 40mm.	2.50
50mm.	2.50
Newbury Leather Bottle, inscribed: *Leather bottle found on battlefield of Newbury 1644 now in museum.* No. 83. 65mm.	2.25
New Forest Roman Jug, not named. No. 174. 67mm.	2.25
Nose of Brasenose College, Oxford (not found numbered). 103mm long.	7.00
Pompeian Vessel, not found named. 43mm.	1.75
Portland Vase, not found named. 60mm.	1.75
Puzzle Jug, original in South Kensington Museum with usual verse. No. 147. 70mm.	3.50
Roman Salopian Ewer found at Uriconium, now in Shrewsbury Museum. 75mm.	2.25
Southwold Jar, (not found numbered). 95mm.	1.75
Winchelsea Roman Cup (3 handles).	1.75

Buildings – white

Highland Cottage, Model of. 60mm.	10.50

Monuments

Baron Burton monument. 130mm.	30.00

Historical/Folklore

Ancient Coaching Hat, Model of. No. 687. 68mm long.	6.00
Witches Cauldron with verse. 47mm.	4.00

Traditional/National Souvenirs

John Bull, bust, eyes and mouth coloured. 100mm.	16.00
Luton Boater, not found named. 78mm dia.	5.50

Melton Mowbray pie, The. Pie with moulded pastry adornments, with verse. 50mm.	16.25
Welsh Lady, bust, with inscription: *Wales! Wales! My Mother's sweet home in Wales* etc. With black Welsh hat. 80mm.	8.25
Welsh Tea Party, 2 sizes: 55mm.	15.25
95mm.	23.00

Seaside Souvenirs

Lifeboat, inscribed: *Margate Lifeboat, friend to all nations.* 118mm long.	5.50
Clam shell menu holder. 62mm.	6.00
Mr. Punch, bust, some colouring – red hearts on cheeks. 80mm.	13.00

Countryside

Haystack, circular. 58mm.	4.00

Animals

Cat, long necked and sitting, can be inscribed: *My word if you're not off.* 108mm.	5.50
Elephant walking. Can be found inscribed: *Baby Jumbo.* No. 237. 70mm.	6.50
Frog, open mouth and green eyes, inscribed: *Always croaking.* 80mm.	5.50
Hare. No. 10. 73mm.	7.50
Sussex pig, Model of, standing inscribed: *You can push or you can shuv but I'm hanged if I'll be druv.* No. 148. 78mm long.	14.00
Teddy Bear, sitting. 90mm.	9.00
Pony, Shetland. 2 sizes: 105mm	19.50
120mm long.	21.50

Birds

Chick emerging from egg. 72mm long.	4.75
Owl. 69mm.	5.50

Great War

Despatch rider, Model of, on motorbike. 120mm long.	40.00
Sailor, bust, inscribed: *HMS Dreadnought* and *The handy man.* With verse: *Hearts of*	19.50
Oak. 95mm. with verse	25.75

Sailor, bust, impressed: *HMS*
Queen Elizabeth. 86mm.   19.50
Tank, Model of. 116mm.   8.75
Tank with inset wheels.
  127mm long.   10.50
Red Cross Van. 90mm long.   17.50
Howitzer (not found named).
  115mm long.   10.50
Field gun with screen.
  112mm long.   13.00
Trench Mortar. 70mm long.   8.75
Bomb dropped from Zeppelin, model
of. 80mm.   5.50
Canister bomb, Model of. 60mm.   8.75
Colonial hat, Model of. 88mm wide. 5.50
Anti Zeppelin candlestick.
  62mm.   8.75
Trench Lamp. 67mm.   8.75

Home/Nostalgic
Anvil on circular base. No. 25.
  68mm.   4.75
Bucket. No. 92. 75mm.   2.25
Dustpan. 44mm long.   5.25
Flat Iron Stand. 70mm.   2.50
Grandfather clock, Model of a,
  inscribed: *Make use of time let not*
  advantage slip. Shakespeare.
  No. 209. 108mm.   10.50
Pillar box, inscribed: *G V R if you*
  haven't time to post a line here's
  the pillar box. 60mm.   8.25

Comic/Novelty
2 Black boys heads popping out
  of box, inscribed: *Box of choco-*
  lates. Much colouring. 60mm. 30.00
Clown, bust, inscribed: *Put me*
  amongst the girls. Some
  colouring. No. 12. 80mm.   15.25

Alcohol
Monk, holding glass with verse.
  112mm.   10.50

Sport
Football. 5mm dia.   4.50

Miscellaneous
Oriental slipper. No. 352.
  105mm long.   4.75

Recorded Numbered Ornamental Wares
No. 16. Globe Vase. 46mm.   1.75

No. 37. Vase, wide mouth.
  50mm.   1.75
No. 45. Trinket Box, spade
  shaped. 40mm.   3.00
No. 63. Pot on 3 small feet. 41mm. 1.75
No. 72. Jug. 60mm.   1.75
No. 74. Jug. 82mm.   1.75
No. 100. Vase. 53mm.   1.75
No. 141. Vase. 47mm.   1.75
No. 144. Vase. 50mm.   1.75
No. 145. Vase. 53mm.   1.75
No. 146. Vase. 50mm.   1.75
No. 215. Vase. 60mm.   1.75
No. 216. Vase. 60mm.   1.75
No. 217. Vase, flat bottomed.
  37mm.   1.75
No. 303. Vase. 52mm.   1.75
No. 305. Beaker. 34mm.   1.75
No. 532. Jug. 70mm.   1.75
No. 587. Taper Vase. 60mm.   1.75
No. 666. Crinkle topped vase.
  40mm.   1.75
Found not numbered. Trinket
  Box, heart shaped. 40mm.   3.00

Clifton China

For mark see *Crested China*, p. 111.

Trademark used by Wildblood, Heath and Sons (Ltd), Peel Works, Longton. The models show great resemblence to those of H & L – Willow Art, also working in Longton and later wares are identical to Arcadian models.

Parian/Unglazed
Bust of Queen Alexandra on
round base. 137mm.   30.00

Ancient Artefacts
Loving Cup. 39mm.   2.25
Egyptian Urn, Model of. No. 130.
48mm.   2.25

Buildings – White
Wainhouse Tower. 135mm.   40.00

Monuments
Burton Statue, Burton on Trent.
Inscribed: *Michael Arthur first
Baron Burton, born 1837. Died
1909.* 130mm.   16.00

Historical/Folklore
Burns chair, Model of. No. 49.
90mm.   5.50

Traditional/National Souvenirs
John Bull, bust of. 90mm.   16.00

Seaside Souvenirs
Lighthouse. 110mm.   3.50

Animals
Cat in boot. No. 65. 68mm.   11.00
Cheshire cat, still smiling, green
right eye. 80mm.   5.50
Elephant, walking. 75mm.   6.50

Bird
Canary on rock, unnamed Nor-
wich Warbler. No. 23. 98mm.   6.50

Great War
Battleship, impressed:
HMS Lion. 140mm long.   13.00
British tank, Model of. 140mm long. 13.00
British tank, Model of, with trailing
steering wheels. No. 120.
130mm long.   10.50
Field Gun with screen. No. 214.
115mm long.   13.00
Shell. No. 114. 70mm.   2.25
Kit Bag with verse: *Pack up your
troubles.* 72mm.   10.50
Drum. 65mm dia.   4.75
Tommy's Steel Helmet.
75mm long.   16.00

Home/Nostalgic
Anvil. 88mm long.   4.75
Watering Can. No. 126. 75mm.   4.75

Novelty
Billiken, The god of luck. 75mm.   3.00

Alcohol
Barrel on legs. No. 85. 60mm.   2.25
Barrel on stand. No. 83.
63mm long.   2.75

Miscellaneous
Bell. No. 12. 55mm.   4.00

Domestic Wares
Hexagonal and octagonal salt
pots can be found inscribed:
Salt. Jugs, beakers and small
vases can also be found.   1.75 to 5.00

C. L. Reis and Co.

For mark see *Crested China*, p. 113.

C. L. Reis is probably a retailer, trademark being used on porcelain with Irish crests. (It seems likely that the china was manufactured by Alfred B. Jones & Sons Ltd. – usual trademark Grafton)

Seaside Souvenirs
Whelk Shell. 82mm long.   3.00

Animal
Pig, standing, inscribed: *Wunt be druv*. 70mm long.   10.00
(One of these pigs is still alive and well and living in Australia!)

Miscellaneous
Basket. No. 240.   2.50

Colleen China

Trademark unidentified but could possibly be Belleek.

National Souvenirs
Bust of *John Redmond MP 1914*
(The bust is hollow and has a Wexford crest) 137mm.   36.50

Collingwood

Columbia China

For marks see *Crested China* p. 113.

For mark see *Crested China*, p. 113.

Trademark used by Collingwood Bros
(Ltd.), St. George's Works, Longton.
This firm produced a range of
'smalls' to commemorate the
British Empire Exhibition,
Wembley, 1924.   £2.25 to £5.00

Trademark used by an English manufacturer for export to British Columbia.
Only one small vase with this
mark is known, it has a British
Columbian crest.

Coral Porcelain

Trademark used by the Coral Porcelain Co. also known as the Scottish Porcelain Co.

A range of 'smalls' with Scottish crests was produced.

The Corona China

For mark see *Crested China*, p. 113.

Trademark used by Sampson Hancock (& Sons), Bridge Works, Stoke and later at the Garden Works, Hanley (renamed Corona Pottery).

Ancient Artefacts

Canterbury Leather Bottle.	
No. 156.	1.75
Hastings Kettle. 57mm.	1.75

Buildings – White

Ann Hathaway's Cottage.	
95mm long.	10.50
Blackpool Tower. 139mm.	5.25
Bottle Oven (inside of). 82mm.	9.50
Bridge, with grassy banks.	
134mm long.	20.00
Canterbury Cathedral, West Front.	
137mm.	19.50
Crosthwaite Church, Keswick.	
110mm long.	50.00

Monuments

Bunyan's Statue. 165mm.	9.50
Tom Hughes Monument, Rugby.	
136mm.	26.00

Historical/Folklore

Noah's Ark. 95mm long.	2.25

Traditional/National Souvenirs

Lancashire Clog. 2 sizes:	
70mm	3.00
102mm long.	6.50
Welsh Harp. 90mm.	4.00
Welsh Hat, can be found with largest place name round brim.	
45mm.	3.25
with wording	4.75

Seaside Souvenirs

Bathing Machine. 71mm.	4.00
Canoe. 102mm long.	3.00
Beachy Head Lighthouse, black band. 150mm.	5.50

Animals

Cat sitting with ruff around neck. 105mm.	8.25
Cheshire Cat. 95mm.	4.75
Manx Cat. 60mm.	13.00
Bulldog, standing. 112mm long.	8.75
Dog, King Charles Spaniel, begging. 69mm.	4.50
Fish Vase. 60mm.	2.00
Hare with raised ears. No. 166. 63mm long.	7.00
Lion, lying down. 140mm long.	16.00
Mouse, eating nut. 44mm.	16.00
Pig, lying down. 65mm long.	6.50
Pig, standing. 84mm long.	7.00
Pony, Shetland. 110mm long.	14.00
Teddy Bear, sitting, can be found completely brown with no crest. No. 194. 85mm.	7.00
brown	21.75
Tortoise. 32mm.	4.00

Birds

Swan. 85mm.	2.25
Swan, Posy Holder. 87mm long.	2.00

Great War

British Airship on base. 128mm long.	13.00
Zeppelin. 134mm long.	13.00
Battleship. 120mm long.	10.50
Lusitania. 163mm long.	56.50
Submarine, inscribed: *E4*. Size varies 102mm–120mm long.	8.75
New submarine, Model of. 146mm long. (This is the submarine usually named E5 by other firms).	8.75
Red Cross Van. 98mm long.	17.50
Renault Tank. 115mm long.	55.00
Tank with inset trailing wheels. 100mm long.	10.50
Field Gun. 2 sizes: 120mm	8.75
140mm long.	9.50
Field Gun with screen. 120mm long.	13.00
Cannon Shell. 100mm.	3.50
Torpedo, Model of. No. 285. 145mm long.	40.00
Bandsman's Drum. 63mm dia.	4.50
Bell Tent, hexagonal tent with open flaps. No. 209. 85mm.	5.50
Ghurka Knife. 140mm long.	13.00
Trench Lamp. 88mm.	6.50

Water Bottle. 68mm.	10.50
Grandfather Clock, same mould as usual Grandfather clock but clockface transfer at 3.25, inscribed: *World War 1914–1919*. *Peace signed 3.25pm June 28th 1919*.	47.50
Cenotaph, Whitehall. 140mm.	4.00
Romsey War Memorial. 155mm.	65.00
Rushden War Memorial. 158mm.	56.50

Home/Nostalgic

Alarm Clock. 85mm.	11.00
Armchair. 60mm.	7.50
Baby in Bootee. 80mm long.	6.50
Grandfather Clock. 128mm.	6.50
Hip Bath. 95mm long.	7.00
Pillar Box. No. 171. 74mm.	4.75
Watering Can. 70mm.	4.75
Writing Slope/Desk top. No. 268. 53mm.	5.50

Comic/Novelty

Cigarette Case. 72mm long.	4.75
Man's Head Cream Jug. 76mm.	3.00

Musical Instruments

Upright Piano. 63mm.	5.50

'Modern' Equipment

Gas Cooker. 70mm.	6.50
Gramophone, square with no horn. 57mm.	12.00

Miscellaneous

Horseshoe, on slope. 70mm long.	1.25
Horseshoe, wall plaque. 60mm long.	1.50
Bishop, Chess Piece. 61mm.	12.50
King, Chess Piece. 115mm.	17.00
Knight, Chess Piece. 70mm.	7.50
Pawn, Chess Piece. 90mm.	10.00
Ladies Button Boot. No. 149. 65mm.	7.50
Ladies 18th Century Shoe. No. 146. 90mm long.	8.00
Lancashire Clog, square toe and gilded buckle. 80mm long.	4.00
Top Hat. 45mm.	3.00

Miniature Domestic

Cheese Dish. 1 piece. 60mm.	4.00
Cheese Dish and Lid. 60mm.	4.75
Teapot and Lid. No. 112. 65mm.	5.00

Coronet Ware

For marks see *Crested China*, p. 117.

A trademark used by Ford & Pointon Ltd, Norfolk Works, Hanley. Subsequently a branch of J.A. Robinson & Sons Ltd, and later Cauldon Ltd. Some late pieces are therefore from Arcadian moulds.

Ancient Artefacts

Fountains Abbey Cup, not found named. 48mm.	2.00
Puzzle Jug. 70mm.	3.50
Roman Oil Lamp. 100mm long.	3.50

Buildings – White

Cottage. 50mm.	4.00

Monuments/Crosses

Celtic Cross, on square base. 108mm.	4.00
Wallace's Memorial at Stirling. 120mm.	17.50

Historical/Folklore

Judge, bust. 60mm.	6.50
Man in stocks. 102mm.	10.50
Mother Shipton. 72mm.	4.00

National Souvenir

Welsh Hat. 57mm.	4.00

Seaside Souvenirs

Bermudan rigged sailing boat. 125m.	13.00
Houseboat. 90mm long.	3.00
Whelk shell. 95mm long.	3.00
Punch and Judy booth, with Punch and dog Toby. 90mm (rare).	26.00
Punch, bust, with red nose. 83mm (quite rare).	13.00

Animals

Cat, large and furry, snarling. 93mm.	6.00

Cat, long necked. 103mm.	5.50
Cat, Manx. 64mm.	13.00
Camel, with 1 hump, kneeling. 56mm.	7.50
Dog, spaniel type, standing. 76mm long.	8.25
Dolphin Vase. 102mm.	2.25
Elephant, kneeling. 60mm.	6.50
Fish, open mouthed. 102mm long.	2.25
Frog, open mouthed and green eyes. 60mm.	4.75
Monkey, wearing coat, sitting. 75mm.	5.50
Mouse playing Mandolin, on base. 80mm.	19.50
Pig, standing, inscribed: *The pig that won't go*. 84mm long.	8.25
Pig, standing. 95mm long.	8.25
Pony, inscribed: *Shetland Pony*. 74mm.	13.00
Seal, with ball on nose.	13.00
Teddy bear. 96mm.	7.50
Toad (or frog) with closed mouth. 50mm.	10.50
Tortoise. 72mm long.	4.00

Birds

Hen, roosting. 55m.	3.00
Kingfisher. 80mm.	7.50
Kingfisher cream jug. 60mm.	4.00
Pelican cream jug. 80mm.	4.00
Swan Posy Holder. 90mm long.	2.25

Great War

Tommy in bayonet attack. 130mm.	95.00
British Airship, on base. 130mm long.	13.00
Monoplane with movable prop and cross hatching. 145mm long.	30.00
Monoplane with movable prop and no cross hatching. 170mm long.	30.00
Battleship. 115mm long.	10.50
Torpedo Boat destroyer, Model of. 105mm long.	16.00
Submarine, inscribed: *E5*. 130mm long.	13.00
Armoured car with turret. 95mm.	19.50
Red Cross Van. 90mm long.	17.50
Tank. 110mm long.	8.75
Tank with large gun turrets. 120mm long.	12.50

Tank with inset steering wheels.
116mm long.   10.50
Field Gun. 145mm long.   11.00
Zeppelin Bomb. 78mm.   4.75
Bandsman's drum. 55mm dia.   4.50
Bell Tent.   5.50
Ghurka Knife. 110mm long.   13.00
Hand Grenade. 60mm.   8.75
Glengarry. 90mm long.   11.25
Peaked Cap. 63mm long.   5.50
Sandbag. 70mm.   8.75
Telescope, folded. 70mm.   7.50
Tommy's hut, unnamed.
105mm long.   40.00
Water Bottle. 63mm.   8.75
Dartford War Memorial (rare).
163mm.   65.00
Cenotaph. 100mm long.   3.00

Home/Nostalgic

Anvil on wooden stump. 66mm.   3.00
The old armchair, with verse. 86mm.   4.00
Carboy. 75mm.   2.25
Coal Scuttle, ornate. 68mm.   2.50
Dustpan. 100mm long.   5.25
Flat Iron.   4.00
Frying pan. 115mm long.   4.00
Grandfather Clock. 127mm.   8.75
Kennel. 52mm.   4.00
Shaving Mug. 58mm.   4.00
Sofa. 82mm.   4.00
Stool, 3 legged. 40mm.   3.50
Watering Can. 70mm.   4.00
Wicker Chair. 92mm.   4.00

Comic/Novelty

Baby in hip bath. 100mm long.   6.50
Boy on scooter. 95mm.   13.00
Clown, bust. 65mm.   4.00
Truck of Coal. 90mm long.   10.50
Jack in the Box. 95mm.   10.50

Alcohol

Bottle of Champagne in Ice
Bucket. 85mm.   5.50
Drunkard, bust of (looks rather
like Ally Sloper). 74mm.   7.50

Sport

Cricket Bat. 115mm long.   21.50
Football. 50mm.   4.50

Musical Instruments

Grand Piano. 82mm long.   11.25

Guitar. 152mm long.   6.50
Harp. 95mm.   6.00
Piano, upright. 65mm long.   8.25
Tambourine. 68mm dia.   4.00

Transport

Saloon Car. 85mm long.   30.00
Motor Horn: *Pip Pip*. 90mm long.   13.00

'Modern' Equipment

Radio Horn. 93mm.   10.00
Square Gramophone. 55mm.   12.00

Miscellaneous

Boot. 70mm.   4.75
Ladies Ankle Boot. 76mm long.   4.75
Ladies 18th century Shoe.
95mm long.   7.50
Solar Topee. 60mm.   8.00

Miniature Domestic

Cheese dish. 2 pieces. 50mm.   4.50
Coffee Pot and lid. 80mm.   3.00
Cup and Saucer. 40mm.   4.00
Teapot and lid. 70mm.   5.50

Craven China

Crown China

For mark see *Crested China*, p. 119.

For mark see *Crested China*, p. 119.

Trademark used by Wiltshaw and Robinson Ltd, Carlton Works, Stoke-on-Trent (usual trademark Carlton).

Trademark used by Wiltshaw and Robinson Ltd, Carlton Works, Stoke-on-Trent (usual trademark Carlton).

Great War

Cannon Shell. 75mm.	4.00
Searchlight. 70mm.	21.75
Glengarry, with coloured thistle. 78mm long.	13.00
Kitbag. 72mm.	10.50

Musical Instruments

Lute. 158mm long.	14.00

Miscellaneous

Ankle Boot, laces undone. 78mm long.	4.00

Buildings – White

Cottage, two chimneys. 50mm.	5.00
Brick cottage, one chimney, on rectangular base. 48mm.	5.00

Traditional/National Souvenirs

Blackpool Big Wheel. 82mm.	6.50
Jenny Jones, Welsh lady, standing figure with black hat, brown basket and red and green shawl. 147mm.	17.50
Welsh Hat, with orange band. 44mm.	4.50

Seaside

Motorboat with driver. 102mm long.	16.00
Lifeboat. 113mm long.	4.75
Luggage Trolley inscribed: *Luggage in Advance*, etc. 80mm long.	30.00
Portmanteau. 55mm.	4.25

Animals

Dog playing banjo, inscribed: *Some band*. 83mm.	18.00
Dog (puppy), sitting with one ear down. 83mm.	5.50
Dog, Scottie, wearing a Tam O'Shanter, some colouring. 82mm.	5.50

Birds

Bird cream jug. 84mm.	4.00
Hen, roosting. 60mm long.	3.75
Owl, wearing black mortar board with red tassel. 75mm.	8.25

Home/Nostalgic

Bellows, ornate. 93mm long.	4.00

Grandfather Clock, inscribed:
Make use of time. Let not
advantage slip. 135mm.   10.50
Rocking Chair. 96mm.   14.50
Sundial, inscribed: *Let others tell of*
storms and showers I'll count the
sunny hours. 90mm.   4.00
Village Pump. Round. 76mm.   5.00
Water Pump with trough. 75mm.   5.00

Comic/Novelty
I'm forever blowing bubbles. Pears
advert blue boy blowing
bubbles. Clothes blue, bubble
and bowl lustre. 110mm.   25.75
Truck of Coal, *Black diamonds from*
. . . 95mm long.   10.50

Alcohol
Beer Barrel on stilts. XXX in red on
sides. 57mm.   2.50
Toby Jug, with verse. 79mm.   5.25

British Sports Series
Tennis player holding a raquet in
front of net, inscribed: *40 Love.*
Some colouring. 83mm.   60.00

Transport
Motorbike and sidecar.
102mm long.   55.00
Open Sports Car, inscribed:
DN999. 105mm long.   30.00

'Modern' Equipment
Gramophone in Cabinet, black
record on turntable, inscribed:
Music hath charms. 92mm.   30.00
Gramophone with dog,
inscribed: *His Masters Voice.*
90mm.   40.00
Telephone, stick type, inscribed:
Hello, hello. 115mm.   11.00

Crown Derby

Trademark used by Crown Derby Porcelain
Company Ltd.

Miscellaneous
Lady's Slipper. 98mm long.   8.00

Crown Devon

The Crown Duchy English China

For mark see *Crested China*, p. 119.

For mark see *Crested China*, p. 120.

Trademark used by S. Fielding and Co (Ltd), Railway Pottery, Devon Pottery, Stoke.

Trade mark probably used for a retailer by an unknown English manufacturer.

Buildings – White
Tower of Refuge, Douglas IOM, also
found in lustre and always with
a Douglas Crest. 68mm.   25.75

Birds
Chicken.   4.75

National Souvenir
Legs of Man, lustre. 101mm.   17.50

A range of domestic ware all with
a Morecambe crest was
produced.

Transport
Racing car with driver and
co-driver, coloured, inscribed:
*Manx International Motor Car
Race*. 140mm long.   65.00

Crown Staffordshire

Curzon Art

For mark see *Crested China*, p. 120.

Trademark used by Crown Staffordshire Porcelain Co. Ltd, Minerva Works, Fenton. Subsequently Crown Staffordshire China Co. Ltd.

Miniature Domestic
Milk Jug.	2.00
Sugar Bowl.	2.00

Trademark probably used for a retailer by Hewitt and Leadbeater, Willow Potteries, Longton (usual trademark Willow Art).

This mark has been found on 'smalls' with World War I commemoratives.
Four flags of the Allies and the
inscription: *United we stand*. 2.50 to 7.50

CW and Co.

For mark see *Crested China*, p. 120.

Trademark used by Charles Waine (and Co.), Derby Works, Longton (usual trademark Venetia China).

This mark has been found on a 'small' with the inscription:
Festival of Empire, Crystal Palace, 1911.   4.00

Cyclone

For marks see *Crested China*, p. 120.

Trademark used by a wholesaler of crested china manufactured by several well-known firms including Taylor and Kent and Wiltshaw and Robinson (usual trademarks Florentine and Carlton).

Ancient Artefacts
Ancient Tyg, one handle, not
    named. 70mm.   1.75
Chester Roman Vase, not named.
    2 sizes: 50mm and 68mm.   1.75
Loving Cup, 3 handled. 38mm.   2.25
Salisbury Kettle, not named.
    100mm.   1.75

Buildings – White
Cottage. 70mm long.   4.00

Monuments/Crosses
Market Cross, not named.
    108mm.   4.00

Historical/Folklore
Man in Pillory. 105mm.   12.50

Traditional/National Souvenirs
Lancashire Clog. 88mm long.   4.75
Highland Quaich. 83mm dia.   5.00

Seaside Souvenirs
Bathing Machine. 76mm.   4.50
Sailing Yacht, in full sail.
    127mm long.   8.75
Lighthouse. 100mm.   4.00
Suitcase. 77mm long.   2.25

Animals
Cat, very plump. 88mm.   7.50
Cat smiling, could be an unnamed
    Cheshire cat. 76mm.   4.75
Manx Cat. 90mm.   13.00
Dog in kennel. 85mm.   8.25
Elephant kneeling. 82mm long.   6.50

Monkey crouching, hands to
  mouth. 90mm.   7.00
Pig, standing, inscribed: *The pig
  that won't go*. 80mm long.   10.50
Rabbit. 70mm long.   4.00
Terrapin. 75mm.   5.50
Toad, very flat. 72mm long only
  32mm high.   6.50

Birds
Pelican milk jug. 83mm long.   4.00
Swan.   2.75
Swan Posy Bowl. 75mm long.   2.25

Great War
Submarine, inscribed: *E9*.
  146mm long.   8.75
Armoured Car, with 3 guns on
  turret, inscribed: *RNAS*.
  116mm long.   82.50
Tank. 125mm long.   13.00
Drum. 32mm.   4.75
Telescope, folded. 70mm.   7.50
Cenotaph, inscribed: *The blood of
  heroes is the seed of freedom*.
  2 sizes: 100 mm   3.50
            140mm.   4.75

Home/Nostalgic
Baby in hip bath. 103mm long.   6.50
Lantern. 65mm.   4.00
Milk Churn, 2 handles. 70mm.   2.25
Oil Lamp. 60mm.   3.50
Pillar Box, inscribed: *I can't get a
  letter from you so send you the box*.
  76mm.   8.25
Sofa. 82mm long.   7.50
Watering Can. 70mm.   4.75

Comic/Novelty
Boy on scooter. 106mm.   13.00

Sport
Boxing Glove. 70mm long (very
  rare).   30.00

'Modern' Equipment
Square Gramophone. No horn.
  53mm.   12.00

Miscellaneous
Shoe, ladies' 18th century.
  95mm long.   7.50

Miniature Domestic
Coffee Pot. 65mm.   3.00
Tea Pot. 75mm.   4.00

The Dainty Ware

For mark see *Crested China*, p. 121.

Trademark used by a London wholesaler on crested china manufactured by a number of companies but mainly Taylor and Kent (usual trademark Florentine).

Historical/Folklore

Man in Pillory. 104mm.	10.50

Traditional/National Souvenirs

Lancashire Clog. 88mm long.	4.75
Welsh Harp. 97mm.	4.00

Seaside Souvenirs

Bathing Machine with figure on steps. 75mm.	7.50
Yacht in full sail. 127mm long.	9.50
Lighthouse on rocks. 95mm.	4.00

Animals

Dogs, two King Charles Spaniels in a Top Hat. 70mm.	10.50
Dog, sitting, head on one side, blue eyes. 69mm.	6.50
Pup, sitting, red eyes, bow around neck. 77mm.	8.25
Mouse. 63mm long.	12.50
Pig, sitting. 63mm long.	6.50
Seal, with ball. 72mm.	8.75

Birds

Baby Bird Cream Jug. 48mm.	4.00
Bird, roosting. 80mm.	7.00
Duck Posy Holder, yellow beak. 80mm long.	6.00
Hen, roosting. 63mm long.	3.00
Parakeet. 75mm.	5.50
Swan Posy Holder. 88mm long.	2.25

Great War

Tommy and his machine gun.	26.00
Tank. 164mm long.	19.50
Drum. 30mm.	4.75
Pickelhaube or Spiked Military Helmet.	13.00
Cenotaph. 142mm.	3.50

Home/Nostalgic

Baby in Hip Bath. 103mm long.	6.50
Coal Scuttle. No. 165. 70mm.	3.00
Grandfather Clock. 130mm.	8.75
Oil lamp. 60mm.	3.25
Old armchair, with usual verse. 85mm.	4.00
Pillar Box. 76mm.	5.50
Sofa. 80mm long.	6.50

Comic/Novelty

Boy on Scooter. 106mm.	13.00
Jack-in-a-Box. 91mm.	10.50

Sport

Boxing Glove. 65mm long.	25.00
Cricket Bag. 110mm long.	6.50

Musical Instruments

Tambourine. 70mm dia.	4.00

Transport

Charabanc with driver. 118mm long.	25.00

'Modern' Equipment

Square gramophone. 57mm.	12.00

Miscellaneous

Book. 57mm.	3.00
Sabot. 70mm long.	4.00

Miniature Domestic

Coffee Pot. 63mm.	3.00

Derwent China

Devonia Art China

For mark see *Crested China*, p. 123.

Trademark used by Hewitt and Leadbeater for a Devonian wholesaler or agent (usual trademark Willow Art).

Ancient Artefacts
Glastonbury Roman Ewer.
60mm.	1.75
Loving Cup, 3 handled. 40mm.	2.25

Buildings – White
Citadel gateway, Plymouth.
110mm.	17.50

Derry's clock tower, Plymouth.
2 sizes: 125mm	9.00
156mm.	12.50

Trademark used for a retailer in Matlock Bath by an unknown English china manufacturer.

Only one model known.

Monuments
Armada memorial. 191mm.	21.50
Drake Statue, Plymouth. 160mm.	11.00

Mayflower Stone, 1620, Model of.
90mm.	32.50

Ancient Artefact
Fountains Abbey Cup. 60mm.	1.75

Historical/Folklore
Bell, inscribed: *Curfew must not ring tonight*. 70mm.   6.50

Traditional/National
Bagpipes. 118mm long.	13.00
Lancashire Clog. 88mm long.	4.00

Seaside Souvenirs
Lighthouse, not named. 110mm.	4.00
Shell on stand, posy holder.	3.50
Scallop shell on coral hatpin	
holder. 80mm.	3.50

Animals
Black Cat, sitting on diamond shaped ashtray, inscribed: *Good luck* and *Ashtray*. Impressed No. 1016.
120mm long.   16.50
Dog, Bulldog, emerging from kennel, inscribed: *The Black Watch*. 70mm long.   7.50

Dog, Collie, sitting, bow round neck. 60mm.	6.50
Dog, Collie, standing. 95mm.	7.50
Dog, Labrador. 90mm.	8.25
Elephant, walking. 52mm.	6.50
Pig, standing. 85mm long.	8.25
Rabbit, sitting, with alert ears. 60mm long.	4.00
Teddy Bear, sitting. 76mm.	7.50

Birds

Chicken. No. 911. 40mm.	4.00
Swan Posy Bowl. 35mm.	2.25

Great War

Monoplane with revolving prop. 150mm long.	30.00
Battleship. 2 sizes: 116mm	10.50
140mm long.	13.00
Battleship, impressed: *HMS Lion*. 140mm long.	13.00
Battleship, inscribed: *HMS Tiger*. 160mm long.	56.50
Troop carrier, Liner converted. No. 213. 140mm long (rare).	90.00
Tank. 120mm long.	13.00
Officer's peaked cap. 80mm long.	5.50
Fireplace, inscribed: *Keep the home fires burning*. Some colouring. 100mm long.	8.25
Cheddar War Memorial, with inscription: *Praise God and remember the men of Cheddar who died for their country in the Great War 1914–1919*. 148mm.	50.00
Plymouth Naval War Memorial. 2 sizes which are slightly different models: 140mm	21.75
160mm.	23.00
Plymouth Armada War Memorial. 115mm size inscribed: *Model of Plymouth War Memorial*	41.50
Plymouth Armada Memorial. inscribed: *Plymouth War Memorial, he blew with his winds and they were scattered*. 170mm.	27.50

Home/Nostalgic

Coal scuttle, helmet shaped. No. 101. 53mm.	3.00
Sundial on circular base, with inscription: 'I mark not the hours'. 118mm.	8.25

Comic/Novelty

Billiken. 60mm.	3.00
Sack of Meal with Mouse, inscribed: *May the mouse ne'er leave yer meal poke wi' a tear drop in its e'e*. 63mm.	8.75

Alcohol

Barrel. 50mm.	2.25
Barrel on stand. 59mm.	3.00
Whiskey Bottle. No. 134. 63mm.	3.00
Whiskey Bottle, inscribed: *One Special Scotch*. 88mm.	4.00

Miniature Domestic

Cup and Saucer. 35mm.	4.00
Shaving Mug. 63mm.	4.00

Diamond China

For marks see *Crested China*, p. 124.

Trademark used by a London wholesaler, the china being manufactured by several leading crested ware specialists, including Birks, Rawlins and Co., Hewitt and Leadbeater and A.B. Jones and Sons Ltd. (usual trademarks Savoy, Willow Art and Grafton).

Historical/Folklore
Bunyan's chair, Model of. No. 42.
90mm.   10.50
Mons Meg, Edinburgh Castle, Model of. 130mm long.   6.50

National Souvenirs
Tam O'Shanter. 73mm dia.   12.50

Seaside Souvenirs
Lighthouse, on rocky circular
  base. 110mm.   3.00
Scallop Shell. 76mm.   2.25

Animals
Elephant, walking. 52mm.   6.50
Grotesque 'animal'. 100mm.   6.00
Pig. 70mm long.   8.25
Rabbit. 88mm long.   7.50

Birds
Canary. 100mm.   6.50

Great War
Airship (observation Balloon),
  inscribed: *Beta*. 80mm long.   30.00
Armoured Car. 125mm long.   40.00
British motor searchlight, Model of.
  103mm long.   70.00
Trench Mortar Gun. 98mm long.   40.00
Cannon Shell. 73mm long.   4.00
Glengarry. 2 sizes: 78mm   13.00
                     100mm long.   13.00
New Zealand Hat. 80mm long.   17.50
Drum. 56mm dia.   4.75

Alcohol
Barrel. 52mm long.   2.50
Man with head in barrel, feet and
  legs protruding. No. 395.
  70mm.   21.75

Miniature Domestic
Cheese dish. 1 piece. 45mm.   4.50
Chesse dish and cover. 45mm.   4.50

Disa Art China

For marks see *Crested China*, p. 125.

Trademark used by Valentine and Sons, Cape Town. China manufactured by Hewitt Bros. (usual trademark Willow Art).

A range of smalls usually with Cape Town and Area Crests and one bowl with a crest of the Municipality of the City of East London.

Birds
Wise Owl winking, with verse:
An aged owl in an oak, etc. 93mm.   7.50

Great War
Pickelhaube. 51mm.   13.00

Home/Nostalgic
Anvil. 57mm.   4.75
Coffee Pot and lid. 70mm.   3.50

Do! Do! Crest China

For marks see *Crested China*, p. 125.

Trademark, used by a wholesaler, manufactured by an unknown English firm.

Animals
Elephant, sitting. 70mm.   6.50

Doric Herald

DRGM

DRGM

Trademark used by Taylor and Kent (Ltd), Florence Works, Longton for the Glasgow wholesaler CR & Co. Glasgow. See also Atlas Heraldic and Caledonia China. (Usual trademark Florentine).

This mark seems to have been used on domestic pieces only. Value £1.50–£5.00.

Impressed mark found on German china.

Novelty
Locomotive and coaltruck, condiment set, lustre. 130mm long.   4.00

The Duchess China

Eglinton China

For mark see *Crested China*, p. 125.

Trademark used by Sampson Hancock (and Sons), Bridge Works, Stoke and later at Gordon Works, Hanley (renamed Corona Pottery). Many of its shapes carry the European War 1914 decoration with crossed flags and bunting to rim. Add £5 for pieces found with this decoration. (Usual trademark Corona).

Ancient Artefacts

Puzzle Jug with verse. 70mm.	3.50
Salisbury Kettle. 110mm.	2.00

Trademark used for a Scottish retailer by an unknown British manufacturer.

Traditional/National Souvenir

Thistle Vase. 50mm.	2.50

Historical

HRH *Prince of Wales*, future Edward VIII, in his investiture costume, standing on base. 88mm long. (Very rare).   75.00

Traditional/National Souvenirs

Lancashire Clog. 87mm long.	4.00
Welsh Hat. 55mm.	3.25

Animals

Bear, sitting. 90mm.	7.00

Birds

Swan Posy Holder.	2.25

Great War

Battleship, four small twin funnels. 140mm long.	19.50
Bell Tent. 70mm.	5.50

Miniature Domestic

Bagware Jug. 51mm.	3.50
Cheese dish and cover. 65mm.	4.75
Cheese dish and cover, circular. 87mm dia.	6.00
Kettle and lid. 80mm.	4.50
Shaving Mug. 55mm.	4.25

Miscellaneous

Pepper Pot, octagonal. 94mm.	2.00

Elite China Series

Empire China

For mark see *Crested China*, p. 127.

For mark see *Crested China*, p. 127.

Trademark used for the retailer David S. Butler of Derby (Forerunner of the Butler Group of Companies) by Hewitt and Leadbeater, Willow Potteries, Longton. (Usual tradmark Willow Art).

Trademark used for an unknown retailer or wholesaler on china manufactured by William Richie & Son Ltd, 24, 26 and 28 Elder Street, Edinburgh. (Usual trademark Porcelle).

Animals

Lion, walking. 110mm long.	8.75
Rabbit. 57mm long.	4.00

Great War

Soldier with rifle, inscribed: *Our brave defender*. 132mm.	25.75
Red Cross Van, red cross on side. No. 218. 84mm long.	17.50
Florence Nightingale Statue, Model of. No. 225. 185mm.	12.50
Mickleover War Memorial inscribed with 26 names of the fallen and *To the glorious dead of Mickleover 1914–1919*. 135mm.	65.00

Home/Nostalgic

Grandfather clock, inscribed. 112mm.	8.75

Cartoon Character

Baby with arms outstretched, inscribed: *Cheerio*. Some colouring on face. 125mm.	16.00

Miscellaneous

Hand holding tulip. 80mm.	2.25

Ancient Artefacts

Loving cup, 2 handled. No. 47. 41mm.	2.25

Seaside Souvenirs

Whelk Shell. No. 451. 80mm long.	2.50

Great War

Bell Tent. 67mm.	5.50

Miniature Domestic

Cheese dish and lid. 46mm.	5.00

Empress China

Endor China

EMPRESS
CHINA

Trademark used by Schmidt and Co, Carlsbad (Bohemia) (Usual trademark Gemma).

Ancient Artefacts
Chester Roman Vase, not named.
  58mm.   1.75

Trademark used for a retailer by an unknown manufacturer, but possibly Birks, Rawlins and Co. (Ltd), Vine Pottery, Stoke. (Usual trademark Savoy).

Only one small found with a
  Newark-on-Trent crest.

English Emporium China

English Souvenir China

For mark see *Crested China*, p. 128.

For mark see *Crested China*, p. 127.

Trademark used for The Golden West Exhibition, 1909, by an unknown English manufacturer.

Trademark used by F. Phillips, Bazaar owner, china thought to have been manufactured by James Reeves, Victoria Works, Fenton. (Usual mark Victoria China).

Seaside Souvenirs
Whelk Shell. 95mm long.   4.50

National Souvenirs
Welsh Hat. 62mm.   3.00

Animals
Camel, with 1 hump, sitting.
110mm.   8.25
Elephant, kneeling. 95mm.   6.50
Fish, with open mouth.
118mm long.   2.00

Animals
Toad, 70mm.   6.50

Birds
Bird Jug. 70mm.   4.00

Home/Nostalgic
Anvil.   4.50

Nostalgic
Baby's cradle. 60mm long.   4.00

Miniature Domestic
Mug. 47mm.   1.75

Erin China

Trademark used for an Irish wholesaler by a
British manufacturer.

Ancient Artefact
Fountain Abbey Abbot's cup, not
  named. 49mm.   1.75

Esbeco

For mark see *Crested China*, p. 128.

Trademark used for the retailer S.B. & Co.
by an unknown manufacturer.

Great War
British Tank, Model of, with inset
  wheels. 95mm long.   10.50

Etruscan China

Exceller

For mark see *Crested China*, p. 128.

For mark see *Crested China*, p. 129.

Trademark used for a retailer or wholesaler AD, probably manufactured by Charles Waine, Longton. (Usual trademark Venetia). Venetia).

This mark has only been found on a heavy small vase with a transfer print of H.M.S. Achilles. (A similar print occurs in the Arcadian range, *but* as print makers sold their wares to all manufacturers this provides no clue!)

Trademark used for a retailer in the south of England by Sampson Hancock (and sons). (Usual trademark Corona).

Traditional/National Souvenirs

Laxey Wheel. 80mm.	30.00
Lancashire Clog. 80mm long.	4.00

Birds

Swan posy holder. 80mm.	2.25

Great War

Ghurka Knife. 140mm long.	13.00

'Modern' Equipment

Gas Cooker. 70mm.	6.50

Excelsior

For mark see *Crested China*, p. 129.

Trademark used by an unknown manufacturer.

A range of smalls with commemorative Four Flags of the Allies was produced. Value £2.00–£4.00.

Animals
Pig, standing. 70mm long.   7.50

Sport
Trophy Cup. 70mm.   6.75

Fairyware

For additional mark see *Crested China*, p. 129.

Trademark used by Schmidt and Co., Carlsbad (Bohemia). (Usual trademark Gemma).

Ancient Artefacts
Loving Cup, 3 handled. 39mm.   2.25

Historical/Folklore
Coronation Chair. 100mm.   4.00

Seaside Souvenirs
Lighthouse on rocks. 105mm.   3.00

Animals
Cow cream jug. 103mm long.
  (Probably a reproduction in
  miniature of an early
  Staffordshire 'creamer'.)   16.00
Dog, pug, lying, paws forward.   11.00
Tortoise dish with lid.
  80mm long.   4.50

Home/Nostalgic
Grandfather clock, with arabic
  numerals. 105mm.   6.50
Grandmother clock, with arabic
  numerals. 85mm.   4.00
Watering Can. 65mm.   4.75

Miscellaneous
Griffin Jug. 85mm.   6.25
Top hat. 43mm.   3.00
Winged Sphinx Vase. 85mm.   8.50

Miniature Domestic

Cheese Dish and Cover. 55mm.	4.00
Cup and saucer. 45mm.	4.00
Milk Jug. 40mm.	1.75
Teapot. 60mm.	4.00

Famous Henley China

For mark see *Crested China*, p. 130.

Trademark used by the retailer Hawkins, Henley-on-Thames, manufactured by Hewitt and Leadbeater, Willow Potteries Ltd, Longton. (Usual trademark Willow Art).

Seaside Souvenirs
Eddystone Lighthouse, not
  named. No. 135. 110mm.   3.00

Animals
Pig, standing. 2 sizes: 80mm.   10.00
                        94mm long.   10.00

Great War
Standing soldier with rifle,
  inscribed: *Our brave Defender*.
  130mm.   21.75

Home/Nostalgic
Watering can. No. 126. 75mm.   4.75

Alcohol
Barrel. No. 100. 35mm long.   3.00

Fenton China

For mark see *Crested China*, p. 130.

Trademark used by E. Hughes and Co., Opal Works, Fenton.

Ancient Artefacts

Leather Bottle. 55mm.	1.75
Loving Cup. 39mm.	2.25

Miniature Domestic

Cheese dish and cover. 55mm.	4.75

A range of useful domestic items such as egg cups, inkwells and sealing wax holders was produced. Value £1.75–£7.50.

Filey China

Trademark used on wares made for a Filey retailer by Taylor and Kent (Ltd), Florence Works, Longton. (Usual trademark Florentine).

Ancient Artefacts

Loving cup, 3 handled. 39mm.	2.25

F.L.

Florentine China

F. L.

Trademark used for a retailer on wares made by Arkinstall & Son Ltd, Arcadian Works, Stoke-on-Trent. (Usual mark Arcadian).

Great War
Tommy on sentry duty, model of.
110mm.   40.00

For mark see *Crested China*, p. 131.

Trademark used by Taylor and Kent (Ltd), Florence Works, Longton.

Ancient Artefacts
Aberdeen Bronze Pot, not named.
58mm.   1.75
Chester Roman Vase, not named.
62mm.   1.75
Loving Cup, not named. 39mm.   2.25
Puzzle Jug. 67mm.   3.50
Roman Lamp. 2 sizes: 63mm.   2.25
                                    100mm.   2.25
Salisbury Kettle, not named.
100mm.   1.75
Southwold Jar, not named.
100mm.   1.75

Buildings – White
Blackpool Tower. 117mm.   5.50
London Bridge. 88mm long.   16.00
Marble Arch, not named. 50mm.   5.50
Old Pete's cottage, near Ramsey.
75mm long.   23.00
St. Paul's Cathedral.
2 sizes: 93mm.   15.25
              130mm.   16.00
Tower Bridge. 115mm long.   17.50
Westminster Abbey, West Front.
85mm.   9.00

Monuments (including Crosses)
Caister-on-Sea, Lifeboat Memorial,
impressed: *1903*. 150mm.   14.50
Glastonbury Tor. 90mm (rare).   45.00
Great Rock of Ages, Model of.
135mm.   9.50
Iona Cross. 108mm.   4.00
Nelson's Column. 121mm.   40.00

Historical/Folklore
Brussels Boy, 120mm.
Impressed: Mannekin pis.   60.00
Man in Pillory. 105mm.   11.00

Traditional/National Souvenirs

Lancashire Clog. 88mm long.	4.00
Laxey Wheel, Isle of Man, not named. 85mm.	30.00
Mother Shipton. 72mm.	6.50
Thistle Jug. 63mm.	2.25
Welsh Bardic Chair. 88mm.	16.00
Welsh Dragon Water Jug, with lid. 120mm.	9.50
Welsh Harp. 100mm.	4.00
Welsh Hat. 57mm.	3.00

Seaside Souvenirs

Basket Beach Chair. 2 sizes: 80mm.	7.50
100mm.	8.25
Bathing Machine. 76mm.	4.75
Houseboat. 57mm.	3.00
Yacht, in full sail. 127mm long.	8.25
Fisherman, bust. 84mm.	10.50
Lighthouse, not named. 90mm.	3.00
Whelk Shell. 100mm long.	2.50
Portmanteau. 60mm long.	2.25
Suitcase. 77mm long.	2.25

Animals

Camel, kneeling. 95mm long.	8.25
Cat, Manx. 61mm.	13.00
Cat, sitting. 112mm.	8.00
Cat, sitting, detailed fur. 90mm.	7.50
Cat, with long neck, sitting. 115mm.	5.50
Cheshire cat, The, inscribed: *Always smiling*. 115mm.	6.50
Dog, with bandaged face. 90mm.	16.00
Dog, bulldog looking out of kennel. 73mm.	7.00
Dog, bulldog, sitting. 56mm.	10.00
Dog, King Charles Spaniel, sitting. 88mm.	7.50
Dog lying in a cradle. 90mm long.	7.50
Dog, puppy, sitting. 92mm.	8.25
Dogs, two King Charles Spaniels in a Top Hat. 65mm.	10.50
Dolphin Vase. 102mm.	4.00
Dragon Jug, mouth open as spout, tail as handle. 100mm.	6.00
Elephant, kneeling. 82mm long.	6.50
Fish, inscribed: *Caught at* .... 120mm long.	2.50
Fish Vase. 115mm.	4.00
Frog cream jug. 45mm.	4.00

Pig, lying down, alert ears. 80mm long.	6.50
Pig, standing. 2 sizes: 80mm.	8.50
95mm long.	9.00
Larger size found inscribed: *The pig that wont go.*	
Piglet, kneeling. 70mm long.	6.50
Polar Bear. 95mm long.	30.00
Pony, small. 105mm long.	10.00
Rabbit. 98mm long.	4.00
Seal, with ball. 72mm.	13.00
Shetland Pony. 66mm.	17.50
Toad, flat. 74mm long.	6.50
Tortoise. 74mm long.	4.00

Birds

Baby Bird Cream Jug. 65mm.	4.00
Canary on rock. 95mm.	6.50
Chicken, hatching from egg. 63mm long.	4.00
Hen roosting. 90mm long.	3.00
Kingfisher Cream Jug. 60mm.	4.00
Kingfisher with long beak. 80mm.	6.50
Owl. 75mm.	5.50
Parakeet. 75mm.	4.75
Parrot. 94mm.	7.50
Pelican Cream Jug. 83mm long.	4.00
Sparrow. 63mm.	8.00
Swan. 2 sizes: 65mm.	3.00
80mm.	4.00
Swan Posy Holder. 88mm long.	2.25

Great War

Monoplane with 4 bladed prop. 170mm long.	40.00
Battleship. 175mm long.	40.00
Red Cross Van. 88mm long.	17.50
Tank with trailing wheels. 127mm long.	13.00
Tank. 125mm long.	8.75
Shell. 75mm.	4.00
Telescope, folded. 70mm.	7.50
Cenotaph, inscribed: *The blood of heroes is the seed of freedom*. 140mm.	4.00
Gravesend War Memorial. 140mm.	52.00
Great Yarmouth War Memorial, with inscription on all four sides. 2 sizes: 145mm.	21.75
175mm.	21.75

Home/Nostalgic

Baby in Bootee. 95mm long.	6.50
Baby in hip bath. 103mm long.	6.50
Case, attaché. 60mm long.	5.50
Chamber pot. 40mm.	2.50
Dolly tub with two pegs and clothes protruding. 82mm.	19.50
Firebucket. 65mm.	3.00
Flat Iron. 76mm.	4.75
Garden Roller. 85mm.	4.75
Grandfather clock. 135mm.	10.50
Lantern. 65mm.	3.50
Milk Churn. 72mm.	3.00
Oil Lamp. 60mm.	3.00
Old armchair, The. 85mm.	4.00
Oriental Lamp (Aladdin's Lamp). 2 sizes: 100mm.	2.25
198mm long.	2.50
Pillar Box, inscribed: *I can't get a letter from you so send you the box*. 76mm.	6.50
Sofa. 82mm long.	6.50
Travel bag, with moulded decoration. 145mm long.	7.50

Comic/Novelty

Boys head on container base, two side holes could be used for flowers, candles? 75mm long.	4.00
Boy on Scooter. 106mm.	13.00
Jack in the Box. 90mm.	10.50
Negro Minstrel, bust. 100mm.	18.50
Pierrot, hands and face flesh coloured, black pompoms on hat and costume. 125mm.	24.50
Pixie sitting on flower pot. 180mm.	11.00
Pixie sitting on thimble. 115mm.	11.00
Screw, inscribed: *You could do with a big fat screw*. 75mm.	21.75

Cartoon/Comedy Characters

Ally Sloper, bust. Not named. 83mm.	12.50

Alcohol

Bottle of Champagne in Ice Bucket, inscribed: *Something good a bottle of the boy*. 85mm.	6.50

Sport

Boxing Glove. 43mm.	30.00

Cricket Bag. 110mm long.	6.50
Golf ball vase on brown base. 55mm.	7.00
Football. 70mm.	6.00

Musical

Grand Piano. 85mm long.	10.50
Tambourine. 70mm.	3.50

Transport

Charabanc with driver. 115mm long.	19.50
Motor Horn, inscribed: Pip Pip. 88mm.	13.00
Saloon Car. 88mm long.	30.00

'Modern Equipment'

Gramophone, hexagonal, with horn. 90mm.	21.50
Gramophone, square, without horn. 53mm.	12.00
Radio Horn. 102mm.	13.00

Miscellaneous

Bunch of Keys on ring. 46mm.	35.00
Carboy. 76mm.	2.25
Oriental shoe with pointed turned up toe. 95mm long.	4.00
Shoe, ladies, 18th century. 95mm long.	7.50
Slipper, open with bow. 100mm long.	20.00
Toby Jug. 65mm.	5.25

Miniature Domestic

Cheese Dish and Cover, 2 pieces. 45mm.	4.75
Coffee Pot. 63mm.	3.00
Cup and saucer. 40mm.	4.00
Hair Brush pin box and lid. 134mm long.	8.75
Kettle. 85mm.	4.00
Shaving Mug. 52mm.	4.00
Teapot. 3 sizes: 50mm, 60mm and 70mm. All sizes.	4.00
Trowel pin box and lid. 140mm long.	8.75

The Foley China

For mark see *Crested China*, p. 135.

Trademark used by Wileman and Co., Foley Potteries, and Foley China Works, Fenton, Longton, subsequently renamed Shelleys Ltd.

All models will be found under
Shelley entry.

Fords China

For mark see *Crested China*, p. 135.

Trademark used by Ford and Pointon Ltd, Norfolk Works, Hanley. Subsequently a branch of J.A. Robinson and Sons Ltd, and later Cauldon Ltd. (Usual trademark Arcadian).

Alcohol
Soda Syphon. 100mm.   7.50

A range of domestic ware, trinket
boxes, ashtrays, jugs and so on.
1.75 – 6.50

FP & S

Furstenberg

For mark see *Crested China*, p. 137.

For mark see *Crested China*, p. 137.

Trademark used by Ford and Pointon Ltd, Norfolk Works, Hanley, subsequently a branch of J.A. Robinson and Sons, Ltd, and later Cauldon Ltd. (Usual trademark Coronet).

Trademark used by a German manufacturer for German Souvenir China.

This mark has only been found on a small 60mm vase with the crest Köln Rh. (Cologne).

Ancient Artefacts
Loving cup, 3 handles. No. 19.
38mm.   2.25

Home/Nostalgic
Baby's Cradle. 63mm long.   4.00

Miscellaneous
Boot. 35mm.   4.75
Oriental Shoe, with pointed toe.
90mm long.   4.00

Miniature Domestic
Beaker. 39mm.   1.75
Cheese dish and cover. 50mm.   4.00

The Garnion Ware

THE GARNION WARE

Mark used by an unknown manufacturer, thought to be foreign.

Only one small with a Guernsey crest has been recorded.

Gemma

For mark see *Crested China*, p. 137.

Trademark used by Schmidt and Co., Carlsbad (Bohemia). Almost all models can be found with a lustre finish.

Ancient Artefacts

Chester Roman Vase. 65mm.	1.75
Loving Cup. 3 handled.	
2 sizes: 39mm.	2.25
68mm.	1.75
Puzzle coffee pot with inscription: *Try your skill, this pot to fill and not to spill don't use the spout except to pour out.* 64mm.	8.75
Puzzle cup, actually a beaker without a handle, with verse: *Try how to drink and not to spill and prove the utmost of thy skill.*	10.50
Puzzle jug, with verse.	
2 sizes: 70mm.	3.50
80mm.	3.50
Puzzle loving cup, 1 or 3 handled with verse. 46mm.	8.75
Puzzle teapot with verse. 45mm.	8.75
Puzzle Tankard. 50mm.	5.50
Puzzle Watering Can. 48mm.	10.50

Buildings – White

First and Last Refreshment House, not named. Also found in yellow/orange lustre. 72mm long.	6.50

Historical/Folklore

Coronation Chair. Can also be found in yellow/orange lustre. 98mm.	4.00
Miners Lamp. 58mm.	7.50

Traditional/National Souvenirs

Kelly from the Isle of Man posy holder, with cat. Inscribed: *A present from the Isle of Man.* 115mm.	40.00

Lancashire Clog. 125mm long.	6.50
Manx Legs inside life belt. 85mm.	9.50
Manx man, three legged with manx cat on triangular base. 115mm.	40.00
Welsh Candlestick, Welsh lady handle. Black hat. 80mm dia.	16.00
Welsh Jug, Welsh lady handle. 88mm.	20.00
Welsh Hat, often found with 'Welsh' transfer print. 75mm dia.	3.50
Welsh Ladies' Head cream jug. 72mm.	17.50
Welsh Lady, coloured, as handle of cheese dish. 74mm long.	20.00
Welsh Lady, coloured, as handle of watering can. 65mm.	20.00

Seaside Souvenirs

Bathing machine Money Box. 83mm.	10.50
Yacht. 102mm long.	8.00
Lighthouse. 95mm.	3.00
Lobster Ashtray, red lobster forming handle. 63mm long.	7.00
Open Bag on four feet.	6.50
Trunk with separate lid. 60mm long.	2.50

Animals

Cat, sleeping, lying on side. Can be found inscribed: *Stop Yer Tickling Jock*. 83mm long.	23.00
Cat wearing boots (Puss in Boots). Cat has pink face and ears. 84mm.	21.75
Cat in Bowler Hat. Cat coloured as above. 63mm.	21.75
Cat, in saucepan with black handle. 70mm long.	17.50
Cat, crouching, blue bead eyes. 50mm.	16.00
Cat, lying down. Comical. 90mm long.	23.00
Cat, sitting in ladies shoe, with shoe tongue flopping out. 80mm.	21.75
Cat, sitting, paw on rat. 80mm.	26.00
Manx Cat. 60mm.	13.00
Manx Cat, sitting. 74mm.	16.00
Manx Cat handle on coffee pot or jug. Cat coloured. 80mm.	13.00

Manx Cat handle, coloured, on miniature cheese dish. 74mm long.	21.50
Manx Cats, as two handles on a vase. 73mm.	13.00
Cat's head bowl. 57mm.	14.00
Cow cream jug, some colouring. 127mm long.	16.00
Dog, cross-eyed, with fly on his nose. Can be found with some colouring. 76mm.	10.50
Dog, curled up. 98mm long.	17.50
Dog, King Charles Spaniel, sitting. 83mm.	4.50
Dolphin Vase. 100mm.	13.50
Fish with open mouth. 140mm long.	3.00
Fish pin cushion holder. 106mm long.	2.75
Frog Prince (Frog with crown on head). 90mm.	21.50
Pig in Top Hat. Pig has pink muzzle and ears. 60mm.	60.00
Pig as above but with Chef's Hat. 93mm.	40.00
Pig in saucepan with black handle. Pig coloured pink as above. 57mm.	30.00
Pig, standing, pink muzzle and ears. Can also be found in yellow/orange lustre. 100mm long.	19.50
Pig, pink, lying on edge of horseshoe ashtray. 65mm long.	13.00
Shetland Pony. 108mm long.	13.00
Tortoise Trinket Box and lid. 80mm long.	5.50

Court Room Pigs

All pink coloured as follows:

Policeman, with helmet coloured black with yellow badge. 80mm.	60.00
Barrister, with monocle. 80mm.	60.00
Prisoner, trotters padlocked. 80mm.	60.00
Witnesses, female with balmoral bonnet, male with bowler. 80mm.	60.00
Judge, robed. 80mm.	60.00
Box with Jury of six piglets. 120mm long.	70.00

Birds

Cockatoo on branch, some colouring. 102mm.	11.00
Hen egg basket, 2 pieces, red comb. 85mm long.	5.25
Swan. 80mm.	3.00
Swan Posy Holder. 90mm long.	2.25

Great War

Despatch Rider's Cap with Goggles. 65mm dia.	25.75

Home/Nostalgic

Armchair, straight backed. 50mm.	4.75
Basket. 60mm.	2.00
Basket, star-shaped. 65mm dia.	1.75
Bucket with looped handle. 80mm.	2.00
Bucket with rope handle. 51mm.	2.25
Candlestick. 80mm.	2.00
Clock, bracket. 76mm.	10.50
Coal scuttle, barrel shaped. 65mm.	3.00
Coal scuttle, box shaped. 50mm.	3.00
Coal scuttle, helmet shaped. 70mm.	3.00
Cradle on rockers. 60mm long.	6.50
Dressing Stool. 4 legged. 62mm long.	4.00
Fireplace, inscribed: *There's no place like home*. Some colouring. 68mm.	8.25
Flat Iron.	4.75
Grandmother Clock. Can be found in yellow/orange lustre. 88mm.	4.00
Jardiniere pot and stand. 121mm.	2.75
Kettle with lid. 75mm.	4.00
Milk Church with lid. 72mm.	2.25
Pillar Box, oval. 90mm.	6.00
Rocking Chair. 60mm.	13.00
Saucepan with silver lid and black handle. 70mm long.	7.50
Shaving Mug. 60mm.	4.00
Shaving Mug, with raised shell pattern. 55mm.	4.00
Sofa, very ornate. 60mm.	6.50
Stool, circular with 3 legs. 55mm.	3.00
Tobacco Jar with brown pipe on lid. 70mm.	9.50
Watering Can, also yellow/orange lustre. 70mm.	4.75

Wheelbarrow, also in yellow/orange lustre.		
3 sizes: 45 mm		3.00
63mm		4.00
95mm		6.00

Comic/Novelty

Briar Pipe, brown. 76mm long.	8.25
Briar Pipe, brown on leaf tray. 72mm long.	5.50

Alcohol

Beer Mug. 47mm.	2.50

Sport

FA Cup, not named. 68mm.	4.25
Trophy, 2 handled with separate lid. 150mm.	5.50

Musical Instruments

Tambourine Ashtray with gilded discs. 68mm long.	3.00

Modern Equipment

Cash Register. 35mm.	7.50

Shoes

Boot. 2 sizes:	88mm	4.75
	135mm long.	7.50
Dinant Wooden Shoe. 80mm long.		4.00
Dutch Sabot. 88mm long.		4.00
Ladies Shoe with high heel and fluted tongue. 75mm long.		7.50
Sabot, high heeled. 80mm long.		4.00
Clog with buckle. 125mm long.		6.50

Hats

Bowler Hat. 32mm long.	12.00
Fireman's Helmet. 74mm.	20.00
Straw Boater. 75mm dia.	3.50
Top Hat, can be match striker. 45mm.	3.00

Miniature Domestic

Complete tea sets can be found on round or square trays. These usually consist of teapot, sugar bowl, milk jug and two cups and saucers. Usually each piece is crested but on really small sets only the tray carries a crest.	15.00–25.00

Cake Dish. Can also be found in
yellow/orange lustre.
70mm dia.   2.00
Candleholder. 78mm dia.   2.00
Cheese dish and cover, round.
45mm dia.   5.00
Cheese dish and cover, square.
2 sizes: 63mm   4.00
        76mm long.   4.00
These can be found coloured,
lustre, beige and with transfers
as well as crested in the usual
manner.
Coffee Pot. 60mm.   3.00
Coffee Pot with ornate handle.
78mm.   4.00
Dressing Table Set, very small.
These usually comprise 1 tray,
2 candlesticks, 1 ring tree and 3
powder bowls with lids.   25.00
Photograph frame, glazed.
100mm.   10.00
Teapot, also found in
yellow/orange lustre.
3 sizes: 50mm   4.00
        60mm   4.00
        70mm   4.00
Toastrack. 2 sizes: 39mm   5.00
               70mm   4.00

W.H. Goss

For marks see *Crested China*, p. 141.

The prices and a full listing of every Goss
piece known to the author will be found in
the companion volume to this guide, *The
1984 Price Guide to Goss China* by Nicholas
Pine.

Values of the thousands of crests and
decorations to be found on Goss china
appear in *Goss China, Arms, Decorations and
Their Values* by the same author.

Full details of marks, including 24 illustrations, will be found on pages 20–24 of *The
1984 Price Guide to Goss China*.

It has been realized during research for
Crested China that many pieces appear
bearing either Arcadian, Willow Art, W.H.
Goss or W.H. Goss England marks as the
later period of crested china (1925–37) saw
much merging of companies and liberal use
of marks.

Any piece with the W.H. Goss or W.H.
Goss England mark is worth a premium
over a similar piece not so marked and a
priced list of Goss England items will be
found in *The 1984 Price Guide to Goss China*
previously referred to. New pieces are constantly coming to light however, and that
list is by no means exhaustive.

The values of Arcadian and Willow Art
models have increased rapidly over the
past few years and the differential between
these and examples marketed by the Goss
factory has narrowed considerably.

Gladstone China

Gothic China

For mark see *Crested China*, p. 155.

Trademark used by Taylor and Kent (Ltd.), Florence Works, Longton (usual trademark Florentine).

Miniature Domestic

Cheese dish and cover. 50mm.   5.00
Mug, one handle. 35mm.   2.00

BRITISH
MANUFACTURE

Trademark used by James Reeves, Victoria Works, Fenton (usual trademark Victoria).

National Souvenirs
Welsh Hat, blue cord and gold
  tassels, longest place name
  round brim. 51mm.   5.50

Crown Devon. Racing Car

Florentine. Pierrot

Florentine. Pixie sitting on thimble

Grafton. Coloured elephant

Grafton. Snail

Grafton. John Peel bust

Grafton. Teapot man

Gemma. Pink Pig on Ashtray

Gemma. Pipe in Leaf Ashtray

Gemma. Lifebelt with legs of Man

Gemma. Bathing Hut

Kensington. Red Cross Nurse

Grafton China

For marks see *Crested China*, p. 153.

Trademark used by Alfred B. Jones and Sons Ltd., Grafton China Works, Longton, Staffs.

NB. Although the Grafton stock numbering system is very reliable, several items have been found with the wrong numbers. The most usual number is given here. It is not unusual to find two models consistently given the same number.

Parian/Unglazed

Bust of John Peel, inscribed: *D'ye ken John Peel with his coat so grey*. 120mm.	24.50
Bust of Albert I of Belgium, inscribed: *Albert I*. 125mm.	43.50
Bust of *Allenby*, impressed, square glazed base. 145mm.	40.00
Bust of George V, inscribed: *George V*. 125mm.	35.00
Bust of David Lloyd George. No. 415. 135mm.	35.00
Bust of *Foch*, impressed. Square glazed base. 135mm.	35.00
Bust of Field Marshal, Sir John French. 135mm.	35.00
Bust of Admiral Sir John Jellicoe. 135mm.	35.00
Bust of General Joffre. 155mm.	42.50
Bust of Lord Kitchener, impressed on back: *Kitchener*. 125mm.	30.00
Bust of Lord Roberts, impressed on back: *Roberts*. 135mm.	30.00
Bust of *Sir Walter Scott*, impressed: *Scott*, on circular glazed base. 120mm.	8.00

Ancient Artefacts

These models are often found not named and are quite often found with a coloured transfer view rather than a crest.

Aberdeen Bronze Pot. No. 267. 65mm.	1.75
Ale Pot. No. 176. 60mm.	3.00

Brading Roman Vase. 3 vases of different shape:	
No. 136. 62mm	2.25
No. 137. 62mm	2.25
No. 139. 55mm.	2.25
Burial Urn, inscribed: *Ancient British Burial Urn excavated in Cornwall*. 64mm.	2.25
British Vase. No. 17. 40mm.	2.25
Butter Pot. No. 185. 40mm.	2.50
Canterbury Pilgrim's Bottle. No. 181. 50mm.	1.75
Chester Roman Vase. No. 165. 60mm.	2.25
Chinese Pilgrim Bottle. No. 669. 88m.	2.25
Chinese Teapot. 2 different models: No. 70. 54mm	4.00
No. 77. 54mm.	4.00
Chinese Vase. 3 vases of different shapes: No. 276. 86mm	2.25
No. 278. 85mm	2.25
No. 282. 75mm	2.25
Cyprus Vase. No. 120. 70mm.	2.25
Ely Drinking cup. 39mm.	3.50
English Wine Glass. 4 glasses of different shape:	
No. 309. 75mm (Ale glass)	3.00
No. 310. 75mm (Goblet)	3.00
No. 311? 70mm (Tumbler)	3.00
No. 312. 70mm (Ovoid bowl).	3.00
Egyptian Pottery – these specimens were discovered by Doctor Flinders Petra (sic)*in Egypt, manufactured about 4,000 BC*.	
No. 155. 60mm	3.00
No. 158. 51mm.	3.00
The following two models have this inscription and further inscriptions.	
Egyptian Bottle. No. 159. 57mm.	3.00
Egyptian Tear Bottle. No. 151. 42mm.	3.00
Egyptian Vase. No. 323. 45mm.	2.50
Hereford Kettle. This model has a separate lid. No. 179. 80mm. (Can be found wrongly numbered 174.)	4.50
London vessels. 5 different models: No. 202. No size details	2.25
No. 205. 48mm	2.25
No. 206. 45mm	2.25
No. 207. 84mm	2.25
No. 208. 70mm.	2.25

Norman Pot, inscribed: *Norman pot from original in Burley Hill Museum*. No. 182. 45mm.   2.25
Portland Vases, not named. No. 150 and No. 530.   1.75
Loving Cup, not found named. No. 145. 40mm.   2.25
Reading Roman Vase. 50mm.   2.25
Roman Lamp. No. 119. 60mm.   2.50
Roman Vase. No. 160. 48mm.   2.25
Salisbury Kettle. No. 174. 105mm.   1.75
(Can be found wrongly numbered No. 179.)
Shakespeare's Jug. No. 124. 76mm.   3.00
Shrewsbury Roman Ewer, inscribed: *Roman Ewer found at Uriconium original now in Shrewsbury Museum*. No. 175. 76mm.   2.25
Southwold Jar.   2.25
Swiss Urn. No. 185. 44mm.   2.25
Yaverland Vase.   2.25

Buildings – Coloured
Bell Hotel, Tewkesbury. 88mm long.   36.50
Captain Cook's house Great Ayton re-erected in Melbourne. 95mm long (rare)   92.50
Couch's House, Polperro, on roof, with arms of Polperro.   85.00
House on the Props, Polperro. 100mm long.   82.50
Old Chapel, Lantern Hill, Ilfracombe. 72mm long.   55.00
Old Toll Bar, Gretna Green. 125mm long.   60.00

Buildings – White
Bath Abbey. 112mm.   21.75
Bath Abbey, West front. 105mm.   13.00
Bargate, Southampton. 90mm.   13.00
The Tower, Blackpool.
2 sizes: 116mm   12.50
135mm.   13.50
Carnarvon Castle. 90mm.   40.00
Citadel Gateway, Plymouth. 105mm.   13.50
First and Last refreshment house in England, Land's End, found numbered 469 and 627. 75mm long.   9.00
Gynn Inn, Blackpool, inscribed:

Model of Blackpools famous landmark, the old Gynn Inn demolished 1921. No. 520. 125mm long.   40.00
Houses of Parliament. No. 424. 115mm.   21.75
Irish Round Tower (not named), often has green shamrocks on base. No. 417. 137mm.   8.25
with shamrocks   10.50
Lincoln Cathedral, West front. 115mm.   16.00
Old Cornish Cottages. 125mm long.   35.00
Old Chapel, Lantern Hill, Ilfracombe. 75mm long.   18.50
Old toll-gate house, including path with gate, inscribed: *Ye olde toll-gate house*. No. 498. 130mm long.   30.00
Old Toll-Gate House, as above but not on base with path and gate, and not named. No. 502. 63mm long.   16.00
Oldest chemists shop in England established 1790, also can be found inscribed: *Model of the oldest pharmacy in England, Knaresborough, Yorkshire. Established in the reign of George 1st 1790*, some colouring. 97mm long.   60.00
Plas Mawr, Conway. 93mm (rare).   43.50
Plymouth, Citadel Gateway. 105mm.   13.50
St. Pauls Cathedral, London. 2 sizes: No. 423. 137mm   13.00
No. 633. 115mm.   11.25
Scarborough Castle Ruins, not named. 104mm.   30.00
Skegness Clock Tower, not named. 127mm.   7.50
Smallest house in Great Britain. No. 560. 92mm.   15.25
Tonbridge Castle. 88mm long.   25.75
Westminster Abbey. No. 422. 121mm.   30.00

Monuments (including Crosses)
Banbury Cross. 141mm.   14.00
Irish Cross, not named, green shamrocks on base. No. 419. 138mm.   7.00
Lloyd George statue Carnarvon. 150mm.   47.50

Ramsgate Lifeboat Memorial
(Statue of Lifeboatman), not
named but often found with the
inscription: *Souvenir from the
Imperial Bazaar Albion Hill,
Ramsgate, which was twice
wrecked by Zeppelin bombs on May
17th 1915 and June 17th 1917* on
base. 140mm.   28.00
Rufus Stone. 96mm.   4.00
(John) Ruskin Memorial Stone,
inscribed: *John Ruskin
MDCCCXIX–MDCCC* and
religious verse. No. 515.
120mm.   12.50
St. Anne's Lifeboat Memorial.
No. 495. 161mm.   12.50
Sandbach Crosses. 130mm.   56.50
Southport Lifeboat Memorial.
121mm.   14.50

Historical/Folklore
Antique Hornware Box, Model of,
plus lid. 70mm long.   5.50
Antique Bureau. 64mm.   8.00
Burn's Chair. No. 667. 88mm.   6.00
Charles I bottle with removable
head lid, not named and
thought by some collectors to be
Guy Fawkes. No. 209. 96mm.   17.00
Coaching Hat, not named.
No. 213. 60mm long.   7.50
*President Wilson's Grandfather's
chair.* No. 492. 75mm.   12.50
Ride a cock horse to Banbury Cross
(lady on horse). No. 569.
106mm long.   43.00
St. Thomas A Becket. 130mm.   30.00
Saint Wilfred of Ripon. 136mm. 34.50
Ye Old Chertsey Bell. 57mm.   8.00

Traditional/National Souvenirs
Blackpool Big Wheel, not named.
78mm.   10.50
Cornish Pasty. No. 340.
95mm long.   7.50
John Peel, Bust. 72mm.   15.00
Lancashire Clog, sometimes
found inscribed: *Model of
Lancashire clog.* No. 407.
90mm long.   4.75
                         with inscription   5.50
Leaking Boot, Cleethorpes, statue of
boy, boot joined to hand by
string. 156mm.   27.50

Lincoln Imp. 108mm.   5.00
Ripon horn blower, often found not
named, inscribed: *The horn is
blown every night at 9. Formerly it
denoted that the watch was set for
the night.* 136mm.   10.50
Toby Jug, Irish. 80mm.   20.00
Toby Jug, Scots. 80mm.   20.00
Yarmouth Bloater. 115mm.   2.50
Welsh Harp. No. 418. 80mm.   4.00
Welsh Hat, with blue band and
bow, found with longest Welsh
place name printed round
brim. No. 183. 50mm.   5.50
Toby Jug, Welsh Lady. 76mm.   20.00
Welsh Milk Can. No. 479.
103mm.   2.50

Seaside Souvenirs
Bathing Machine. No. 256.
55mm long.   6.00
Boat with billowing sail,
inscribed: *Polly.* No. 448.
115mm long.   14.50
Boat, flat bottomed with bird's
head as figurehead. No. 462.
80mm long.   4.50
Lifeboat. No. 332. 110mm long.   5.50
Punt with two girls aboard.
115mm long.   30.00
Rowing boat, can be found
inscribed: *Sant Cybi* (patron
saint of Holyhead) on models
with a Holyhead crest. *Robin
Hoods Bay* and *Whitby.* No. 169.
130mm long.   3.50
                                    inscribed   5.00
Fisherman's Creel with lid. No.
292. 72mm long.   3.50
Beachy Head Lighthouse, with black
band. No. 3. 135mm.   6.50
Eddystone Lighthouse. No. 315.
102mm.   5.00
Lighthouse, with steps on base
and gilded windows. No. 47.
145mm.   4.00
Lighthouse pepper pot.
108mm.   3.00
Shell dish. No. 533. 63mm long.   2.00
Oyster Shell, on Coral legs.
51mm.   2.50
Oyster Shell, on stand. 83mm dia. 2.50
Shell dish with handle. No. 537.
80mm.   2.25

Whelk Shell, 4 sizes:

No. 65. 45mm long	2.50
No. 65. 85mm long	2.50
No. 528. 70mm long	2.50
No. 528. 115mm long.	3.00

Bathing Beauty, reclining, wearing swimsuit and mob-cap, holding parasol. 135mm (uncommon). 40.00

Boy holding model yacht, on beach base, coloured hair and yacht. No. 563. 85mm. 50.00

Boy swimming on a rectangular 'sea' base. Hair and eyes coloured. No. 565. 120mm long. 40.00

Girl kneeling on 'beach' base, with red bucket and spade, brown hair and red hat brim. No. 564. 75mm (563–565 are all quite rare). 55.00

Toddler on donkey. 85mm and 109mm. 40.00

Animals

Some 'Grafton' animals were given tiny glass bead eyes, more often than not these are missing, leaving small holes. Even without these beads the models remain very attractive, but obviously a complete model is more desirable and £5.00 should be deducted for models having no glass eyes. The range of large comical cats with these coloured bead eyes and coloured bows are particularly appealing but are hard to find.

Bear, dressed as boy, standing on shell tray. 85mm. 24.75

Bear and Ragged Staff.

2 sizes: 85mm	13.00
100mm.	16.00

The larger version is No. 224 and has bead eyes.

Calf, not named, but mostly found with cartoon transfer of farmer and wife behind gate with bull on the other side. No. 287. 100mm long. 12.50

Camel, 2 humps. No. 242. 16.00

Cat, Cheshire, inscribed: The Cheshire Cat and Always smiling. 1 yellow glass eye. No. 288. 86mm. 11.00

Cat, Cheshire, with red mouth and nose, one bead eye (green)

and one eye closed, inscribed: The Cheshire Cat. Found with and without separate shield carrying crest. No. 171.

2 sizes: 86mm	7.50
100mm.	8.50

Cat, crouching and angry. 55mm. 25.00

Cat, crouching, fat and angry with tail in the air. Found with bead eyes. No. 303. 88mm long. 30.00

Cat in Jar, inscribed: From Chicago Perishable. No. 277. 80mm. 24.75

Cat singing, red mouth and green bow. 75mm. 30.00

Cat, sitting and comical, green bow and tail at front with bead eyes (blue or green). No. 319.

2 sizes: 88mm	23.00
103mm.	27.00

Cat, sitting and winking, orange or red bow. No. 612. 80mm. 24.50

Cat, sitting and comical, yellow bow. Found with verse: As I was going to St. Ives. No. 351. 94mm. 21.75

Cat, sitting and comical, green bow and tail at front with bead eyes. No. 339. 154mm. 27.00

Cat, sitting and comical, yellow bow and tail at back with bead eyes. No. 344.

2 sizes: 100mm	27.00
146mm.	30.00

Cat, standing, arched back and tail in the air with green bow. No. 303. 100mm. 30.00

Cat, standing, arched back, small tail, green bow. No. 527. 78mm. 28.00

Cat, standing and comical, blue bow and green eyes. 88mm long. 20.50

(Cat) Kitten. No. 211. 50mm. 8.75

Cow, standing, not named. 60mm. 13.00

Bulldog, British, inscribed: Slow to start but what a hold. 83mm. 14.00

Bulldog, standing with feet wide apart. No. 391. 51mm. 10.50

Bulldog, sitting with bead eyes (yellow or green). No. 250.

2 sizes: 88mm	23.00
102mm.	27.00

Dog in boater and clothes. 88mm. 26.00

Dog, bottle with separate head lid. No. 232. 100mm. 13.00

Dog, Greyhound, standing with
front legs on small oval base.
No. 709. 102mm long.   40.00
Dog, with 2 heads, one head is
smiling and the other is sad.
Two varieties.
No. 645. 38mm   40.00
No. 646. 63mm.   40.00
Dog, King Charles Spaniel,
sitting. No. 390. 53mm.   9.50
Dog, kneeling, wearing a green
cap. No. 488. Can be found
coloured with match holder.
85mm.   37.50
Dog, Labrador Pup, sitting with
bead eyes (yellow or green).
Can be found painted yellow.   26.00
No. 355. 85mm.   painted   30.00
Dog, Puppy, sitting, one ear
raised and scratching with back
leg. (Often found coloured with   7.50
no crest.) No. 410. 85mm coloured   12.00
Dog, running, with fly or bee on
tail. 95mm long.   47.50
Dog, Scottie, standing. No. 432.
Can be found with bead eyes.
94mm long.   23.00
Three varieties of dog, all with
some colouring and marked
Swains Studdy Series are as
follows:
Dog, yawning, on ashtray base.
105mm long.   30.00
Dog, yawning, with ball in
mouth, on ashtray base.
105mm.   30.00
Dog, yawning. 46mm.   30.00
Elephant, circus, standing on
forelegs on stool. 105mm.   55.00
Elephant, sitting and comical.
No. 438. 127mm.   35.00
Elephant, walking. No. 426.
100mm.   21.50
Elephant, walking. No. 470.
2 sizes: 50mm   9.50
         80mm.   7.50
Can be found painted red.
Elephant, with sandwich boards,
crest one side and inscribed:
Turn me round on the other.
102mm.   24.50
Fish, curved vase. 57mm.   2.00
Fish, curved tail and open
mouth. No. 392. 105mm long.   2.50

Fish, curved. No. 196.   4.50
Fish, curved body and open
mouth. No. 393. 80mm long.   5.00
Fish. No. 244. 110mm long.   4.50
Fish, straight and fat. No. 247.
2 sizes: 88mm   2.50
          110mm.   3.00
Fish, straight and fat with open
mouth. No. 341. 102mm long.   3.50
Fish, straight with open mouth.
No. 97. 100mm long.   3.50
Fish, straight and thin. No. 302.
2 sizes: 76mm   3.00
          112mm long.   4.00
Large size can be found with
bead eyes.
Fox with bead eyes (yellow).
No. 462. 140mm long.   50.00
Fox, without bead eyes (i.e.
model designed without them).
135mm long.   50.00
Fox with pheasant on stand.
No. 434. Can be found painted
red.   60.00
Frog, with closed mouth, can be
found with bead eyes. No. 204.
72mm.   20.50
Lion, standing. 105mm long.   11.25
Monkey with bead eyes.
No. 242. 87mm.   27.00
No. 245. 70mm.   23.00
No. 286. 70mm. Can be found   23.00
painted yellow, red or green.   27.00
Monkey, sitting, wearing coat.
No. 245. 62mm.   23.00
Can be found painted yellow.   27.00
Mouse, sitting up. No. 210.
2 sizes: 42mm   16.00
         65mm.   16.00
Mouse, sitting up, holding nut,
yellow bead eyes. No. 243.
43mm.   27.00
Mouse on cheese, can be found
blue with pink ears. No. 459.
47mm.   30.00
Pig, fat, lying asleep, inscribed:
Wunt be druv. No. 421. 83mm.   21.75
Pig, running, red bead eyes.
No. 416. 87mm.   26.00
Pig, sitting, long pointed nose
and long ears tilted forward.
No. 263. 90mm long.   30.00
Pig, sitting with raised ears.
No. 203. 70mm.   24.50

Pig, sitting and laughing,
inscribed: *Wunt be druv.*
No. 338. 65mm.   21.75
Pig, sitting, is much fatter than
the above, inscribed: *Wunt be
druv.*   21.75
Pig, sitting up on hind legs,
found inscribed: *Wunt be druv*,
or *I Won't be drove.*
No. 417. 70mm.   20.50
No. 420. 80mm.   21.75
Pig, standing, can be found with
no inscription but normally
found inscribed: *Wunt be druv* or
I won't be drove. No. 343.
70mm long.   10.00
Pig, standing, inscribed: *Wunt be
druv.* 88mm long. (This could be
a larger version of 343).   15.25
Polar Bear. No. 102. 105mm long.   34.50
Polar Bear, standing on rocky
base. 117mm long.   50.00
Pony, not named. No. 493.
2 sizes: 70mm   17.50
           105mm long.   20.50
Rabbit, with bead eyes (yellow).
No. 240. 112mm long.   13.00
Rabbit trinket dish, pink eyes.
No. 734. 120mm long.   12.00
Seal. No. 402. 70mm long. (This is
a very delicate model).   10.00
Snail. No. 328. 80mm long.   10.00
Squirrel holding nut, can be
found with bead eyes. No. 327.
75mm.   12.50
Terrapin. No. 253. 92mm long.   5.50
Wallaby. No. 222. 68mm.   20.50

Birds

Bird/fledgling, some colouring.
No. 435. 65mm (very plump
and pretty).   11.25
Bird posy holder, grotesque chick
with orange legs. No. 737.
68mm.   20.50
Chicken hatching from Egg, can
be found with bead eyes.
No. 326. 73mm long.   9.50
Chick. 60mm.   4.50
Cock on circular base. No. 454.
100mm (pair with hen).   13.00
Duck, occasionally found
inscribed: *Aylesbury duck.*
No. 377. 96mm long.   12.50

Duck posy holder. 80mm.   4.50
Duck Posy or cigarette holder,
some colouring. No. 732.
115mm.   5.50
Hen, on circular base. No. 453.
100mm (pair with cock).   13.00
Hen, roosting on basket base.
82mm.   9.50
Kingfisher on base. No. 670.
62mm.   15.50
Owl on rocky base. No. 687.
132mm.   11.25
(very impressive model).
Penguin. No. 329. 88mm.   7.50
Swan, head under wing. No. 409.
85mm long.   10.50

Great War

American soldier, squatting, fully
coloured. One model found all
black except for cigar and can
be found with no colouring at
all. No. 85. 80mm.   100.00
British Territorial Bulldog, seated
figure of Tommy with bulldog
face, red and blue bands on hat.
No. 262. 88mm.   87.50
Kitchener Bust (glazed) on
circular base, inscribed: *Lord
Kitchener of Khartoum creator of
British Army 1914/1918. Born
June 24th 1850. Died serving his
country June 5th 1916 by the
sinking of HMS Hampshire off the
Orkneys.* No. 395.
2 sizes: 100mm   17.50
         130mm   21.50
Kitchener Match Holder,
caricature of Kitchener with
left-belt, some colouring. plain 17.50
No. 214. 95mm dia.   coloured   26.50
Or could it possibly be the
Kaiser?
Sailor, seated and holding a
model submarine, hat band
impressed: *Victory.* Is often
found inscribed: *Weve got 'U'
well in hand.*   40.00
Can also be found coloured.
No. 452. 80mm.   56.50
Soldier leaving Trench, inscribed:
Over the top. No. 483. 118mm.   110.00
Soldier throwing hand grenade,
inscribed: *The Bomb Thrower.*
No. 425. 140mm.   110.00

Soldier throwing hand grenade, without the ammunition box which must have been added for stability. A forerunner of above. 140mm (very rare). 120.00

Biplane, fixed prop. No. 450. 145mm long. 60.00

Monoplane, fixed prop. No. 414. 135mm long. 35.00

HMS Dreadnought, ship with high prow. No. 408. 142mm long. Same ship with same stock number found inscribed: HMS Gosport or HMS Henry of Blois or HMS Victory. 65.00

HMS Iron Duke. No. 431. 155mm long. 85.00

Submarine, inscribed: E9. No. 406. 145mm long. 25.75

Motor Ambulance with curtains, inscribed: Motor ambulance car given by Staffordshire china operatives. British Red Cross Society: St John Ambulance Association. Load not to exceed 1 driver, 1 attendant and patients. No. 397. 98mm long. 30.00

Motor Tractor, inscribed: Model of motor tractor used on western front. No. 456. 80mm long. 110.00

Renault Tank. 100mm long. 41.50

Tank with steering wheels, inscribed: H.M. Landship Creme de Menthe. No. 413. 118mm long. 21.75

Tank, no steering wheels, inscribed: H.M. Landship Creme de Menthe. No. 413. 98mm long. 24.50

Whippet Tank, inscribed: Model of Whippet Tank. No. 449. 115mm long. 75.00

Alpine Gun with moving wheels, inscribed: Model of Alpine gun. No. 394. 105mm long. 130.00

Desert Gun. No. 430. 155mm long. 40.00

Field Gun on sledge, inscribed: French 75. No. 412. 160mm long. 40.00

German gun captured by British. No. 403. 153mm long. 26.50

Trench Howitzer (found with Ramsgate Imperial Bazaar inscription. See Monuments. Ramsgate Lifeboat Memorial) No. 404. 75mm long. 7.50

Cannon Shell. No. 400. 76mm. 3.00

Cannon Shell, inscribed: Jack Johnson. No. 339. 90mm. 4.00

German Incendiary Bomb. No. 405. 80mm. 6.50

Mills hand grenade with removable metal pin, often found without inscription. No. 411. 83mm. 15.50

Bandsman's Drum. 45mm. 4.75

Bell Tent with open flaps, with or without base. No. 239. 65mm. 5.50

Boot with Puttee. No. 389. 75mm. 13.00

Anzac Hat with blue band. 110mm long. 17.50

Colonial Soldier's Hat. No. 238. 89mm long. 7.50

Water Bottle. No. 234. 80mm. 8.75

Cenotaph, inscribed: MCMXIV– MCMXIX – The Glorious Dead and 3 coloured flags on reverse. 2 sizes: 135mm. 11.00
                       155mm. 14.00

Home/Nostalgic

Anvil on heavy base. No. 352. 70mm. 4.75

Baby crawling naked, brown hair, blue eyes. No. 544. 100mm long. 25.75

Baby sitting up. No. 481. 63mm. 12.50

Baby's rocking cradle. No. 294. 62mm long. 5.50

Basket with handle. No. 29. 52mm. 2.00

Boy Scout holding bugle. 133mm. 46.50

Flat Iron. No. 162. 65mm long. 4.75

Grandfather clock. 110mm. 9.50

Horn Lantern, inscribed. No. 306. 76mm. 4.00

Laundry Basket. No. 534. 75mm long. 3.50

Rocking Horse. 125mm long. 50.00

Village Water Pump. No. 331. 80mm. 5.75

Wing Chair. 73mm. 15.25

Comic/Novelty

Billiken. No. 291. 44mm. 3.00

Boy, grotesque, sitting cross-legged, top of head on egg-cup. 62mm. 4.50

Chinese Man Pepper Pot, some colouring. No. 726. 70mm. (There must be a matching Salt Pot). 9.50

Deep Sea Diver. No. 261.
105mm.   80.00
Dutchman, sitting cross-legged,
and holding cheese. No. 230.
85mm.   .   8.25
Fu Hing God of Happiness? Chinese
Priest sitting upright, holding
baby, some colouring. 115mm.   30.00
Head on a rock, comic, could be
Kitchener wearing a pharaoh's
headress. 67mm.   20.50
Head, Comic Salt Pot, miserable
face and droopy bow tie. No.
25. 85mm (matches below).   4.00
Head, Comic Pepper Pot,
happy face and perky bow tie.
No. 258. 85mm (matches
above).   4.00
Lemon with lid, stalk handle.
No. 62. 60mm.   5.50
Pierrot, sitting cross-legged on
box playing banjo, some
colouring. Found with
inscription: *As I was going to St.
Ives*. No. 566. 103mm.   16.00
Teapot Man, face on lid, spout
and handle form arms, some
colouring. 48mm.   9.50
Watch Stand, Father Time head
with beard forming legs.
No. 154. 110mm.   12.75

Alcohol
Bottle with Stopper. No. 715.
68mm.   4.00
Champagne Bottle. No. 221.
102mm.   4.75
Champagne Bottle Pepper Pot.
No. 225. 102mm.   4.00
Man in Barrel, head and feet
protruding, inscribed: *No beer*.
115mm.   19.50

Sport
Canoe. No. 169. 125mm long.   5.50
Footballer with ball on small base.
130mm.   80.00
Golfer holding bag of golf clubs,
comic figure, inscribed: *The
Colonel*. No. 352. 90mm.   30.00
Can be found fully coloured.   40.00
Golf Ball Salt Pot. 52mm.   3.00
Golf Ball Pepper Pot. No. 293.
52mm.   3.00

Tennis player, lady holding
racquet (reputedly Suzanne
Lenglen). 133mm.   75.00

Transport
Car, inscribed: *Dreadnought*.
102mm long.   30.00
Charabanc, with 5 rows of seats,
inscribed: *Dreadnought*. No.
568. 100mm long.   40.00
                              if inscribed   60.00
Mons Blieriot, bust, inscribed: *First
man to fly across the channel in an
aeroplane July 25th 1900*. 85mm.   38.00

'Modern' Equipment
Horn Gramophone, square base.
No. 641. 92mm.   17.00

Miscellaneous
Top Hat. No. 189. 37mm.   3.00
Fireman's helmet. No. 66. 65mm.   22.00
Boot. No. 237. 80mm long.   7.50
Sabot. No. 212. 80mm long.   4.75
Oriental Shoe, pointed. No. 170.
95mm long.   4.75
Shoe, lady's 18th century. No. 50.
83mm long.   8.25
Bell, miniature. No. 250. 55mm.   3.00
Handbell. 2 sizes: No. 15. 82mm   3.50
                              No. 265. 51mm.   3.50
Horse's Hoof. No. 236.
72mm long.   3.00
Dice, Trump Indicator, heart,
diamond, club and spade and
no trump on five sides. 35mm.   23.00

Miniature Domestic
Beaker. No. 73. 52mm.   1.75
Cheese dish and cover (2 pieces).
No. 78. 65mm long.   7.50
Cup. No. 147. 39mm.   1.75
Cup and Saucer. No. 122. Cup:
36mm dia. Saucer: 67mm dia.   4.00
Mug with one handle. No. 36.
48mm.   1.75
Mug with one handle. No. 143.
41mm.   1.75
Shaving Mug. 40mm.   5.00

**Numbered Domestic and
Ornamental Wares**
No. 3. Jug, elongated spout.
80mm.   1.75

No. 4. Crinkle dish. 69mm.	1.75	No. 184. Vase, 5 sided. 40mm.	1.75
No. 5. Bagware Vase. 45mm.	2.00	No. 191. Vase. 70mm.	1.75
No. 8. Vase. 61mm.	1.75	No. 242. Stamp Box. 47mm long.	2.50
No. 10. Vase, shaped. 70mm.	1.75	No. 260. Vase, 2 handles. 37mm.	1.75
No. 13. Jug. 67mm.	1.75	No. 263. Salve Pot. 45mm dia.	2.50
No. 19. Vase, shaped. 65mm.	1.75	No. 297. Pill Box, oval.	
No. 20. Crinkle top vase. 70mm.	1.75	45mm long.	2.50
No. 22. Bulbous Vase. 50mm.	1.75	No. 298. Pill Box, rectangular.	3.00
No. 23. Vase, with moulding.		No. 299. Pill Box, 5 sided. 28mm.	3.00
60mm.	1.75	No. 300. Stamp Box, 5 sided.	
No. 25. Vase, 2 handles. 60mm.	1.75	50mm dia.	3.00
No. 27. Vase, bulbous. 60mm.	1.75	No. 301. Vase, bulbous. 50mm.	1.75
No. 45. Bagware Jug. 40mm.	2.00	No. 302. Vase. 48mm.	1.75
No. 53. Ewer. 76mm.	1.75	No. 318. Pill Box, decorated with	
No. 65. Posy bowl. 68mm long.	1.75	angel's heads. 63mm.	4.00
No. 67. Tray, diamond shaped.		No. 348. Jug. 63mm.	1.75
121mm long.	2.25	No. 349. Jug, slim. 66mm.	1.75
No. 68. Tray, heart shaped.		No. 360. Pin Tray, triangular.	
100mm long.	2.25	85mm long.	2.00
No. 71. Tray, club shaped.		No. 367. Pin Box, oval.	
100mm long.	2.25	90mm long.	2.50
No. 71. Vase, 2 handles. 40mm.	1.75	No. 372. Jug, slim neck. 76mm.	1.75
No. 74. Pot with 3 blunt feet.		No. 373. Jug, long necked. 75mm.	1.75
47mm.	1.75	No. 374. Jug, fluted base. 73mm.	1.75
No. 75. Jug. 39mm.	1.75	No. 375. Vase, double mouthed.	
No. 84. Spade or heart shaped		63mm.	1.75
pin box. 68mm.	3.50	No. 378. Sauce Boat. 120mm long.	2.75
No. 85. Club shaped pin box.		No. 386. Ashtray, triangular on 3	
68mm.	3.50	feet. 75mm dia.	2.00
No. 86. Bowl. 48mm dia.	1.75	No. 387. Candlestick. 160mm.	2.00
No. 88. Vase. 40mm.	1.75	No. 500. Casket with lid.	
No. 91. Vase. 39mm.	1.75	84mm long.	2.50
No. 92. Tray, hexagonal.		No. 502. Mustard Pot with lid and	
69mm dia.	2.00	spoon. 70mm.	3.00
No. 94. Vase. 44mm.	1.75	No. 504. Vase, octagonal. 60mm.	2.00
No. 95. Globe Vase, crinkle top.		No. 505. Vase. 56mm.	1.75
43mm.	1.75	No. 506. Vase. 54mm.	1.75
No. 96. Taper Vase. 45mm.	1.75	No. 507. Taper Vase, octagonal.	
No. 100. Tray, spade shaped.		60mm.	1.75
78mm long.	2.25	No. 529. Vase, with moulding.	
No. 102. Ewer (Polar Bear found		45mm.	1.75
with same no.)	1.75	No. 531. Vase, curious wedge	
No. 104. Vase. 65mm.	1.75	shaped. 50mm.	1.75
No. 106. Jar. 60mm.	1.75	No. 535. Vase, shaped. 52mm.	1.75
No. 121. Vase, 2 handles. 70mm.	1.75	No. 590. Tray. 150mm long.	2.00
No. 125. Pot, round. 52mm.	1.75	No. 649. Vase, hexagonal wide	
No. 127. Vase, long neck. 62mm.	1.75	top. 51mm.	1.75
No. 130. Bowl with handle.	1.75	No. 650. Vase, hexagonal wide	
No. 131. Basket. 123mm long.	2.50	top, readed base. 55mm.	1.75
No. 140./6. *Hair tidy*. 90mm.	4.50	No. 652. Vase, hexagonal shaped	
No. 152. Vase with ornate handle.		top. 57mm.	1.75
145mm.	1.75	No. 653. Vase, pentagonal	
No. 156. Vase. 63mm.	1.75	tapered. 57mm.	1.75
No. 177. Vase, bulbous. 40mm.	1.75		

No. 654. Vase, hexagonal wide
top. 51mm.   1.75
No. 657. Vase, bulbous hexagonal
base. 44mm.   1.75
No. 658. Vase, octagonal. 50mm.   1.75
No. 676. Cream Jug. 60mm.   2.00
No. 682. Pepper Pot,
egg-shaped. 45mm.   2.25
No. 713. Vase. 70mm.   1.75
No. 714. Vase. 69mm.   1.75
Not numbered. Pill Box, ivy leaf
shaped. 57mm long.   3.00

Granic China

Trademark used by an unknown manufacturer but possibly Sampson Hancock (and Sons), Bridge Works, Stoke and later at the Gordon Works, Hanley (usual trademark Corona).

Only one piece known with
Liverpool Crest. Crinkle edged
vase. No. 262. 55mm.   2.00

Grays Sports China

The Griffin China

For mark see *Crested China*, p. 174.

For mark see *Crested China*, p. 174.

Trademark used by A.E. Gray & Co., Glebe Works, Mayer Street, Hanley.
The firm does not appear to have made crested china but the mark is included here because the 'Sports China' series very much appeals to collectors of pre-Great War souvenir china. Vases, jugs and beakers are found with transfer prints of footballers in the colours of League teams.

each 15.00

Trademark used by the London wholesalers, Sanderson & Young, 21 Red Lion Square. Manufactured by several potteries, probably branches of J.A. Robinson & Sons.

Ancient Artefacts

Fountains Abbey, Abbot's Cup, not named. 49mm.	1.75
Loving Cup, 3 handles. 39mm.	2.25
Newbury Leather Bottle, inscribed: *Leather bottle found at Newbury 1044 on Battlefield now in Museum*. No. 83. 65mm.	2.25

Buildings – Coloured

Cottage. 95mm.	7.50

Monuments

Iona Cross. 110mm.	4.00
Sailor's Stone, Hindhead. 94mm.	8.75

National Souvenirs

Welsh Hat, blue cord. 55mm.	3.00

Seaside Souvenirs

Suitcase, closed. 80mm long.	2.25

Animals

Cat, *The Cheshire Cat Always Smiling*. 88mm.	4.75
Cat, Manx. 83mm long.	13.00
Camel, one hump. 88mm.	8.25
Pig, standing. 90mm long.	8.75

Birds

Parrot. 78mm.	4.75
Baby bird cream jug. 66mm.	4.00

Home/Nostalgic

Coal scuttle. 75mm.	3.00
Coal scuttle, helmet shaped. 60mm.	3.00
Pillar Box. 75mm.	5.50
Watering Can.	4.75

Sport
Cricket Bag. 115mm long.   6.50

Musical Instruments
Tambourine.   5.50

Miscellaneous
Lady's 18th Century Shoe.
  90mm long.   7.50

Grimwades

Trademark used by Grimwades Ltd,
Winton, Upper Hanley and Elgin Potteries,
Stoke.
    Earthenware firm more noted for hotel
and domestic ware. Obviously made this
one late piece for export.

Jug. No. 1823. 69mm. Crest
Dominion of Canada.   3.00

Grimwades also produced a range of Great
War miniature domestic pieces of great
interest.
The War Time Butter Dish (for a
  family of ten), inscribed: *Made by*
  the girls of Staffordshire during the
  winter of 1917/18. When the boys
  were in the trenches, fighting for
  Liberty and Civilisation.
  Special message from Rt. Hon. D.
  Lloyd George, Prime Minister:
  'I have no hesitation in saying that
  economy in the consumption and
  use of food in this country is a
  matter of the greatest possible
  importance to the Empire at the
  present time'. 110mm dia.
The War Time Bread and Butter
  plate, similar inscription.
  200mm dia.
  Approximate value of pieces
  in this range.   15.00

Grosvenor Ware

For marks see *Crested China*, p. 175.

Trademark used by Sampson Hancock (& Sons), Bridge Works, Stoke and later at the Gordon Works, Hanley (renamed Corona Pottery. Usual trademark Corona).

Ancient Artefacts
Jersey Milk Can. 53mm.	3.00
Leather Jack. 58mm.	1.75

Buildings – White
Blackpool Tower, on heavy detailed base. 127mm.	4.50

National Souvenirs
Welsh Harp. 90mm.	4.00

Animals
Cat, sitting, large ruff of fur. 100mm.	8.25
Cow Creamer. No. 376. 130mm long.	13.00
Fish. 88mm long.	3.00
Lion, lying down. No. 369. 140mm long.	16.00
Pig, standing. No. 158. 84mm long.	7.00

Great War
Submarine, inscribed: *E4*. 110mm long.	8.75
Renault Tank. 100mm long.	55.00
Torpedo, Model of. 150mm long.	40.00
Ghurka Knife. 140mm long.	13.00
Newnham War Memorial. No details of size (rare).	65.00

Novelty
Cigarette Case. 70mm long.	4.75
Desk top. 35mm.	4.00

Sport
Tennis racquet. 136mm long.	6.50

Musical Instruments
Piano with open lid. 60mm.	9.50

'Modern' Equipment
Gas Cooker. 70mm.	6.50

Miscellaneous
Horseshoe on slope. 70mm long.	2.00

Gwalia Ware

H & L

Oldbury, Knighton,
& Llandrindod Wells.

Trademark used for a LLandrindod Wells
retailer by an unknown manufacturer. Only
one piece recorded.

Ancient Artefacts
Chester Roman Kettle, not
named. Crest. L. Wells.   2.00

For mark see *Crested China*, p. 175.

Impressed mark used by Hewitt & Leadbeater, Willow Potteries, Longton. Usual
trademark Willow Art, these impressed
initials are often found on models that also
carry the Willow Art mark.

Parian/Unglazed
Ann Hathaway's Cottage.
  Coloured. 60mm long.   16.00
  Also a large size known.   25.00
Bust of Shakespeare. 112mm.   5.50
Bust of Lord Roberts on square
  glazed base. 166mm.   30.00
Font in which Shakespeare was
  baptized, Model of. 95mm dia.   6.00
Lincoln Imp, not named. 130mm.   4.00

H & S

Hamilton China

For mark see *Crested China*, p. 176.

For mark see *Crested China*, p. 176.

Trademark used for a Plymouth retailer by Hewitt & Leadbeater, Willow Potteries, Longton.

Trademark used for H. Hamilton, Milton & Amber, Saltburn, and made by an unknown manufacturer.

Buildings – White

Derry's Clock, Plymouth. 150mm.	10.50
Hastings Castle Ruins. 100mm.	17.50

Monuments

Burns, statue on square base. 170mm.	11.00
Drake, statue, Plymouth. 160mm.	8.75

Great War

Battleship, impressed: *HMS Lion*. 140mm long.	13.00

Home/Nostalgic

Garden Trug. 70mm.	2.25
Church Bell, inscribed: *Curfew must not ring tonight*. 70mm.	5.50

Seaside Souvenir

Two curling waves on an octagonal base, inscribed: *The glad sea waves*. 50mm.	13.00

Birds

Kingfisher. 77mm.	7.50

Heathcote China

Herald China

For mark see *Crested China*, p. 176.

MADE IN ENGLAND
Heathcote China
BEST BONE

Trademark used for a wholesaler or retailer probably by Alfred B. Jones & Sons Ltd, Grafton China Works, Longton, Staffs. (Usual trademark Grafton).

Ancient Artefacts
Aberdeen Bronze Pot, not named.
60mm.   1.75

Novelty
Trademark used by H.M. Williamson & Sons, Bridge Pottery, Longton.

Dutchman, sitting cross legged
holding cheese. 85mm.   8.25

Domestic manufacturer not
known to have made crested
souvenirs, only domestic wares
found.

Miscellaneous
Diamond Pintray. 120mm long.   2.25

Cup and saucer with Troon crest.   2.50

Heraldic China

For mark see *Crested China*, p. 177.

Trademark used by Sampson Hancock (and Sons), Bridge Works, Stoke. (Usual trademark Corona).

Animals
Bulldog in kennel. 66mm.   6.50

Alcohol
Barrel on legs.   3.00
Tankard. 70mm.   3.00

Miscellaneous
Queen, Chess piece. 90mm.   17.00
King, Chess piece. 108mm.   17.00

Heraldic China

Trademark used by an unknown manufacturer.

Only 42mm jug has been found with a Whitehead crest.

Herald Series

E. Hughes and Co. China

For mark see *Crested China*, p. 177.

For mark see *Crested China*, p. 177.

Trademark used for William Holmes & Co, fancy goods importers, Glasgow, on china manufactured by Alfred B. Jones & Sons Ltd, Grafton China Works, Longton, Staffs. (Usual trademark Grafton).

Trademark used by E. Hughes & Co., Opal Works, Fenton. (Usual trademarks Fenton & Royal).

Ancient Artefacts

Chester Roman Vase. 60mm.	2.25

Seaside Souvenirs

Whelk Shell. 83mm long.	2.50

Seaside Souvenirs

Oyster Shell dish. 130mm long.	2.25
Some Domestic ware found too.	1.50–5.00

Animals

Bulldog, sitting. No. 250. 88mm.	13.00
Dog, King Charles Spaniel, sitting. No. 390. 55mm.	9.50
Dog, Puppy, sitting with one ear up. No. 410. 85mm.	5.50
Shetland Pony, not named. 105mm long. (This model can be found with a crest of Shetland.)	13.00

Birds

Duck, sitting. No. 47. 90mm long.	6.50

Great War

Hand Grenade with removable pin. 83mm.	13.00
Cannon Shell, inscribed: *Jack Johnson*. No. 399. 90mm.	4.00
Bell Tent with open flaps. No. 239. 65mm.	5.50
Killin War Memorial, with extended base and railings. 160mm.	75.00

Iceni Crest China

For mark see *Crested China*, p. 178.

Trademark used for wholesalers by J.A. Robinson & Sons, subsequently Cauldon Ltd. (Usual trademark Arcadian).

Ancient Artefacts
Goodwin Sands Carafe. 82mm.	2.25

Seaside Souvenirs
Lighthouse. 150mm.	4.00

Monuments
Caister on Sea Lifeboat Memorial. 150mm.	14.50

Animals
Cat, sitting and smiling (grotesque, rather similar to Cheshire Cat). 75mm.	5.50
Black Cats, 3 on sledge. 118mm long.	75.00
Sussex pig, Model of, sitting inscribed: *You can push or you can shuv but I'm hanged if I'll be druv*. No. 148. 88mm long.	10.50
Sussex pig. Model of, standing. Inscribed as above. No. 148. 88mm long.	10.50

Birds/Eggs
Chick, breaking out of egg. 63mm long	4.00
Hen, red comb. 80mm.	10.50

Great War
Clip of bullets, Model of. 57mm.	10.50
Tank. 100mm long.	8.75
German Incendiary Bomb. 80mm.	4.75

Home/Nostalgic
Candlestick, square. 35mm.	2.00
Chair, highbacked. 90mm.	4.25
Ankle Boot. 74mm long.	4.00

Imperial

For mark see *Crested China*, p. 178.

Trademark used by Wedgwood and Co (Ltd), Unicorn and Pinnox Works, Tunstall, on cheaply produced souvenir wares.

Ancient Artefacts
Lincoln Jack, not named. 54mm.	1.75

Seaside Souvenirs
Suitcase.	2.25

Birds
Pelican Jug.	4.00

Sport
Football. 65mm.	4.50

Miscellanous
Dutch Sabot. 83mm long.	4.00
Top Hat. 40mm.	3.00

Impero

Ionic Heraldic

For mark see *Crested China*, p. 178.

For mark see *Crested China*, p. 179.

Trademark used by the German manufacturer Kutzscher & Co., Schwarzenberg, Saxony (now in East Germany) on crested china for export to Britain.

Trademark used for the Glasgow wholesaler CR & Co. by an unknown manufacturer, but probably Taylor & Kent. (Usual trademark Florentine).

Buildings – White
Boston Stump Church. 125mm.	17.50
Skegness Clock Tower. 122mm.	4.00
York, *Bootham Bar*. 135mm.	13.00

Home
Bucket with rope handle. 75mm.	2.25

Monuments
Captain Scott, figure on square base. 2 sizes: 135mm.	13.00
150mm.	13.00
Hull soldiers' war memorial, with inscription: *Erected to the memory of the men of Hull who fell in the late South African War*. 120mm.	18.00

Traditional/National Souvenirs
Devil looking over Lincoln. 95mm.	7.50
Lincoln Stonebow. 105mm long.	10.50
The Fiddler, York. 120mm (rare).	19.50

Seaside Souvenirs
The Lighthouse, Flamborough. 125mm.	11.00

Animals
Two Elephants on Sledge. Comic. 70mm.	21.50

Birds
Swan posy bowl. 74mm.	2.25

Ivora Ware

For mark see *Crested China*, p. 179.

Trademark used by William Richie and Sons Ltd., on a range of domestic ware (Usual trademark Porcelle).

Miscellaneous

Boot. 65mm long.	5.25
Coal Bucket. 70mm.	3.50

Miniature Domestic

Cheese dish and cover. 50mm.	4.50

NB. Badly printed marks which appear to by *Ivyknot?* are *Wyknot?* (see Wy not?).

JBC

For mark see *Crested China*, p. 180.

Trademark used for a Manchester wholesaler by Hewitt & Leadbeater, Willow Potteries, Longton. (Usual trademark Willow Art).

Traditional/National Souvenirs

Model of James' the fifth chair at Stirling Castle. 100mm.	5.50
Welsh hat, blue band. Can be found with the longest place name round brim. No. 75. 57mm.	5.50

Animals

Pig, fat and standing. Tail forms a circle and rejoins the body. 80mm long.	10.00

Alcohol

Bottle inscribed: *One Special scotch*. 90mm.	3.50

Miscellaneous

Hand holding tulip vase. 80mm.	2.25

JP

JW

For mark see *Crested China*, p. 180.

For mark see *Crested China*, p. 180.

Trademark used by a French manufacturer for the French souvenir market.

One Vase, 70mm high, has been recorded with this mark with the crest Boulogne Sur Mer.   1.50

Trademark used for a retailer by J.A. Robinson Ltd. (Usual trademark Arcadian).

Great War
Tommy and his machine gun, Model of. 130mm.   26.00
Red Cross Van. 80mm long.   17.50

Miscellaneous
Dutch Clog. 102mm.   4.50

Kangaroo Art China

An Australian retailer or wholesaler of British heraldic china. No other details known.

Keltic

For mark see *Crested China*, p. 180.

Trademark used by an unknown manufacturer for Irish and Scottish towns.

Ancient Artefacts
Puzzle Jug. 68mm.   3.50

Seaside Souvenirs
The Glad Sea Waves. 50mm.   13.00

Animals
Camel, kneeling. 95mm long.   8.25

Home/Nostalgic
Shaving Mug. 55mm.   4.00

Miscellaneous
Shoe, Ladies' 18th Century.
   95mm long.   7.50

Kensington China

Miscellaneous

Clog. 70mm long.	4.00
Hand holding Tulip. No. 74. 80mm.	2.25

For mark see *Crested China*, p. 181.

Trademark used by Royal Crown Pottery Co., Burslem, a branch of J.A. Robinson Ltd. (Usual trademark Arcadian and Willow Art).

Seaside Souvenirs

Lighthouse, octagonal. 112mm.	4.50

Animals

Cat, Cheshire, inscribed: *Still smiling*. No. 159. 95mm.	4.75
Cat, haunched. 70mm.	7.50
Elephant, walking. No. 113. 52mm.	6.50
Teddy Bear, sitting. 90mm.	10.50
Shetland Pony. 108mm long.	19.50

Great War

Nurse, inscribed: *A friend in need*. 130mm.	25.75
Battleship. 140mm long.	13.00
Field Gun, with screen. 115mm long.	13.00
Fireplace with cooking pot, inscribed: *Keep the home fires burning*. 77mm.	7.50

Home/Nostalgic

Coal scuttle. 52mm.	3.00
Grandfather Clock, inscribed: *Make use of time let not advantage slip. Shakespeare.* No. 149. 128mm.	8.75

Novelty

Pixie, crouching on a rectangular base. 78mm. (Could well be Billiken the God of Luck).	4.50

Alcohol

Barrel on Stand. 58mm.	3.00

Transport

Open Tourer. 115mm long.	21.75

King China

For mark see *Crested China*, p. 181.

Trademark used for a retailer or wholesaler by Alfred B. Jones and Son Ltd., Grafton China Works. Longton, Staffs.

One 64mm fluted vase with a Swansea crest found with this mark.

Kingsway Art or Crest China

For mark see *Crested China*, p. 183.

Trademark used for W.H. Smith by Hewitt and Leadbeater, Willow Potteries, Longton. (Usual trademark Willow Art).

Ancient Artefacts
Pilgrims bottle.	2.25
Salt maller, Model of.	2.25

Buildings – White
St. Botolph's Church, Boston. 112mm.	20.50

Monuments
Princetown Lifeboatmans Monument. 130mm.	37.50

Historical/Folklore
Bunyan's chair. 92mm.	8.25
Burn's Chair, Dumfries. 85mm.	5.50
James V Chair, Stirling Castle. 100mm.	6.50
Mary Queen of Scots Chair, Edinburgh Castle, Model of. 75mm.	4.75

Traditional/National Souvenirs
Bagpipes with turquoise ribbon. 118mm long.	13.00
Burns and Highland Mary, sitting on a rock. 112mm (rare).	19.50
Welsh Lady, bust, with black hat. 110mm.	12.50
Welsh Leek. 55mm.	2.50

Seaside Souvenirs
Yacht in full sail. 122mm.	11.00
Lifeboat, blue and yellow ropes. 116mm long.	4.75
Lighthouse on base, not named. 110mm.	4.50
Lighthouse, octagonal. No. 174. 192mm.	5.00
Eddystone Lighthouse, Model of. 86mm.	4.00
Crab. 83mm long.	6.50

Animals

Cat, Cheshire, inscribed: Still smiling. 95mm.	4.75
Cat, sitting.	
2 sizes: 57mm	7.50
67mm.	8.50
Cat, standing, with blue bow. 70mm.	8.25
Dog, Dachshund. No. 021. 75mm long.	40.00
Dog, Scottie, wearing a Glengarry. Some colouring.	
2 sizes: 58mm.	5.50
87mm.	6.50
Dog, Scottish Terrier, standing. 90mm long.	6.50
Elephant, sitting with trunk in air. 97mm.	8.25
Elephant, walking. 98mm.	21.50
Elephant Jug. No. 78. 70mm.	4.00
Hare. 77mm long.	4.00
Monkey, holding a Coconut. No. 429. 80mm.	7.00
Three Wise Monkeys, with usual verse. 77mm.	8.75
Ram with curly horns. 90mm long.	23.00

Birds

Chick, fluffy, large feet. 70mm.	8.00
Goose. 95mm.	22.50
Owl. 115mm.	7.00

Great War

Standing soldier inscribed: Our Brave Defender. 130mm.	21.75
Submarine, E4. 125mm long.	8.75
Red Cross Van. 87mm.	17.50
Field Gun with screen. 115mm long.	13.00
Bugle. 70mm long.	7.50
Drum. No. 030. 60mm dia.	4.75
Edith Cavell, nurse. Patriot and Martyr, Memorial Statue, Norwich. 115mm. (Found impressed 296).	19.50
Florence Nightingale Statue, Model of. 160mm.	12.50

Home/Nostalgic

Basket. No. 244. 80mm long.	2.00
Bell, inscribed: Curfew must not ring tonight. No. 107. 65mm.	4.50
Book. No. 76. 60mm.	3.50

Flat Iron. No. 018. 65mm.	4.75
Pillar Box, inscribed: GVR and If you haven't time to post a line, here's the pillar box.	
No. 18. 80mm.	8.50
Pillar Box, impressed: G.R.. No. 203 and 024. 90mm.	6.50
Sundial, circular, with round base, and inscription I Mark not the hours. 118mm.	7.50
Sundial, circular base. No. 205 and 024. 93mm.	4.75
Thimble, large.	8.75

Comic/Novelty

Baby with outstretched arms, inscribed: Cheerio.	
No. 024. 128mm.	16.00
Dutch Girl. 80mm. (It is very probable that the Dutch boy was also made with this mark, but has not yet been recorded.)	6.25
Sack of Meal with mouse, inscribed: May the mouse ne'er leave yer meal wi' a tear-drop'n its e'e. 63mm.	8.75

Alcohol

Beer Barrel. 60mm.	3.00
Foaming Tankard, inscribed: The more we are together the merrier we will be. 58mm.	4.00
Whisky Bottle, inscribed: A Special Scotch. 100mm.	4.00

Sport

Cricket Ball. 48mm.	14.00
Golf Ball. 45mm.	4.50

Miscellaneous

Club Pintray. No. 009. 58mm long.	2.25
Diamond, trump indicator. No. 009. 65mm.	4.00
Diamond Pintray. No. 009. 58mm long.	2.25
Handbell. 82mm.	3.50
Shoe with blue painted bow. 115mm long.	13.00
Two models reported from Shelley range:	
Cycle Lamp (No. 342). 83mm.	19.50
Roll Topped Desk (No. 380), here No. 030. 86mm.	16.00

Kyle Series

LAB

For mark see *Crested China*, p. 184.

Trademark used by Charles Waine (& Co.), Derby Works, Longton. (Usual trademark Venetia).

Great War
Biplane with fixed prop. 150mm
   long.   60.00

Transport
Tram. 50mm.   85.00

ENGLAND

Mark used for a retailer by an unknown English manufacturer.

One 62mm Vase, with Arms of Seaford, found.

Lawrence Sheriffe Ware   Leadbeater Art China

For mark see *Crested China*, p. 184.

For mark see *Crested China*, p. 184.

Trademark used by an unidentified manufacturer. (Only crest known – Rugby, with retailers name, Hands & Son, Rugby).

Ancient Artefacts

Loving Cup, 3 handles. 37mm.	2.25

Trademark used by Edwin Leadbeater, Drewery Place, Commerce Street, Longton.

Parian/Unglazed
Bust of *Scott* on column base.

172mm.	14.00

Buildings – Coloured
Gate House, Stokesay Castle.

102mm long.	110.00
Isaac Walton's Cottage, Shallowford.	
114mm long.	110.00
Old Market Hall, Church Stretton 1617–1839. 2 sizes:	
95mm and 105mm long.	110.00
The Tan House, Little Stretton.	
109mm long.	90.00

Buildings – White
Ann Hathaway's Cottage, not

named. 58mm long.	6.00
Burns Cottage, with inscription.	
70mm long.	10.50
Margate Clock Tower, Margate.	
150mm.	10.50

Monuments
Limerick Monument, inscribed:

The treaty of Limerick signed AD 1696. 120mm.	41.50
Margate Lifeboat Memorial. 160mm.	15.25
Sir Walter Scott. Statue. 178mm.	12.50

Historical

Bunyan's Chair. 95mm.	8.25
James Vth Chair, Stirling Castle, Model of. 102mm.	6.50

Traditional/National

Welsh Hat. No. 57. 60mm.	3.00

Seaside Souvenirs

Lifeboat.	4.75
Lighthouse. 110mm.	4.00

Animals

Cheshire Cat, inscribed: *Still*	
smiling. 2 sizes: 85mm.	4.75
115mm.	5.50
Dog, sitting, with bow.	
No. 77. 75mm.	8.25
Dog, labrador, sitting. 76mm.	6.50
Lion, walking. 114mm long.	8.75
Pig, fat. 102mm long.	8.25

Birds

Chick Posy Holder. 60mm long.	3.00
Duck Posy Holder. 45mm.	6.00

Great War

Red Cross Van.	
No. 105. 88mm long.	17.50
Cumberland and Westmorland war	
memorial. 148mm.	65.00
Derby war memorial. 150mm.	65.00
Harrogate war memorial, on	
unglazed obelisk on base with	
spiral steps. 153mm.	65.00
Nottingham war memorial. 150mm.	46.50
Nurse Cavell, Memorial. 200mm.	40.00
Plymouth armada war memorial,	
with inscription: *He blew with*	
his winds and they were scattered.	
No. 107. 168mm.	21.75
Crich Stand, Notts and Derby	
War Memorial. 150mm.	65.00
Ulster War Memorial, Thiepvel,	
with inscription: *They died that*	
we might live. 140mm.	110.00

Home/Nostalgic

Anvil. No. 78. 58mm.	4.75

Novelty

Monk, standing. 91mm.	6.00

Miscellaneous

Sabot. 80mm long.	4.00
School Boy's Cap. 67mm long.	19.50

Lion China

For mark see *Crested China*, p. 186.

Trademark used by Wiltshaw & Robinson, Ltd., Carlton Works, Stoke-on-Trent. (Usual trademark Carlton).

Monuments

Rock of Ages, with inscriptions.	
82mm.	6.50

Animals

Dog. (Puppy) sitting on a glass	
hand mirror, inscribed: *Me*	
twice. 105mm long.	24.50

Limoges

Liverpool Rd Pottery

No details of mark available.

For mark see *Crested China*, p. 186.

A range of smalls only was made by this famous manufacturer with the exception of the following.

Transport
Open Motor Car. 90mm long.   20.00

Trademark used by Liverpool Rd. Pottery Ltd.

Seaside Souvenirs
Scallop Shell standing upright. 110mm long. (This carries a map as well as a crest of Norfolk).   11.00

Transport
Open motor car. 90mm long.   20.00

Lochinvar

N. & C.

or with Nicholson and Carter in place of N & C.

Trademark used for the retailers Nicholson & Cartner by Hewitt and Leadbeater, Willow Potteries, Longton. (Usual trademark Willow Art).

National Souvenirs

Welsh Hat. No. 75. 54mm.	3.00

Great War

Field Gun. 115mm.	8.75
Bell Tent with open flaps. 85mm.	5.50

Alcohol

Whiskey Quaich or bowl. No. 110. 100mm long.	5.25

Locke and Co

For mark see *Crested China*, p. 186.

Trademark used by Locke and Co. (Ltd) Shrub Hill Works, Worcester, and subsequently taken over by the Worcester Royal Porcelain Co. Ltd., in 1904.

Ancient Artefacts

Newbury Leather Bottle, not named. 70mm (found with biscuit ground).	4.00
Roman Lamp. 100mm long (found with biscuit ground).	4.50

National Souvenirs

Welsh Hat, can be found in 'biscuit ware'. No. 61 or 19. 56mm.	9.00

Alcohol

Tankard, very ornate. 70mm.	4.50

Miscellaneous

Dutch sabot. 60mm long.	5.00
Cup and Saucer, miniature. 78mm dia.	7.50

Numbered ornamental and domestic wares

No. 16. Large Pot. 65mm.	3.00
No. 36. Vase. 41mm.	3.00
No. 41. Cream Jug. 63mm.	3.00
No. 43. Vase, no details of size.	3.00
No. 47. Jug. 55mm.	3.00
No. 95. Vase. 63mm.	3.00

Lynton China

M

For mark see *Crested China*, p. 187.

LYNTON CHINA

MADE IN ENGLAND

Trademark used by an unknown English manufacturer.

This very obscure and unusual mark has only been found on one Great War Commemorative.

The colour transfer print of five flags and a field gun is found on a mug with a large handle. 59mm high. Inscribed: *Allies United 1914*.   8.00

Trademark used by an unknown English manufacturer.

Mark found only on one small – no details of crest.

Marine Art China

Macintyre

For mark see *Crested China*, p. 187.

For mark see *Crested China*, p. 187.

Trademark used by Hewitt & Leadbeater, Drewery Place, Commerce St., Longton. (Usual marks Willow and Leadbeater).

Birds
Chick Posy Holder. 60mm long.　　3.00

Trademark used by James Macintyre & Co. Ltd., Washington Works, Burslem. (Usual trademark Argonauta Porcelain).

A 62mm vase is the only piece recorded.

Mayfair Ware

Maxim China

For mark see *Crested China*, p. 187.

For mark see *Crested China*, p. 189.

Trademark used for a retailer by Hewitt & Leadbeater, Willow Potteries, Longton. (Usual trademark Willow Art).

Animal
Bulldog, standing. 125mm long.   13.00

Trademark used by Max Emanuel & Co., Mitterteich, (Bavaria). (Usual trademark Mosanic).

A range of 'smalls' and a trinket
    box.   1.50–3.50

Miscellaneous
Sabot, pointed toe. 93mm long.   4.00

Meir Arms China

For mark see *Crested China*, p. 189.

Trademark used by Barker Bros. Ltd., Meir
Works, Barker Street, Longton.

Ancient Artefacts
Puzzle Jug with verse. 70mm.   3.50

Historical/Folklore
Mary Queen of Scots Chair.
  No details of size.   4.75
*Mons Meg, Edinburgh Castle, Model
of.* 57mm.   7.50

Seaside Souvenirs
Eddystone Lighthouse. 109mm.   4.00

Animals
Pig, standing. 88mm long.   7.00

Great War
Red Cross Van. 85mm long.   17.00
Tank.   8.75

Alcohol
Barrel. 52mm.   2.00

Miscellaneous
Sabot.   4.50
Shoe, embossed buckle.
  115mm long.   4.00

Melba Bone China

Trademark used by Mayer & Sherratt,
Clifton Works, Longton.

This mark is only found on late
crested domestic ware.   1.00–3.00

Mermaid

The Milton China

For mark see *Crested China*, p. 189.

Trademark used by William Ritchie and Sons Ltd, 24, 26 and 28 Elder Street, Edinburgh. (Usual trademark Porcelle).

Mark mostly found on crested
domestic ware.   1.00–3.00

Great War
Tank, sometimes inscribed: *HMS
Donner Blitzen*, with details of
Ancre. 130mm long.   21.50

Sport
Cricket Bag. 110mm long.   6.50

For alternative mark see *Crested China*,
p. 189.

Trademark used by Hewitt Bros., Willow
Potteries, Longton, on china for a London
wholesaler (G.G & Co.). (Usual trademark Willow Art).

Ancient Artefacts
Ancient tyg, 2 handled.   1.75
Loving Cup, 3 handled. 55mm.   2.25

Monuments
Drake statue, Plymouth. 160mm.   8.75

Historical/Folklore
Model of Mons Meg, Edinburgh
Castle. 130mm long.   7.50

Traditional/National Souvenirs
Bagpipes with turquoise ribbon.
115mm long.   13.00
Welsh Hat. 62mm.   3.00

Seaside Souvenirs
Bathing Machine. 70mm long.   4.00
Lighthouse, octagonal. 114mm.   4.00
Shell on coral base. 93mm.   3.00

Animals
Bear, polar, standing upright.
95mm.   30.00
Dog, Scottie, wearing a
glengarry. 60mm.   5.50
Donkey with saddle. No. 904.
120mm long.   12.50

Elephant, with trunk in the air.
80mm long.   8.25
Elephant (trunk down).
75mm long.   6.50
Elephant Jug. 70mm. (Trunk is
handle).   4.00
Frog, with open mouth. 60mm.   4.00
Lion, poised to pounce, red
roaring mouth. 83mm long.   16.50
Lion standing on ashtray,
inscribed: *Ash Tray* and *Who
burned the tablecloth*.
110mm long.   12.50
Lion, roaring at mouse, sitting on
apple. Inscribed: *Much Ado
About Nothing*. Some colouring.   22.50
Pig, standing. 95mm long.   12.50
Ram, with curly horns.
90mm long.   23.00

Birds
Chicken, very fluffy. No. 325.
65mm.   4.00
Swan. 69mm.   3.50

Great War
Nurse, inscribed: *A friend in need*.
130mm.   25.75
Aeroplane Propeller. Rarely
factory marked. 150mm long.   13.00
Submarine, impressed: *E4*.
116mm long.   8.75
British Tank, Model of. 98mm long.   8.75
Red Cross Van. 90mm long.   17.50
Field Gun. 116mm long.   8.75
Bandsman's Drum with cording.
60mm.   4.75
Bugle. 70mm.   7.50
Kit Bag with verse: *Pack up your
troubles*. 74mm.   10.50
Incendiary bomb, rope handle.
82mm.   4.75
Kitchen range, pot on fire.
Inscribed: *Keep the home fires
burning*. Some colouring. No. 6.
80mm long.   7.50

Home/Nostalgic
Coal Scuttle. 65mm.   3.00
Watering Can. No. 126. 74mm.   4.75
Wheelbarrow. 105mm long.   6.50

Comic/Novelty
Dutch Girl, standing. 76mm.   6.50

Girl in dress and bonnet. 78mm.   7.50
A truck of coal from ..... Wagon of
black coal. 90mm long.   10.50

Cartoon/Comedy Characters
Baby, saluting, inscribed: *One of
the b'hoys*. Some colouring.
160mm.   16.00
(Great War cartoon character
could be 'Pooksie').
Dr Beetle, impressed: Charlie
Tolkard's character in Daily
Mail. 142mm.   47.50

Sport
Racehorse. 102mm.   40.00

Musical Instruments
Guitar. 163mm long.   6.50

Miscellaneous
Dagger, in decorative scabbard.
135mm long (rare).   37.50
Ladies' 18th century shoe.
90mm long.   7.50
Slipper Wall Pocket, blue bow.
No. 259. 150mm long.   12.50

Miniature Domestic
Mug, one handled. 38mm.   1.75

Moore Bros

Mosanic

For mark see *Crested China*, p. 190.

MOORE BROS.
STAFF
Rᵈ Nᵒ
442279

Trademark used by the German firm, Max Emanuel & Co., The Mosanic Pottery, Mitterteich. They exported a range of brown/stone unglazed buildings to Britain.

All models unglazed and brown/stone coloured.

Buildings

Trademark used by Moore (Bros.), St Mary's Works, Longton.

A range of 'smalls' with a Christmas Crest and a sprig of holly recorded.   10.00

Abbots of Buckfast Town House, inscribed: *Ye olde town house of ye Abbots of Buckfast ye close Exeter.* No. 0372. Rd. No. 567827. 100mm long.	20.50
Aberdeen, Old Machor Cathedral. No. 1313. Rd. No. 55628(?). 75mm long.	21.75
Aberystwyth, The College. No. 0350. Rd. No. 561630. 110mm long.	21.75
Bank of Ireland. No. 0365. Rd. No. 587364. 129mm long.	23.00
Birmingham Town Hall. 72mm long.	19.50
Bridlington Priory Church. No. 7533. 65mm.	21.875
Canterbury Cathedral. No. 0326. Rd. No. 558188. 112mm long.	21.75
Carlisle Cathedral. No. 0361. Rd. No. 876552. 97mm long.	21.75
Chester Cathedral. No. 0340. Rd. No. 559941. 100mm long. Two varieties with East and West transepts transposed.	21.75
Christchurch Priory. Rd No. 562002. 2 sizes: No. 0345I. 98mm long.	19.50
No. 0345II. 133mm long.	21.75
Croswaite Church, Keswick. Rd. No. 579266. 127mm long.	21.75
Crystal Palace. No. 0386. Rd. No. 58157(?). 170mm long.	21.75
Dartmouth, The Old Butterwalk. No. 0375. Rd. No. 576629. 105mm long.	19.50

Douglas, Tower of Refuge.		*Manchester Cathedral.*	
75mm long.	21.75	No. 0356. Rd. No. 564098.	
Edinburgh Castle. No. 0327.		100mm long.	21.75
Rd. No. 559939. 113mm long.	21.75	*Marble Arch* (white). No. 0422.	
Exeter Cathedral. No. 0348.		90mm.	17.50
Rd. No. 364035. 150mm long.	21.75	*Molls Coffee House, Exeter.*	
Exeter Guildhall, inscribed: *Ye olde*		No. 6936. 70mm long.	19.50
Guilde Hall of ye Ancient and		*Newark Castle.* No. 0307.	
Loyal Cittie of Exeter. 65mm.	19.50	Rd. No. 554738. 108mm long.	21.75
Exeter, St Mary's Steps & Stepcote		*Newcastle Cathedral.* No. 0343.	
Hill. No. 0304. Rd. No. 598554.		Rd. No. 560727. 95mm long.	21.75
93mm long.	19.50	*Newcastle-on-Tyne, Black Gate.*	
Fairmaids House, Perth. No. 0318.		No. 0389. 80mm long.	19.50
Rd. No. 558196. 72mm.	23.00	*Newcastle-on-Tyne, The Castle.*	
Gloucester Cathedral. No. 0347.		No. 0307, 0309 or 0419.	
Rd. No. 579265. 120mm long.	21.75	Rd. No. 554738 or 585809. (it is	
Guy's Cliff, The Mill. No. 2480.		possible that there is more than	
Rd. No. 554739. 93mm long.	21.75	one model). 95mm.	21.75
Halifax, Parish Church. No. 0323.		*Ripon Cathedral.* No. 0385.	
Rd. No. 558194. 90mm long.	21.75	Rd. No. 580773. 109mm long.	21.75
Harrogate, Royal Pump Room, Old		*Robinson Brewers Ltd, Ho'ton*	
Sulphur Well. No. 1301.		*(Ales & Stout).* No. 0379.	
Rd. No. 554744. 60mm.	19.50	112mm long.	20.50
Hathaways Cottage, Stratford.		Rowton Tower, inscribed: *King*	
No. 0378. Rd. No. 576880.		*Charles stood on this tower*	
120mm long.	10.50	*Sep 2nd 1645 and saw his army*	
Hereford Cathedral.		*defeated on Rowton Moor.* 85mm.	21.75
No. 0325. 92mm long.	21.75	*St Johns Church, Perth.* No. 0357.	
Hexham, The Abbey. No. 0371.		Rd. No. 568187. 85mm.	21.75
Rd. No. 581571. 109mm long.	21.75	*St Mary's Church, Scarborough.*	
Hawarden Castle. No. 0335.		No. 0303. 97mm long.	21.75
Rd. No. 559936. 110mm long.	21.75	*St Patrick's Cathedral.* 103mm.	21.75
Hawarden Church. No. 0323.		*St Pauls Cathedral,* not named.	
Rd. No. 559934. 85mm long.	21.75	No. 7332. Rd. No. 564098.	
Hawarden, Gladstone Memorial		88mm long.	17.50
Library. No. 0330. 115mm long.	23.00	*St Tudno's Church, Llandudno.*	
Houses of Parliament. No. 0398.		No. 0303. Rd. No. 564142.	
Rd. No. 599955. 70mm.	21.75	84mm.	21.75
Iffley Church. No. 0360.		*Salisbury Cathedral.* No. 0351.	
Rd. No. 587402. 113mm long.	21.75	Rd. No. 567854. 105mm long.	21.75
Kirk Braddon Church.		*Scarborough, The Castle.*	
Rd. No. 557800. 80mm long.	21.75	No. 0398. 78mm.	21.75
Lancaster Castle. No. 0365.		*Shakespeares House,*	
130mm long.	21.75	*Stratford-on-Avon.* No. 0380.	
Lichfield Cathedral. No. 0352.		Rd. No. 576829. 110mm long.	19.50
Rd. No. 580372.	21.75	*Upleatham Church.* No. 0331.	
Lincoln Castle. No. 0315.		Rd. No. 582362. 97mm long.	20.50
Rd. No. 556282. 110mm long.	21.75	*Westminster Abbey.* No. 0341.	
Lowther Castle. No. 0317.		Rd. No. 560726. 110mm long.	21.75
Rd. No. 566283. 105mm long.	21.75	*Winchester Cathedral.* No. 0430.	
Madame Tussauds.	23.00	Rd. No. 632519. 144mm long.	23.00
Malvern Priory. No. 0322.		*York Minster.* Rd. No. 556287.	
Rd. No. 558186. 95mm long.	21.75	2 sizes: No. 0312. 82mm long.	19.50
		No. 0312II. 138mm long.	22.50

Historical/Folklore
Old Norman Font, St Mary's Church
Steps, Exeter. No. 0376.
Rd. No. 579668.   18.50

Seaside Souvenirs
Corbierre Lighthouse, Jersey, Model
of. No. 0419. Rd. No. 558636.
84mm.   18.50
Flamborohead Lighthouse. 67mm.   18.50

Moschendorf

For mark see *Crested China*, p. 191.

Trademark used by the German firm
Hof-Moschendorf (Bayern).

This mark has only been found on
a crested 6 inch tea plate.   1.00

Mother Shipton China

For mark see *Crested China*, p. 191.

Trademark used for the retailer J.W. Simpson, Dropping Well, Knaresboro' by Wiltshaw and Robinson Ltd, Carlton Works, Stoke-on-Trent. (Usual trademark Carlton).

Historical/Folklore

Knaresborough Dropping Well, with inscription. 103mm.	18.50
Mother Shipton, with some colouring. 2 sizes: 92mm.	14.00
190mm.	18.50
Mother Shipton with some colouring, standing on lustre oval base. 90mm.	18.00
Mother Shipton, some colouring, standing on ashtray base, with inscription.	8.00

Seaside Souvenir

Suitcase. 36mm.	3.50

Animals

Deer, with antlers. 217mm to top of antler.	47.50

Great War

Munitions worker, inscribed: *Doing her bit. Shells and more shells.* Some colouring. 140mm.	75.00
French 75mm Field Gun. 125mm.	13.00
Edith Cavell, statue, inscribed: *Brussels dawn October 12th 1915. Sacrifice, Humanity.* 163mm.	10.50

Home/Nostalgic

Frying Pan. 110mm long.	5.50
Warming Pan. No. 392. 127mm long.	4.75

Comic/Novelty

I'm forever blowing bubbles. Pears advert blue boy blowing bubbles. Clothes blue, bubble and bowl lustre. 110mm.	24.50

Alcohol

Toby Jug, with inscription. 70mm.	5.25

Musical Instruments

Upright Piano. 64mm.	8.75

Nautilus Porcelain

Nelson China

For mark see *Crested China*, p. 193.

Trademark used by the Nautilus Porcelain
Co., Possil Pottery, Glasgow.

Ancient Artefacts

Aberdeen Bronze Pot. 65mm.	3.75
Hastings Kettle. 52mm.	3.50
Loving Cup, three handled.	
2 sizes: 39mm.	5.00
50mm.	4.50
Puzzle Jug. 70mm.	00.00

Traditional/National

Irish Wooden Noggin. 57mm.	5.25
Highland Whiskey Bowl. Can	
have 2 or 3 handles. 60mm dia.	7.50
Thistle Jug. 64mm.	5.00

Animals

Pig, fat and standing. 70mm long.	12.50

Home/Nostalgic

Coal scuttle, cylindrical on bow	
feet. 70mm long.	3.00
Dust Pan. 50mm long.	5.00
Garden Urn. 63mm.	4.00
Milk Churn. 76mm.	8.50
Miner's Lamp. 63mm.	10.50

Miscellaneous

Dutch Sabot. 90mm long.	7.00
Old Boot. 63mm long.	8.50
Oriental Slipper. 92mm long.	8.50
Top Hat, match striker. 46mm.	6.00
Milk Jug, tall and ornate. 95mm.	5.00

Miniature Domestic

Beaker. 39mm.	3.00
Cheese dish, 2 pieces.	
70mm long.	10.50
Cup. 39mm.	3.00

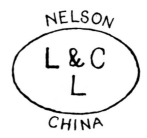

Trademark used for a Liverpool retailer by
an unknown English manufacturer but
probably a branch of J.A. Robinson & Sons.

Seaside Souvenir

Bathing Machine.	4.50

Great War

Model of a pair of field glasses.	
60mm long.	8.75

Ness

Niagara Art China

"NESS CHINA"

NIAGARA
ART
CHINA

Trademark used for an Inverness firm by Schmidt and Co., Carlesbad (Bohemia). (Usual trademark Gemma).

Great War
French Infantry Helmet.
    60mm long.   40.00

Trademark used by Birks, Rawlins and Co (Ltd), Vine Pottery, Stoke. (Usual trademark Savoy).

Great War
Tommy's Steel Helmet. The only
    recorded model, it has a Gains-
    borough crest. 76mm long.   23.00

Norfolk Crest China

For mark see *Crested China*, p. 193.

Trademark used for W.H. Smith & Sons by Hewitt & Leadbeater, Willow Potteries, Longton – subsequently Hewitt Bros. (Usual trademark Willow Art).

Buildings – White
Shakespeare's House.
59mm long.   5.50

Monuments
Sir Robert Peel statue. 168mm.   16.00

Historical/Folklore
James V Chair. 101mm.   6.50

Traditional/National
Lancashire clog. 88mm long.   3.50
Welsh Hat, with blue band.
No. 75. 57mm.   3.00

Seaside Souvenirs
Lifeboat. 95mm long.   4.75

Animals
Cat, on cushion, playing fiddle,
  holding bow. 110mm.
  Inscribed: *Cat and Fiddle, Buxton*.   40.00
Dog, Bull Terrier, standing.
  60mm.   7.50
Dog, sitting, head to one side.
  No. 23. 70mm.   8.00
Elephant, walking. 52mm.   6.50
Elephant, walking, trunk over
  head. No. 113. 53mm.   8.25
Pig, standing. 85mm long.   10.00

Birds
Duck Posy Holder, yellow beak.
  80mm long.   4.00
Hen egg cup. 76mm long.   5.00

Great War
Battleship, impressed:
  H.M.S. Lion. 140mm long.   13.00

British Tank. 102mm long.   8.75
Tank with trailing wheels.
  123mm long.   10.50
Military Cap. 80mm dia.   5.50
Kitbag with verse. 74mm.   10.50
Matlock Bath War Memorial.
  182mm.   65.00

Home/Nostalgic
Grandfather Clock, inscribed:
  *Make use of time let not advantage
  slip. Shakespeare*. 128mm.   9.00

Comic/Novelty
Jester, double faced bust. Some
  colouring. 3 sizes: 65mm.   4.00
                          80mm.   5.00
                          90mm.   7.50
Monk, jovial and plump.
  No glass. 90mm.   12.50

Alcohol
Monk, jovial and holding glass.
  70mm.   8.75

Sport
Cricket Cap. 67mm long.   19.50

Nornesford China

One and All

For mark see *Crested China*, p. 194.

For mark see *Crested China*, p. 194.

Trademark used by a Longton firm, probably R.H. and S.L. Plant (Ltd), Tuscan Works, Longton. (Usual trademark Tuscan).

Animals

Cheshire Cat, with brown bead right eye. 90mm.	7.50

Home/Nostalgic

Bellows. 105mm.	4.00
Loaf of Bread. 55mm.	17.00
Pillar Box. No. 181. 73mm.	6.50
Shaving Mug. 53mm.	4.00

Miscellaneous

Top Hat. No. 173. 45mm.	3.00

Trademark used by J.A. Robinson & Sons, Stoke-on-Trent. (Usual trademark Arcadian).

Ancient Artefacts

Salisbury Jack, not named. 50mm.	1.75

Buildings – White

Anne Hathaway's Cottage. 105mm long.	8.00

Animals

Bulldog, sitting. 50mm.	8.75
Teddy Bear. No. 27. 65mm.	7.00
Squirrel, eating nut. 60mm.	10.50

Bird

Goose. 95mm.	12.00

Home/Nostalgic

Cauldron with handle. 82mm.	3.00
Fire Bucket. 53mm.	2.50

Comic/Novelty

Jester, sitting on heart shaped ashtray. 65mm.	10.50

Miscellaneous

Domed Jampot with cover. 80mm.	3.50

Oxford Art China   P

For mark see *Crested China*, p. 195.

For mark see *Crested China*, p. 195.

Trademark used for an Oxfordshire retailer by Hewitt & Leadbeater, Willow Potteries, Longton. (Usual trademark Willow Art).

Trademark used by Hutschenreuther, Probstzella, Thüringia. (not the more famous Bavarian firm of the same name).

Historical/Folklore

Sir Walter Scott's Chair, Abbotsford.	
80mm.	6.50

Ancient Artefacts

Aberdeen Bronze Pot. 68mm.	1.50
Ancient tyg, 2 handled.	1.50
Loving Cup, 3 handled.	2.00

Home/Nostalgic

Cauldron.	2.00

Miniature Domestic

Cheese dish and cover, 2 pieces.	
55mm.	4.00
Teapot. 65mm.	4.00
Tea Urn, tapered. 65mm.	6.50

Palatine China

P.A.L.T.

For mark see *Crested China*, p. 195.

For mark see *Crested China*, p. 195.

Trademark used for Pearsons, of Blackpool by J.A. Robinson Ltd, (Usual trademark Arcadian).

Trademark used by a German firm on domestic wares, after the Great War.

Domestic ware only.   1.00–5.00

Animals
Dog, sitting with a tear on cheek.
  80mm.   14.50

Great War
Armoured car, Model of.
  120mm long.   22.50
Red Cross Van, inscribed, *EH 139*.
  88mm long.   17.50
Tank, Model of. 115mm.   8.75

Panorama

Panorama   173

Miscellaneous

School Boy's Cap. 67mm long.	19.50
Toby Jug. 74mm.	5.25

For mark see *Crested China*, p. 197.

Trademark used by Wagstaff and Brunt on china manufactured by Edwin Leadbeater, Commerce Street, Longton.

Many of these wares are found with a transfer print view rather than a crest.

Unglazed/Parian

Burns and Highland Mary. 125mm.	16.00
Bust of Dickens, on circular glazed base. 170mm.	35.00

Monuments

Sir Robert Peel statue on large plinth. 165mm.	16.00

Historical

Bunyans Chair, Model of. 95mm.	8.25
Model of Mons Meg Edinburgh Castle. 130mm long.	7.50
Sir Walter Scott's Chair at Abbotsford. No. 85. 80mm.	6.50

Traditional/National

Welsh Hat. No. 57. 60mm.	3.00

Animals

Cat sitting, left ear raised, one green eye. 105mm.	9.50
Pug dog, sitting. 67mm.	7.50

Birds

Chick. 33mm.	4.00

Great War

Red Cross Van. No. 103. 88mm long.	17.50

Home/Nostalgic

Anvil. No. 78. 58mm.	4.75
Monk. 88mm.	6.50

Paragon China

PARAGON
CHINA
ENGLAND

Trademark used by Star China Co., Atlas Works (and other addresses), Longton. Subsequently Paragon China (Co) Ltd.

Mark used on domestic wares with Great War Commemorative, Four Flags of the Allies with inscription: *For right and freedom*.   4.00–7.00

Park, For the People, China

PARK
FOR THE PEOPLE
CHINA

Mark used by unknown English manufacturer for a charity, (possibly) in Newtown, Mid-Wales.

This mark has been found on several smalls all with a Newtown crest, could they have been sold at a charity or fund raising bazaar?

Patriotic China

Pearl Arms China

For mark see *Crested China*, p. 197.

For mark see *Crested China*, p. 197.

Trademark used during the Great War by Birks, Rawlins and Co (Ltd), Vine Pottery, Stoke. (Usual trademark Savoy).

Trademark used for a wholesaler by Hewitt Bros, Willow Potteries Ltd, Longton. (Usual trademark Willow Art).

Range of domestic wares all with Military Crests and Great War inscriptions.	2.00–10.00

Miniature Domestic

Teapot. 65mm.	7.50

Ancient Artefacts

Carlisle Salt Pot, not named. 46mm.	1.75

Historical/Folklore

James V Chair, Stirling Castle. 100mm.	6.50
Royal Crown. 55mm.	20.00

Traditional/National Souvenirs

Blackpool Big Wheel. 100mm.	6.50
Lancashire Clog. 88mm long.	4.00
Welsh Hat with longest Welsh place name around brim. No. 75. 55mm.	4.50

Seaside Souvenirs

Lighthouse. 110mm.	3.00

Animals

Cat, sitting. 70mm.	7.50
Cat sitting in boot, blue bow. 88mm long.	11.00
Bulldog, black, emerging from kennel, inscribed: *The Black Watch*. 70mm long.	7.50
Dog, Collie, standing. 52mm.	8.25
Elephant, walking. 52mm.	6.50
Elephant, cream jug. 72mm.	4.00
Mouse. 62mm.	12.50
Pig, sitting, inscribed: *You may push me* etc. 73mm.	8.25
Pig, standing. 85mm long.	10.00
Rabbit, right ear erect. 66mm long.	4.00

Birds

Canary on rock. 98mm.	6.50
Swan, with head on breast. 58mm.	3.00

Great War

Sailor, inscribed: *Our Brave Defender*. 130mm.	25.75
Monoplane, with fixed prop. 146mm long.	30.00
Battleship, 4 funnels. 127mm long.	13.00
Battleship, 3 funnels. Impressed *H.M.S. Lion*. 140mm long.	17.00
British tank, Model of, with trailing wheels. 130mm long.	10.50
British Tank, Model of. 92mm long.	8.75
Bugle. No. 370. 70mm.	12.50
Kit Bag with verse: *Pack up your troubles in your old kit bag*. 74mm.	10.50
Officer's Peaked Cap. 70mm dia.	5.50
Pickelhaube. (German spiked helmet). 50mm.	13.00
Fireplace inscribed: *Keep the home fires burning*. Some colouring. 100mm long.	8.25

Home/Nostalgic

Anvil. 60mm.	4.75
Basket, oblong with handle. 76mm long.	2.00
Book, leather bound. 60mm.	3.00
Coal scuttle, helmet shaped. No. 101. 53mm.	4.00
Grandfather Clock, inscribed: *Make use of time let not advantage slip. Shakespeare*. 128mm.	9.00
Pillar Box, outpressed: *G.R.* 90mm.	6.50
Sundial, circular on square base, with inscription: *I mark not the hours*. 98mm.	5.50
Watering Can. 72mm.	4.75

Comic/Novelty

Billiken, the God of Luck, often found unnamed. 73mm.	3.00
Billiken, the God of Luck, sitting on high-backed chair. 100mm.	4.00

Alcohol

Whiskey Bottle with cork, inscribed: *One special scotch*. 88mm.	4.00

Transport

Open Tourer, 4 seater. 114mm long.	21.75

Miscellaneous

Hand holding a tulip. 80mm.	2.25
Policeman's Helmet.	18.50

Miniature Domestic

Cheese dish and cover. 45mm.	4.50
Coffee Pot. 69mm.	3.00

Pheonix China

For additional mark see *Crested China*, p. 198.

Trademark used by Thomas Forester & Sons (Ltd.), Phoenix Works, Longton.

A range of crested domestic ware was produced.

Miniature Domestic

Wash Basin. 50mm.	2.50
Wash Jug. 80mm.	2.50

Podmore China

For mark see *Crested China*, p. 199.

Trademark used by Podmore China Co., Elm Street, Hawley.

Unglazed/Parian

Bust of *Bunyan*, square unglazed base. 135mm.	16.00
Bust of Burns, on square unglazed base with crest. 150mm.	12.50

Buildings – Coloured

Bell Hotel, Abel Fletcher's house in *John Halifax gentleman*. 67mm.	40.00

Buildings – White

Bell Hotel, Abel Fletcher's house in *John Halifax gentleman*. 67mm.	17.50
Big Ben. 101mm.	10.50
Clifton Suspension Bridge. 190mm long.	26.00
God's Providence House, Chester. AD1652. 2 sizes: 70mm	14.50
90mm.	19.50
Hastings Clock Tower. 167mm.	10.50
King Charles Tower, Chester. 88mm.	20.50
Leicester, Clock Tower. 191mm.	16.00
Lincoln Cathedral, West front. 106mm.	14.00
Margate Clock Tower. 143mm.	10.50
Matlock Bath, The Tower, 120mm.	17.00
St Albans, Clock Tower. 125mm.	18.50
St. Pauls Cathedral. 105mm.	12.50
Westminster Abbey. 127mm.	17.50

Monuments (including Crosses)

Banbury, The Cross. 158mm.	13.00
Bunyan's Statue, Model of. 2 sizes: 173mm.	10.50
206mm.	11.25
Nelsons Column. 140mm.	40.00
St Albans Statue. 160mm.	40.00

Historical/Folklore

Armour, Breast plate. 75mm.	35.00

Bunyan's Chair. 99mm.	10.50
Burns Chair, Model of. 93mm.	6.50
Mary Queen of Scots Chair in	
Edinburgh Castle, Model of.	4.75
Mother Shipton, standing figure.	
75mm.	6.00
Tewkesbury Cross Stocks and	
Whipping Post. 105mm (rare).	31.50

Traditional/National Souvenirs

Chester Imp, recumbent.	
100mm long.	28.00
Lancashire Clog. 73mm long.	4.00
Lincoln Imp sitting on round	
base. 105mm.	4.00

Seaside Souvenirs

Lifeboat with deep blue cord.	
115mm long.	4.75
Lifeboatman on plinth. 142mm.	7.50
Beachy Head Lighthouse, with	
black band. 120mm.	5.00
Needles Rocks and Lighthouse, Isle of	
Wight. 125mm long.	21.75
North Foreland Lighthouse,	
Broadstairs. 128mm.	16.00
Oyster Shell on log base. 80mm.	3.00
Whelk shell, inscribed: *Listen to*	
the sea. 100mm long.	3.50
Child, sitting with knees under	
chin, wearing bathing suit.	
Impressed: *Splash me.* Some	
colouring. 140mm (rare).	30.00
Child, standing on rock draped	
in towel. Some colouring.	
115mm. and 140mm.	17.00

Animals

Cat, standing with arched back	
and tail up. Coloured eyes and	
mouth. 110mm.	8.25
Cat, grotesque with almost	
human face and wearing a black	
cap. Inscribed: *Puss Puss.*	
105mm.	23.00
Cat with long neck. 120mm.	5.50
Dog, Scottie, looking out of	
kennel. Inscribed: *Black Watch.*	6.50
Dog, black with green bow.	
70mm.	7.50
Dog, Scottie, wearing a Tam	
O'Shanter. 75mm.	5.50
Dog, sitting. 68mm.	6.50
Elephant. 64mm long.	6.50

Pig, standing. 100mm long.	7.50
Shetland Pony. 100mm long.	10.50

Birds

Cock with red comb, on green	
base. 45mm.	7.50
Hen, with red comb. 66mm.	7.50
Penguin. 88mm.	8.50

Great War

Bust of *HRH, Prince of Wales,* in	
uniform, on square base.	
155mm.	56.50
Monoplane with revolving	
prop.	30.00
Cenotaph, inscribed: *The Glorious*	
Dead. MCMXIV–MCMXIX.	
Green wreaths. 3 sizes:	
84mm.	4.00
130mm.	4.75
165mm.	5.50
Edith Cavell Memorial, London.	
Inscribed: *Edith Cavell Brussels*	
dawn October 12th 1915.	
Humanity Sacrifice. 2 sizes:	
142mm.	12.00
170mm.	17.50
Edith Cavell Statue, Norwich.	
165mm.	22.50
Black Watch War Memorial.	
130mm.	60.00
Leek War Memorial. *Model of War*	
Memorial Leek, presented by Sir	
Arthur & Lady Nicholson.	
158mm.	65.00
Matlock Bath War Memorial. Often	
found un-named. 190mm.	14.50
R.A.F. Memorial. 152mm.	
(Details as Alexandra model).	52.50
Rushden War Memorial. *Their*	
names liveth for ever, To keep in	
mind those from this town who	
gave their lives in the Great War.	
1914–1915. 155mm.	50.00
Blackpool War Memorial, inscribed:	
1914 in memory of our glorious	
dead 1918. 145mm.	35.00

Home/Nostalgic

Baby's Bootee. 52mm.	6.50
Baby's Cradle. 65mm long.	4.00
Grandfather Clock, with	
inscription: *Make use of Time.*	
123mm.	8.00

Fireplace with clock on
mantelpiece, inscribed: *Home
sweet home. East or west home is
best*. Some colouring. 98mm.   13.00

Comic/Novelty
Billiken, sitting on high backed
chair, inscribed: *The God of
things as they ought to be*.
102mm.   4.00
The Bridegroom, God Help Him.
145mm.   24.50
Sack of Coal, some colouring.
2 sizes: 60mm.   5.50
         95mm.   6.50
Can be found inscribed: *If you
can't afford a truck – buy a sack*.
Schoolboy, comic coloured face.
100mm.   29.50

Cartoon/Comedy Characters
*Mr Pussy Foot. All water we don't
think*. Standing figure, some
colouring. 96mm.   22.50

Alcohol
Beer Barrel on stand, fixed.
60mm.   2.50

Sport
Golf Ball, inscribed: *The ancient
game of golf was first played in
1448*. 40mm.   4.50
The Sprinter, gangly athlete with
comic face, kneeling, on oval
base. 98mm.   65.00

Transport
Charabanc. 127mm long.   17.00

Modern Equipment
Horn Gramophone. 93mm.   14.50

Miscellaneous
A hand holding a tulip. 95mm.   2.25

Miniature Domestic
Cheese Dish, 1 piece. 50mm.   4.00
Cheese Dish, 2 pieces.
71mm long.   5.50

Porcelle

For mark see *Crested China*, p. 201.

Trademark used by William Ritchie & Son
Ltd., 24, 26, 28 Elder Street, Edinburgh.

Many, if not all, these models are from
Savoy moulds and this firm may have been a
wholesaler or retailer or heraldic china,
obtaining supplies from Birks, Rawlins and
Co. (Usual trademark Savoy).

Unglazed/Parian
Bust of Robbie Burns on glazed
plinth. 135mm.   12.50
Bust of Sir John Jellicoe, impressed: *W.C. Lawton sculp. copy-
right. 23rd Sept 1914*. 170mm.   47.50

Ancient Artefacts
Newbury Leather Bottle. 65mm.   2.25
Whiskey Quaich. 30mm.   4.00

Buildings – White
Burns Cottage, Model of.
70mm long.   10.50
Cottage. 75mm long.   6.50
Windmill, with revolving sails.
108mm.   16.00

Historical/Folklore
Hindu God or Pixie on circular
base. No. 35. 88mm.   5.00
*Mary Queen of Scot's chair, Edin-
burgh Castle, Model of*. 70mm.   4.75

Traditional/National Souvenirs
Irish Harp with moulded
shamrocks. 105mm.   4.00
Bagpipes. 115mm long.   13.00
Thistle Vase. 48mm.   2.25

Seaside Souvenirs
Bathing Machine, inscribed:
Morning dip. 87mm.   5.50
Lighthouse on rocky base.
104mm.   3.00

Fisherman, with Tub, inscribed:
Waiting for the smacks. 67mm. 19.50
Shell ashtray. 81mm long. 2.50
Scallop Shell. 70mm long. 2.00
Whelk Shell. No. 451. 2 sizes:
98mm. 3.50
100mm long. 3.50

Animals
Cat, sitting, long neck and tail
joined to shoulders. 105mm. 16.00
Cat, sitting. 51mm. 7.00
Cat, squatting, wide grin.
105mm. 9.00
Dog, puppy begging. 68mm. 5.50
Dog, Terrier, looking out of
kennel, inscribed: *Black Watch*,
dog black. 55mm. 6.50
Hare, sitting up. 106mm. 21.25
Pig, lying down. 80mm long. 6.50
Pig, standing. 70mm long. 8.25
Rabbit, crouching with flat ears.
30mm. 4.00
Rabbit, sitting. 80mm. 20.00
Seal. 50mm. 8.75
Grotesque animal/bird. 105mm. 5.00
Animal jug, tail is handle. 70mm. 4.00

Birds
Duck. 70mm long. 6.00

Great War
Sailor, standing with hands on
hips. 130mm. 56.50
British Airship on stand.
130mm long. 13.00
HMS Queen Elizabeth.
165mm long. 49.50
Torpedo Boat Destroyer, Model of.
140mm long. - 87.50
Submarine, inscribed: *E1*.
150mm long. 30.00
Submarine, inscribed: *E4*. 95mm. 8.75
Armoured Car with 2 guns.
127mm long. 40.00
British motor searchlight, Model of.
90mm long. 70.00
Red Cross Van. 110mm long. 17.50
Tank with 2 steering wheels,
inscribed: *HMS Donner Blitzen*
and *Model of British tank first
used by British troops at the Battle
of Ancre Sept. 1916*.
Two sizes: 130mm long. 25.00
160mm long. 30.00

Field Gun. 170mm long. 13.00
Howitzer. 2 sizes: 140mm. 13.00
168mm long. 24.50
Machine gun, Model of, on tripod
(2 pieces). 80mm. 110.00
Trench Mortar. 8.75
Land Mine. Similar to curling
stone but with rectangular
firing mechanism. No. 429.
52mm. 24.50
Mills Bomb. 80mm. 11.00
Shell inscribed: *Iron rations for
Fritz.* 78mm. 4.00
Glengarry. 2 sizes: 70mm. 13.00
100mm long. 16.00
Larger model has coloured
heather in band.
Anzacs Cap, Model of, with maple
leaf, impressed: *CANADA.*
90mm long. 20.50
Colonial soldiers Hat.
90mm long. 13.00
Peaked Cap. No. 516.
70mm long. 5.50
Poilu, French Trench Helmet.
84mm long. 40.00
Sailors Cap. 70mm dia. 40.00
Tommy's Steel Helmet.
82mm long. 16.00
Fireplace, inscribed: *Keep the home
fires burning.* 70mm. 9.50

Home/Nostalgic
Baby's cradle. 55mm. 6.50
Iron and stand. 70mm long. 8.00
Jelly Mould. 55mm. 9.50
Milk Churn with fixed top.
60mm. 2.50
Watering Can, miniature. 50mm. 6.00
Wheelbarrow. 114mm long. 6.50
Wooden tub. 39mm. 3.00

Comic/Novelty
Policeman, hands behind back.
No. 327. 113mm. 18.00

Cartoon/Comedy Characters
Winkie the Gladeye Bird cruet
set, salt, pepper and mustard.
68mm. Set 40.00

Sport
Curling Stone. 52mm. 12.50
Golf Club Head. 65mm. 5.50

Musical Instrument
Banjo. 137mm long.   4.50

Transport
Open Motor Car.   21.75

Modern Equipment
Square Gramophone. 55mm.   12.00

Miscellaneous
Ankle Boot. 72mm long.   4.00
Boot. 58mm long.   3.50
Oriental Shoe with turned up
    toe. 88mm long.   4.00
Top Hat. 45mm.   .   3.00

Miniature Domestic
Cup and Saucer. 40mm.   4.00
Mug. 47mm.   1.75

Premier

For mark see *Crested China*, p. 202.

Trademark used by a wholesaler on china manufactured by Taylor & Kent (Ltd), Florence Works, Longton. (Usual trademark Florentine).

Monuments
Iona Cross. 108mm.   6.00

Traditional/National Souvenirs
Welsh Hat. 57mm.   3.00

Seaside Souvenirs
Suitcase. 77mm.   2.25

Animals
Cheshire Cat always smiling. 87mm.   5.00
Manx Cat. 61mm.   13.00
Frog. 72mm long.   6.50
Pig, standing, inscribed: *The pig
    that won't go*. 95mm long.   7.50

Home/Nostalgic
Coal scuttle, helmet shaped.
    65mm.   3.00
Oriental lamp. (Aladdin's
    Lamp). 100mm long.   2.25

Musical
Tambourine. 70mm dia.   3.50

Miscellaneous
Shoe, Ladies, 18th Century.
    95mm long.   7.50

Miniature Domestic
Coffee Pot. 55mm.   3.00

Princess China

For mark see *Crested China*, p. 203.

Trademark used for a Blackpool retailer probably by Wilhelm Kutzscher & Co., Schwarzenberger Porzellanfabrik, Schwarzenberg, Saxony. (Now in East Germany). (This firm used several trademarks and produced a great deal of the German models just labelled; Germany, Saxony or foreign).

Buildings – White

Blackpool Tower, with buildings. 155mm.	10.50

Traditional/National Souvenirs

Blackpool, Big Wheel. 89mm.	6.00

Bird

Bird standing on rock. 80mm.	6.50

Queens China or Ware

For mark see *Crested China*, p. 203.

Trademark used by Birks, Rawlins & Co (Ltd), Vine Pottery, Stoke. (Usual trademark Savoy).

Ancient Artefacts

Chester Roman Vase. 60mm.	1.75
Glastonbury Bowl. 40mm.	1.75
Shakespeare's Jug. 63mm.	3.00

Historical/Folklore

Burns Chair. 76mm.	6.50
Execution Block. 98mm long.	9.50
Rufus Stone. 100mm.	3.50

Traditional/National Souvenirs

Balmoral Bonnet. 70mm long.	22.50
Tam O'Shanter. 78mm dia.	12.50
Welsh Hat. 50mm.	3.00

Seaside Souvenirs

Bathing Machine. No. 425. 60mm.	4.50
Lighthouse on rocky base. 134mm.	3.00
Rowing Boat. 127mm long.	5.50

Countryside

Beehive. 70mm.	4.75

Animals

Bear dancing, with muzzle. 102mm.	27.50
Cat, detailed fur. 80mm.	7.50
Dog, angry and barking. 100mm long.	21.50
Fish. 102mm long.	2.00
Frog, realistic, giant-size. 73mm.	30.00
Hare. 74mm.	8.00
Lion, sitting on base. (This was originally designed by Alfred Stevens for the British Museum). 104mm.	7.50
Pig, lying down. 80mm long.	8.25
Seal. 55mm long.	8.75

Birds

Birds on tree trunk.	23.00
Duck, swimming. 40mm long.	6.50
Penguin. 76mm.	8.75

Great War

Submarine, E1. 149mm long.	8.75
Ambulance, Red Cross Van.	
108mm long.	17.50
Ambulance, with Rolls Royce	
front. 115mm long.	25.75
Armoured Car. 125mm long.	40.00
Field Gun, with fish tail.	
140mm long (scarce).	52.50
Machine gun on tripod,	
two-piece. 80mm.	110.00
British Trench Mortar Gun.	
110mm long.	40.00
Shell. 70mm.	4.00
R.F.C. Cap. 72mm long.	26.00
Colonial Hat. 92mm long.	8.25
French Trench Helmet.	
72mm long.	40.00
Glengarry. 70mm long.	13.00
Officer's Peaked Cap.	
72mm long.	5.50
New Zealand Hat. 83mm long.	13.00
Sailors Cap. No. 533. 70mm.	40.00
Bandsman's Drum. 55mm dia.	4.75

Home/Nostalgic

Grandfather Clock. 149mm.	21.50
Post Box. 60mm.	6.00

Comic/Novelty

Humpty Dumpty Salt and	
Pepper Post. 80mm.	pair 49.50
Man, shirt off, working in barrel.	
68mm long.	18.25
Policeman holding truncheon.	
105mm.	16.50

Cartoon/Comedy

Bonzo, not named. 118mm.	24.50

Sport

Golf Caddie with bag of clubs on	
heart shaped pin tray/ash tray.	
80mm.	37.50
Curling Stone, not named.	
53mm.	12.50

Musical Instruments

Banjo. 136mm long.	4.75

Queens Crest China

For mark see *Crested China*, p. 205.

Trademark used for S.P. & Co Ltd, of 57 King St, Manchester, by Arkinstall & Son Ltd, Arcadian Works, Stoke-on-Trent. (Usual trademark Arcadian).

Ancient Artefacts

Colchester Vase. No. 504. 50mm.	1.75
Dorchester Jug, inscribed: *Model*	
of old jug found in North Square,	
Dorchester. No. 1774. 52mm.	2.25
Fountains Abbey Cup.	
No. 23821. 50mm.	2.25
Irish Bronze Pot.	
No. 1834. 45mm.	1.75
Jersey Milk Can. No. 3424. 60mm.	3.00
Lincoln Jack from original in	
museum. No. 1564. 65mm.	2.25
Newbury Bottle, inscribed:	
Leather bottle found at Newbury	
1644 on Battlefield now in	
museum. No. 2294. 65mm.	2.25

Animals

Manx Cat, crouching. 65mm.	13.00
Elephant, Indian. 77mm long.	6.50
Tortoise. 72mm long.	4.00

Numbered Ornamental Wares

Some of these could be un-named ancient artefacts. Value £1.25 each.

No. 594. Fluted jug. 54mm.
No. 1724. Small pot on three feet. 43mm.
No. 1824. Ewer. 60mm.
No. 3164. Pot. 50mm.
No. 3594. Vase. 50mm.
No. 3884. Vase. 54mm.
No. 7061. Vase. 65mm.
No. 14715. Vase, with narrow neck. 100mm.

Queeny China

R & L

No details of mark available.

For mark see *Crested China*, p. 205. Also found with a printed mark.

Mark used by an unknown manufacturer.

Both the models known sport Hastings crests.

Buildings

Cottage. 70mm long.   4.00

Trademark used by Robinson & Leadbetter, Wolfe Street, Stoke-upon-Trent and subsequently a branch of J.A. Robinson Ltd.

Ancient Artefacts

Chester Roman Vase. 2 sizes:	
63mm and 76mm.	2.25
Loving Cup, 2 handled. 45mm.	2.25
Loving Cup, 3 handled. 39mm.	2.25

Buildings – Coloured

Mason Croft, the house of Miss Marie Corelli.	
2 sizes: 75mm long.	85.00
90mm long.	95.00
Shakespeares Cottage.	
40mm long.	14.00

Birds/Eggs

Egg Flower Holder. 80mm long.	2.75
Swan with yellow beak and feet.	
70mm.	3.00

Miscellaneous

Thimble Salt Pot. 37mm.	7.00

R & M

Raleigh China

For mark see *Crested China*, p. 206.

For mark see *Crested China*, p. 206.

Trademark used by Roper & Meredith, Garfield Pottery, Longton.

Birds
Bird, with open wings.
75mm long.   7.50

Great War
March War Memorial. 174mm.   60.00
St. Ives War Memorial Cross.
135mm.   60.00

Comic/Novelty
Truck of coal, inscribed: *Black Diamonds*. Black coal. 79mm long.   10.50

Sport
Rugby player, holding rugby ball,
on oval ashtray. Inscribed: *Play
up*. Fully coloured. 126mm.   55.00

Trademark used for a retailer by Sampson Hancock (and Sons), Bridge Works, Stoke and later at the Gordon Works, Hanley. (renamed Corona Pottery). (Usual trademark Corona).

Historical/Folklore
Ark. 92mm long.   2.25

Traditional/National Souvenirs
Lancashire Clog. 102mm long.   4.00
Welsh Hat. No. 198. 45mm.   3.50

Great War
Submarine, inscribed: *E4*.   8.75
Field Gun. 125mm long.   8.75
Bell Tent, open flap. 80mm.   5.50

Miniature Domestic
Cheese Dish. 45mm.   4.75

Raphael China

Trademark used for S.P. & Co. Ltd, of 57 King St, Manchester, by Arkinstall & Son Ltd, Arcadian Works, Stoke-on-Trent. (Usual trademark Arcadian).

The only other items known are smalls with either printed decorations or the crests of Switzerland or Austria. (Spelt that way so not for export).

Ancient Artefacts
Kendal jug. 76mm.   2.50

Regency Ware

For mark see *Crested China*, p. 207.

Trademark used for a retailer by Sampson Hancock (& Sons), Bridge Works, Stoke. (Usual trademark Corona).

Buildings
Model of Clifton Suspension Bridge.
    120mm long.   30.00

Animals
Cat, sitting with ruff of fur round
    neck. 100mm.   8.25
Cat, standing. 60mm.   7.50
Pig, standing. 85mm long.   7.00

Great War
Zeppelin. 153mm long.   13.00
Flash Lamp. 85mm.   4.00

Comic/Novelty
Cigarette Case. 70mm.   4.75

Modern Equipment
Gas Cooker. 68mm.   6.50
Gramophone, square cabinet, no
    horn. 85mm.   12.00

Miscellaneous
Pawn, Chess Piece. 90mm.   10.00

Regis

For mark see *Crested China*, p. 207.

Trademark used by Hewitt Bros, Willow Potteries, Longton. (Usual trademark Willow Art).

Parian/Unglazed

Bust of Lord Beatty. 165mm.	56.50

Buildings – White

Weymouth Jubilee Clock Tower. 126mm.	13.00

Monuments

Highland Mary statue. 155mm.	24.50

Historical/Folklore

Dutch girl. 78mm.	6.25
Mary Queen of Scots Chair, Edinburgh Castle, Model of. No. 163. 75mm.	4.75

Traditional/National Souvenirs

Welsh Hat. 58mm.	3.00

Seaside Souvenirs

Lifeboat, coloured ropes. 118mm long.	4.75
Lighthouse, not named. 100mm.	3.00
Corbiere Lighthouse, with coloured rock base. 96mm.	11.00

Animals

Cat with bow, standing. 85mm.	8.25
Dog, Collie, standing. 85mm.	8.25
Dog, Scottie, wearing a Glengarry, some colouring on hat. 85mm.	6.50
Elephant with hunter and two Indian riders on back. 90mm.	25.75

Great War

Airship, *Beta*. 80mm long.	30.00
British Tank. 92mm.	8.75
British Tank with trailing wheels. 2 sizes: 95mm.	20.50
127mm long.	10.50

Cannon Shell Salt Pot. 83mm.	2.50
Kit Bag with verse: *Pack up your troubles in your old kit bag.* 74mm.	10.50
Forage Cap. 83mm long.	16.00
Cenotaph. 145mm.	4.00
Florence Nightingale Statue, inscribed: *Florence Nightingale 1820–1910.* 160mm.	12.50
Black Watch War Memorial. 130mm.	60.00
Weymouth War Memorial. 152mm.	30.00

Home/Nostalgic

Anvil. 76mm.	4.75
Shaving Mug. 55mm.	5.00

Comic/Novelty

Billiken. 73mm.	3.00
Billiken, the God of Luck, sitting on high backed chair. 100mm.	4.00
Baby, standing to attention, some colouring. Inscribed: *One of the B'hoys* 160mm	16.00

Alcohol

Toby Jug. 83mm.	4.75

Miscellaneous

Hand holding tulip. 80mm.	2.25

Registry Ware

Trademark used by an unknown
manufacturer.

This mark has been found with
Scarborough crests on a curve
sided lip salve pot and a small
vase.

Rex China

For mark see *Crested China*, p. 209.

The trademark of Moschendorf, Hof,
Bavaria.

Traditional/National Souvenirs
Tam O'Shanter. 72mm dia.   9.50

Miniature Domestic
Cheese Dish, with gilded rope
    handle. 70mm.   4.00

Rialto China

Rita China Series

For mark see *Crested China*, p. 209.

For mark see *Crested China*, p. 210.

Trademark used by British Art Pottery Co. (Fenton) Ltd, Rialto Works, High Street, Fenton.

Trademark used for the retailer L & L of Weston-Super-Mare by an unknown manufacturer.

Ancient Artefacts
Salisbury Kettle. 88mm.	1.75

Seaside Souvenirs
Dolphin supporting sea shell. 85mm.	6.00

Animals
Bulldog in kennel, inscribed: *The Black Watch*. 79mm.	6.50
Bulldog coloured black	8.50

Great War
Battleship with inscription: *Great War 1914–1918. The German Fleet surrendered 74 warships Nov 21st 1918*. 153mm long.	35.00

Home/Nostalgic
Watchman's Lamp.	4.00
Ornate carved wooden chair 110mm	5.50

Unglazed/Parian
Bunyan Statue. 125mm.	10.50
Burns, bust, on circular unglazed base. 176mm.	12.00
Scott, bust, on circular unglazed base. 176mm.	10.50

Ancient Artefacts
Loving cup, 2 handled.	2.25

Buildings – White
Ann Hathaway's Cottage. 55mm long.	6.50
Llangynwyd Church. 107mm long.	40.00

Monuments
Glastonbury Tor. 83mm.	47.50
Great Rock of Ages, Burrington Coombe, Near Cheddar, Som. Model of, with verses of hymn. 125mm.	7.50
King Alfred's Statue. 160mm.	30.00
Robert Blake, statue. 170mm.	17.00

Historical/Folklore
Burns Chair, Model of. 88mm.	6.50
James V Chair, Stirling Castle.	6.50

Animals
Dog, sitting with bow. 75mm.	6.50
Cat, long neck, features coloured. 110mm.	5.50
Fish. 115mm long.	2.50

Birds
Duck Posy Bowl, yellow beak. 74mm long.	7.50

Comic/Novelty
Clown.	8.50

Jester, double faced, inscribed:
Awake Asleep.   7.50

'Modern' Equipment
Horn Gramophone. 90mm.   17.50

Miscellaneous
Dutch Sabot. 85mm long.   4.50
Schoolboy's Cap. 65mm long.   19.50

Roman Bath China

Trademark used for a retailer by Hewitt &
Leadbeater, Willow Potteries Ltd, Longton.
(Usual trademark Willow Art).

One small found with this mark
  and Chester crest.

Rosina Queens China

Rowena China

For mark see *Crested China* p.210

For mark see *Crested China*, p. 210

Trademark used by George Warrilow & Sons (Ltd), Queens Pottery, Longton.

A small quantity of crested domestic ware has been found.

Trademark used by R.H. & S.L. Plant (Ltd), Tuscan Works, Longton. (Usual trademark Tuscan).

Ancient Artefacts
Gastrica Cyprian Bottle. 71mm.   2.25

Animals
Fish Posy Vase. 130mm long.   2.50
Giant open-mouthed fish.
130mm long.   5.50

Comic/Novelty
Two seater car ashtray, inscribed:
Petrol consumption nil. 135mm
long.   82.50

Cartoon Characters
These fine coloured models form
a series. Some white, glazed,
examples have been seen.
Don, little boy in short trousers
and blue cardigan. 130mm.   56.50
Dr. Dromedary, camel, in black top
hat and suit. 130mm.   56.50
Lord Lion, lion in pale blue jacket.
130mm.   56.50
Oo Jah, Flip Flap, Elephant, in pink
striped pyjamas. 130mm.   56.50
Pa Piggins, Pig, in Edwardian
Sporting clothes. 130mm.   56.50
Snooker, or the kitten cat, yellow
with crown on head. 130mm.   56.50

Royal Albert Crown China

Royal Arms China

For additional mark see *Crested China*, p. 211
Trademark used by Thomas C. Wild, Crown China Works, High St, Longton.

A small range of domestic ware and 'smalls' found with this mark.

Trademark used for a retailer by an unknown manufacturer.

One 'small' with a Birmingham crest recorded.

Buildings – white
Thatched cottage 48mm   7.50

Royal China

For mark see *Crested China*, p. 211.

Trademark used by E. Hughes and Co., Opal Works, Fenton. (Also used marks, Fenton & E. Hughes & Co.).

Miniatrue Domestic

Cheese dish and cover. 50mm.   4.00

Royal China Works, Worcester

For mark see *Crested China*, p. 211.

Trademark used by Grainger, Worcester, when taken over by the Worcester Porcelain Co. Ltd.

Miniature Domestic

Mug, with one handle. 40mm.   10.00

Royal Coburg

Royal Crown

For mark see *Crested China*, p. 212.

No details of mark available

Trademark used by an unknown manufacturer.

Trademark used by an unknown manufacturer.

Home/Nostalgic
Chair with 2 gold tassels.   5.50

Animals
Open mouthed fish. 128mm long.   3.00

Miniature Domestic
Cheese dish and cover. 50mm.   4.00

Great War
Field gun with screen. 118mm.   12.00

Royal Doulton

Royal Ivory Porcelain

For mark see *Crested China*, p. 212.

For marks see *Crested China*, p. 212.

Trademark used by Doulton & Co. (Ltd), Nile St, Burslem.

Range of small with foreign and English crests.

Ancient Artefacts
Loving Cup, 3 handled. 49mm.   4.25

Trademark used by Robinson & Leadbeater Ltd and for the London wholesalers E.B. & Co. (Usual trademark R&L).

Ancient Artefacts
Chester Roman Vase. 63mm.   2.25
Loving Cup, 2 and 3 handled.
45mm.   2.25

Home/Nostalgic
Bellows. 115mm long.   4.75

Miscellaneous
Bishop's Mitre.   4.00

Miniature Domestic
Tea Pot with lid. 55mm.   4.00

Pearl. Crown

Podmore. Sack of coal

Podmore. Cock on green base

Porcelle. Black Terrier looking
out of kennel

Queens China. 'Bonzo'

Shelley. Blackpool Big Wheel

Savoy. Pig sitting

Savoy. Comic Owl

Savoy. Camel Jug

Unmarked. Savoy cat with
crown

Savoy. Monmouth Cap

Savoy. Fireplace

Royal Stafford China

Royal 'Vale' China

For mark see *Crested China*, p. 213.

For mark see *Crested China*, p. 213.

Trademark used by Thomas Poole, Cobden Works, Longton.

Trademark used by H.J. Colcough, Vale Works, Goddard Street, Longton.

Animals

Elephant, walking, 52mm.	6.50

Great War

Submarine, inscribed: *E4*. 115mm long.	8.75
Brick Kiln, inscribed: *Keep the home fires burning*. 78mm.	6.50
Bell tent, open flap 70mm	5.50

Miscellaneous

Spade, playing card suit. 68mm.	2.50

Seaside Souvenirs

Lighthouse. 105mm.	3.00
Lighthouse on circular base. 115mm.	3.00

Animals

Pig, fat, lying forward, pricked ears. 100mm long.	55.00
Pig, fat, sitting. 63mm.	9.50

Great War

Water Bottle. 70mm.	4.00
Cenotaph. 146mm.	4.75

Miscellaneous

Ladies 18th Century shoe. 95mm long.	7.50

Royal Worcester

Ryecroft China Series

For mark see *Crested China*, p. 213.

See mark in *Crested China*, p. 215.

Trademark used by Worcester Royal Porcelain Company Ltd. (Royal Worcester).

Ancient Artefacts
Chester Roman Vase. 60mm.   5.25
Loving Cup. 2 and 3 handled.
40mm.   10.00

Miniature Domestic
Mug, one handled. 45mm.   10.00

Trademark used by an unknown manufacturer. The initials in the mark should probably be GWP not CWP.

Buildings – White
Roche Abbey, ruins, unglazed.
85mm.   41.50
Town Hall, Stockton-on-Tees,
glazed. 94mm.   43.50

Monuments
Woodhouse Eaves Cross.   33.50

Seaside Souvenirs
Lifeboat. 101mm long.   4.75

S

St. George China

For mark see *Crested China*, p. 215.

For mark see *Crested China*, p. 215.

Trademark used by P. Donath, Tiefenfurt. (Silesia).

Very little crested china of this manufacture has been found and all known pieces are small domestic items of only nominal value. One of the firms main areas of specialization was pink souvenir ware.

Trademark used by Wilhelm Kutzscher & Co., Schwarzenberger Porzellanfabric, Schwarzenberg, Saxony. (Now in East Germany).

This manufacturer made many unmarked pieces for the English market.

Ancient Artefacts
Puzzle jug, with verse. 60mm. 3.00

Seaside Souvenirs
Lighthouse. 121mm. 2.50

Animals
Two puppies and a kitten in a basket. 62mm. 21.75
Cat, with drumstick, sitting on a drum. 90mm. 15.25
Elephants, two on a sledge or slope. 70mm. 19.50
Grotesque animal with winged legs, sitting. 80mm. 6.50

Birds
Hen and Cock on circular base. 80mm. 10.50

Sport
Tennis racquet with ball. 140mm long. 10.00

Miscellaneous
Ladies heeled shoe 84mm long 7.50

St. Pauls

Trademark used for export to Canada by Hewitt & Leadbeater, Willow Pottery, Longton. (Usual trademark Willow Art).

National Souvenirs
Welsh Hat. No. 75. 54mm.   5.00
(the only model recorded has
Yukon crest).

Sandifords Ceramic China

Trademark used by an unknown manufacturer for the retailer Sandifords.

Only a pin tray and one 'small' recorded both with Chorley crest.

San Juan

Savoy China

For mark see *Crested China*, p. 216.

Mark used by an unknown manufacturer.

Only model carried a Madrid crest.

Ancient Artefact

Portland Vase. 51mm.	1.75

CHINA
MADE IN ENGLAND

Mark found on a Carlton mould fisherman – obviously after firms merged

For additional mark see *Crested China*, p. 216.

Trademark used by Birks, Rawlins and Co (Ltd), Vine Pottery, Stoke. Merged in 1932 with Wiltshaw & Robinson Ltd. (Makers of Carlton).

Parian/Unglazed Busts

Bust of Albert King of the Belgians. 150mm.	40.00
Bust of Admiral Sir David Beatty, found with inscription *British Naval Victory, German Cruiser Blucher sunk January 24th 1915. England declared War on Germany August 4th 1914.* 150mm.	56.50
Bust of David Lloyd George with inscription on reverse. 186mm.	40.00
Bust of Lord Kitchener, found with inscription *Lord Kitchener of Khartoum Field Marshal KG KP Secretary for War. Born 1851. June 15th, drowned at sea off the Orkneys 1916.* 120mm.	30.00
Bust of Sailor, can be inscribed: *HMS Iron Duke, HMS Tiger,* or *HMS Warspite.* 108mm.	21.75
Bust of Sailor, inscribed: *HMS Iron Duke, HMS Lion* and *HMS Ocean* (rare), on round glazed base. 135mm.	47.50

Bust of John Travers Cornwell,
inscription *John Travers
Cornwell, age 16. Faithful unto
death. Hero Battle of Jutland.*
108mm.   195.00

Ancient Artefacts
Ancient Jug. No. 87. 74mm.   2.25
*Ancient Jug, Model of. Dug out of the
Foundations of Lichfield Museum.*
62mm.   2.25
Bottle, not named. No. 408.
90mm.   3.50
Carlisle Elizabethan Measure, no
details.   3.00
Carlisle Jug, *14th Century jug found
in an old tank at Carlisle gaol by
permission of Col. Sullie Hovsk.*
No. 179. 70mm.   2.25
Carlisle Vase, no details.   2.25
Chinese Vase. No. 67. 70mm.   2.25
*Chinese Vase in South Kensington
Museum.* No. 219. 70mm.   2.25
Colchester Vase. *Ancient Vase
original in Colchester Museum.*
No. 349. 50mm.   2.25
Colchester Roman Vase,
inscribed: *Roman Vase found in
Cloaca, now in Colchester Castle.*
No. 196. 30mm.   2.25
Globe Vase. No. 62. 42mm.   2.25
Greek Vase. No. 77. 69mm.   2.25
Hastings Kettle. No. 140. 60mm.   2.25
Italian Vase. No. 30.   2.25
Itford Urn. 44mm.   2.25
Launceston Bottle. No. 193.
65mm.   2.25
Lewes Vase, not named. No. 196.
35mm.   1.75
Loving Cup, 3 handled, not
named. 38mm.   2.25
Maltese Fire Grate. No. 39 and No.
721. 45mm.   6.00
Newbury Leather Bottle. No. 14.
63mm.   2.25
Pear Bottle. No. 17.   2.25
Penrith Salt Pot. No. 182. 60mm.   2.25
Persian Bottle. No. 68. 95mm.   2.25
Pilgrims bottle Nevers ware. No.
172. 75mm.   2.25
Pompeian Vase. No. 161. 124mm.   2.25
Portland Vase. No. 16. 51mm.   2.25
Puzzle Jug. No. 378. 68mm.   3.50
Scarborough Jug. No. 454 or No.
10. 48mm.   2.25

Silchester Roman Urn. No. 74.
51mm.   2.25
Shakespeares Jug, *the jug of
William Shakespeare,* with his
signature. 60mm.   3.00
Tear Bottle. 70mm.   2.25
Teapot, copy of early 18th
century stoneware (shaped as
a camel). 100mm long (rare).   25.25
Windsor Roman Urn. *Roman urn
dug up at old Windsor from
original now in British Museum.*
No. 138. 45mm.   2.25
York Roman Ewer. *Roman Ewer
from the original in Hospitium
found at York.* No. 20.   2.25

Buildings – Coloured
Exeter Cathedral, brown coloured.
150mm long.   40.00
Tumbledown cottage, not
named, highly coloured and
glazed. Impressed 1800.
105mm long.   47.50

Buildings – White
Aberystwyth, The University. No.
68. 146mm long.   26.00
Burns cottage. 70mm long.   8.75
Citadel Gateway, Plymouth. No.
209. 114mm.   17.50
Clifton Suspension Bridge. 132mm
long.   30.00
Derry's Clock, Plymouth. No. 17.
152mm.   10.50
*First and Last Refreshment House in
England.* No. 301. 72mm.   7.50
Hastings Clock Tower. No. 274.
156mm.   10.50
Margate Clock Tower. 160mm.   10.50
Monnow Gate, Monmouth.
112mm.   21.75
Portsmouth Town Hall. No. 7.
80mm.   35.00
Tumbledown Cottage.
105mm long.   26.00

Historical/Folklore
Burns Chair, Dumfries. 85mm.   6.50
Gargoyle or Devils Head,
inscribed: *My word if you're not
off.* No. 230. 90mm long.   7.00
*Mary Queen of Scots Chair,
Edinburgh.* 77mm.   4.75

Traditional/National Souvenirs

A Cornish Pasty. 100mm long.	4.00
Ripon Horn Blower. No. 497. 100mm.	8.25
Bagpipes. 110mm long.	13.00
Monmouth Cap. 50mm.	11.50
Thistle Vase. 47mm.	2.25
Welsh Hat with longest place name round brim. No. 6	
2 sizes: 35mm	4.00
55mm.	6.00
Welsh Lady carrying a basket. 110mm.	23.00

Seaside Souvenirs

Bathing Machine, inscribed: *Morning dip*. 62mm.	4.50
Lifeboat, inscribed: *Zetland*.	7.00
Rowing Boat. No. 118. 130mm long.	4.75
Yacht. 115mm long.	11.00
Beachy Head Lighthouse. No. 371. 130mm.	4.00
Eddystone Lighthouse. No. 136. Also found inscribed: *St Catherines Lighthouse*. 92mm.	3.50
Lizard Lighthouse.	5.50
Crab Ashtray or dish. 52mm long.	5.00
Lobster pintray with lid. 97mm long.	16.00

Countryside

Acorn, Model of. No. 110. 56mm.	3.50

Animals

Cat, Cheshire. No. 17. 80mm.	4.50
Cat sitting, miniature, with long neck 68mm	9.50
Cat, angry with arched back, inscribed: *Me backs up*. No. 195. 100mm long.	10.50
Cat with long neck. No. 217.	
2 sizes: 65mm	5.50
105mm.	13.00
Larger model also found with feet apart.	
Cat, sitting, detailed fur. 90mm.	7.50
Cat, squatting with huge grin, comic. 105mm long.	15.25
Dog cream jug No. 106 60mm	11.25
Dog (no particular breed) sitting. 55mm.	5.50
Dog (curly tail) standing. 65mm.	8.75
Dog, Basset/Dachshund. No. 296. 132mm long.	30.00

Bulldog, lying, inscribed: *Another Dreadnought*. 118mm long.	16.00
Bulldog, standing, with verse. No. 364. 130mm long.	12.00
Dog, crouched and barking. No. 253. 100mm long.	11.00
Dog, Scottie, wearing Glengarry. No. 477. 86mm.	6.50
Dog, Scottie, wearing Tam O'Shanter. 2 sizes: 63mm.	5.50
80mm.	6.50
Dog, Scottie, looking out of kennel. 80mm long.	6.50
Dog, Spaniel, begging. 65mm.	7.50
Donkey, standing. 120mm long.	25.25
Elephant, sitting with trunk in the air. No. 218. 63mm.	8.25
Elephant, standing, trunk in air. No. 110. 100mm long.	25.25
Elephant, standing. No. 250. 65mm.	6.50
Fish. 104mm long.	2.00
Fish Vase. No. 33. 88mm.	3.00
Grotesque animal (a horrid looking creature which could be a pig or a dog). No. 398. 102mm.	7.50
Hare, crouching. No. 235. 80mm long.	20.00
Hippo, with pointed teeth. 113mm long.	50.00
Lion, sitting on square base. 108mm.	24.50
Lion, walking, sometimes inscribed: *Another Dreadnought*. No. 788. 135mm long.	16.00
Mouse. 65mm long.	14.50
Pig, lying down. 80mm long.	7.50
Pig, standing and fat. No. 109. 2 sizes: 70mm and 100mm long.	8.25
Large size can be found inscribed: *Model of Irish Pig*.	20.00
Pig, sitting, long nose. 110mm.	35.00
Piglet with long ears. 65mm long.	7.50
Polar Bear. No. 236. Length 145mm.	45.00
Rabbit. 88mm long.	7.50
Rabbit, sitting, one ear up. No. 548. 70mm long.	14.50
Rhino, grotesque. No. 284. 130mm long.	40.00
Seal. 2 sizes: 63mm.	6.50
80mm long.	7.50
Snail. No. 252. 84mm long.	8.50
Teddy Bear. 90mm.	10.00

Tiger, Sabre Toothed, with
inscription: *My word if you're not
off*. 128mm long. 37.50
Toad. No. 331. 75mm. 20.00

Birds

Duck, swimming. No. 562.
2 sizes: 40mm. 5.50
65mm long. 6.50
Duck, standing. 150mm. 25.75
Duck, standing on green base.
Can be found coloured.
170mm. 20.00
Duckling, standing on tree trunk,
colouring on trunk and beak.
186mm. 20.50
Goose in full length cloak. 72mm. 19.50
Hen, sitting, red comb. No. 23.
55mm. 4.00
Owl, comic. No. 33 or No. 329.
60mm. 8.25
Penguin. No. 549. 76mm. 8.75
Penguin on heart shaped *ashtray*.
85mm. 8.00
Swan, detailed plumage. 50mm. 6.00

Great War

Highland infrantryman, with
pack, rifle and bayonet.
165mm. 75.00
Sailor, standing, arms folded.
No. 538. 160mm. 95.00
British Lion, wearing puttees,
inscribed: *Another Dreadnought*.
130mm long. 47.50
Nurse, with red cross on chest,
holding bandage. Can be found
inscribed: *Nurse Cavell*. No. 531.
165mm. 69.00
Sailor, bust, inscribed on cap
badge: *HMS Warspite* or *HMS
Lion*. No. 532. 135mm. 30.00
Sailor with arms folded.
Unglazed on glazed base.
130mm approx. 85.00
Scottish soldier on circular base.
160mm. 75.00
Biplane, with fixed prop.,
inscribed: *RAF*. 153mm long. 90.00
Monoplane, with fixed prop.
128mm long. 40.00
Monoplane, pointed wings and

revolving prop. No. 521.
130mm. 40.00
Zeppelin with revolving 2-bladed
propeller, can be found with
inscription *Zeppelin destroyed by
Lt. Robinson V.C. at Cuffley Essex
Sept. 3rd 1916*. No. 567. 175mm
long. 117.50
Battleship, 3 funnels, inscribed:
HMS Lion. 168mm long. 56.50
Battleship, 2 funnels, inscribed:
*HMS Iron Duke, HMS Queen
Elizabeth, H.M.S. Barham* or
HMS Warspite. 168mm long. 56.50
British Minesweeper, Model of. No.
641. 150mm long (very rare). 125.00
Torpedo Boat Destroyer. 140mm
long. 87.50
Submarine, inscribed: *E1*.
Usually found with inscription
*Commander Moltke torpedoed
August 19th 1915*. No. 575.
150mm long. 35.00
Ambulance, with 3 red crosses –
one on cab top. No. 520. 150mm
long. 21.75
Ambulance with 'Rolls Royce'
front. No. 520. 115mm long. 25.75
Armoured Car (reputedly a
'Talbot' but not named).
125mm long. 40.00
British motor searchlight. No. 123.
103mm long. 70.00
Tank with trailing steering
wheels, inscribed: *HMS Donner
Blitzen* and 515 on side, with
further inscription: *Model of
British Tank first used by British
Troops at the Battle of Ancre Sept.
1916*. 4 sizes:
108mm. 45.00
125mm. 30.00
140mm. 30.00
155mm long. 30.00
Tank with inset steering wheels,
inscribed as above. 2 sizes:
125mm. 21.75
115mm long. 21.75
Tank with no trailing wheels,
inscribed exactly as above. No.
597. 135mm long. 30.00
Field Gun, Model of, with fish
tail. No. 616. 140mm long
(rare). 52.50

Howitzer. 170mm long.   24.50
Machine Gun, 2 pieces, swivels
on tripod. No. 402. 153mm
long.   110.00
British Trench Mortar Gun. No.
613. 98mm long.   47.50
Shell, inscribed: Iron rations for
Fritz. No. 5. 2 sizes:
    No. 556. 70mm.   4.00
    No. 558. 110mm.   5.50
(Shell 'Salt' and 'Pepper' pots also
found. 80mm).   2.50
Model of Stokes Bomb. No. 575.
24mm dia. at base (very rare).
100mm.   200.00
Trench Mortar Bomb. Often found
not named.
2 sizes: No. 574. 65mm   47.50
        No. 575. 86mm.   47.50
Hand Grenade. No. 556. 75mm.   8.75
Anzacs Hat, Model of. No. 111.
90mm long.   16.00
Balmoral Bonnet, Model of. 74mm
long.   22.00
Colonial Hat. No. 48. 92mm long.   8.25
French Trench Helmet, worn by the
Dauntless French Poilu. No. 69.
82mm long.   40.00
Glengarry. No. 508. 78mm long.   13.00
New Zealand Hat, Model of. No.
613. 80mm long.   17.50
Officer's Peaked Cap. No. 516.
72mm long.   5.50
Rumanian soldier's steel helmet,
Model of, found with Bucharest
Crest and Rumanian War
declaration inscription. 82mm
long.   40.00
R.F.C. Cap, Model of. Cap badge
clearly moulded. No. 577.
80mm long.   26.00
Sailor's Hat, inscribed on band:
HMS Lion, HMS Queen Elizabeth
or HMS Tiger. Blue bow. No.
533. 71mm dia.   56.50
Tommy's Steel Helmet. 82mm
long.   20.00
Bandsman's Drum. 55mm dia.   4.75
Bell Tent. No. 118. 65mm.   5.50
Water Bottle. No. 219. 57mm.   8.75
Tommy in Dug Out, not named.
No. 669. 85mm. Very rare.   157.00
Fireplace, inscribed: Keep the home
fires burning. No. 68. 94mm.   10.00

Cenotaph, inscribed: The Glorious
Dead. 130mm.   4.50
Edith Cavell Memorial, Norwich,
inscribed: Nurse Cavell. Red
Cross on apron. No. 110.
168mm.   17.50

Home/Nostalgic
Dog kennel, inscribed Beware of
the dog.   5.00
Flat iron. 65mm.   5.00
Trivet for flat iron. No. 544. 70mm
long   3.00
Grandfather Clock, inscribed: Nae
man can tether time nor tide.
No. 622.   12.50
Jardiniere on stand. No. 86.
77mm.   3.25
Pillar Box. 56mm.   10.50
Watering Can. No. 455. 76mm.   4.75

Comic/Novelty
Billiken. 75mm.   3.00
Candlesnuffer in form or young
boy in nightwear, yawning and
stretching. 80mm.   16.50
Caterpillar with human face. No.
543. 74mm.   8.25
Choirboy. No. 542. 85mm.   9.50
Hindu god sitting on rock, blue
beads. No. 28 or No. 554.
90mm.   5.25
Policeman, short and fat. 103mm.   18.50

Cartoon/Comedy Characters
Bonzo, dog (1920s cartoon
character). No. 927. 80mm.   24.50
Tweedledum and Tweedledee,
fully coloured, pair of separate
sitting figures. each   30.00
Winkie the Gladeye Bird.   16.00
Can be found as salt, pepper and
mustard cover set, in colour. each   20.00

Alcohol
Beer Barrel. No. 406. 55mm.   3.00
Beer Barrel with separate base.
57mm.   7.50
Old Beer Jug, Model of. No. 84.
80mm.   4.50

Sport
Cricket Bag. No. 745. 95mm long.   6.50
Golf Ball, Model of. No. 111. 40mm.   5.00

Golf Club with broken shaft. No.
442. 70mm.   7.00

Musical Instruments

Banjo. 137mm long.   4.50
Double Base. 145mm long.   16.00
Upright Piano. No. 887. 83mm
  long.   6.50
Violin. 136mm long.   21.75

Transport

Charabanc, (24 seater). No. 811.
  134mm long.   34.50

Modern Equipment

Gramophone, square with large
  horn. 102mm.   18.50

Miscellaneous

Bell, Model of, porcelain clapper.
  No. 5. 85mm.   5.50
Clog, gilded studs. 83mm. long   5.00
Dutch clog. No. 424. 70mm long.   4.00
Top Hat. 44mm.   3.00

Miniature Domestic

Cheese Dish, one piece. 40mm.   8.75
Cheese Stand, Model of, with lid.
  No. 200. 55mm long.   10.50
Extinguisher, Model of. (Candle
  Snuffer). No. 42. 51mm and
  64mm.   3.25
Soda Syphon.   7.50

Scotch Porcelain

For mark see Crested China. p. 226.

Trademark used for a Scottish retailer by an
unknown manufacturer.

Parian/Unglazed

Bust of Scott, on circular glazed
  base. 108mm.   8.00

Alcohol

Tankard. 62mm.   3.00

Shamrock China

Shamrock Crest China

For mark see *Crested China*, p. 226.

Trademark used by Belleek Pottery. (David McBirney and Co), Belleek, Co. Fermanagh, N. Ireland.

Birds
Cockerel, with orange face and
  yellow beak. 100mm.   10.50

For alternative mark see *Crested China*, p. 227.

Trademark used for a Belfast wholesaler by R.H. & S.L. Plant (Ltd), Tuscan Works, Longton. (Usual trademark Tuscan).

Seaside Souvenirs
Shell. No. 56. 82mm long.   2.50

Alcohol
Carboy. 68mm.   2.25

J. Shaw

Shell China

For mark see *Crested China*, p. 227.

For mark see *Crested China*, p. 227.

Trademark used by J. Shaw & Sons, Longton, subsequently John Shaw & Sons (Longton) Ltd, Willow Pottery, Longton.

Trademark used by an unknown Staffordshire Pottery.

Miniature Domestic

Cheese dish and cover. 45mm.   5.00

Novelty
Biscuit impressed: *Huntley and Palmer*. Biscuit coloured on white shaped base. 68mm long. (Has been recorded with a Dolgelly crest.)   30.00

Shelley China

For marks see *Crested China*, p. 228.

Trademark used by Wileman & Co, Foley Potteries and Foley China Works, Fenton, Longton and subsequently renamed Shelleys Ltd.

NB
These lists include pieces marked Shelley, Foley and Shelley late Foley.

Unglazed/Parian

Bust of *Albert*, King of the Belgians, 1915. 118mm.	40.00
Bust of *Burns*, on square glazed base. 140mm	14.00
Bust of HM King George V. 130mm.	40.00
Bust of French, with inscription: *Field Marshall Sir John French, Commander in Chief of the Expeditionary Force.* 118mm.	30.00
Bust of Jellicoe, with inscription: *Admiral Sir John Jellicoe. In Supreme Command of the North Sea Fleet.* 118mm.	40.00
Bust of Joffre, with inscription: *General Joffre, Commander in Chief of the French Army 1915.* 130mm.	40.00
Bust of Kitchener, with inscription: *Field Marshall Earl Kitchener, Secretary of State for War.* 118mm.	22.50
Bust of *The Rt Hon David Lloyd George.* 2 sizes: 118mm & 130mm.	40.00
Sailor standing with hands on hips, square base. Inscribed: *Ready! Aye! Ready!* and impressed: *HMS Lion.* Coloured. 170mm.	82.50

Ancient Artefacts

Early models (marked Foley) are sometimes found with no printed number or inscription. Models can be found with coloured transfer views, etc., instead of crests. *All* inscriptions begin: *Model of* so this will not be repeated throughout the list.

Ancient Cyprian water bottle. No. 140. 45mm.	3.00
Antique tea caddy – Queen Anne. No. 153. 70mm.	6.50
Aqua Mivel for pouring water over the hands of the priest. No. 137. 74mm wide.	6.50
Arabian wine vessel. No. 203. 75mm.	3.00
Caerswys roman vessel. No. 204	5.24
Cauldron with two handles. Unnamed Foley model. No. 31. 35mm.	3.50
Celtic jar (an ancient). No. 200. 65mm.	4.00
Celtic water bottle. No. 205. 63mm.	3.50
Chester Roman Urn, inscribed: *A very rare Roman urn found near Chester now in possession of J.W. Salt Esq.* No. 118. 54mm.	3.00
Chinese jar 12th Century. No. 304. 121mm.	11.00
Chinese vase of great antiquity and beauty date about 5000 BC. Belongs to the nation. No. 115. 62mm.	3.00
Chinese vase, about 500 AD. No. 213. 60mm.	3.00
Cinerary urn of rare form. No. 134.	4.25
Cleopatra's Vase, inscribed: *An Egyptian vase taken from the tomb of Cleopatra.* No. 114. 50mm.	4.00
Colchester Famous Vase, inscribed: *Famous Colchester vase in the museum.* No. 110. 48mm.	3.00
Cyprian vase about 5000 BC. No. 206.	3.00
Cyprian water bottle. No. 192. 76mm.	3.50
Derby Roman Vase, inscribed: *Roman vase found at Little Chester, Derby.* No. 83.	3.00
Dorset Cinerary Urn, inscribed: *Cinerary urn with handles found at Dorset.* No. 132. 56mm.	3.00
Dover Cinerary Urn, inscribed: *Cinerary urn found in Dover.* No. 141. 63mm.	3.00

Eastern Olive jar. No. 208. 53mm.   3.00

Egyptian Vase, inscribed: *Ancient Egyptian vase about 250 BC*. No. 84. 43mm.   3.00

Ely Saxon Vase, inscribed: *Ancient Saxon vase, found in Ely*. No. 310. 88mm.   3.00

Exeter Vase, Unnamed Foley model. No. 117. 55mm.   3.00

Flemish jug 14th century. No. 312. 70mm.   3.00

Gastrica Vase, inscribed: *Vase or bottle found in Gastrica. Ancient Cyprian pottery 900 BC*. No. 138. 51mm.   4.50

Glastonbury Bowl, inscribed: *Bowl from the ancient British lake village near Glastonbury*. No. 101. 50mm.   2.25

Glastonbury Vase, inscribed: *Vase from the Ancient British Lake Village near Glastonbury*. No. 104. 50mm.   2.25

Hanley Chinese Vase, inscribed: *Chinese vase, originally in Hanley Museum*. No. 80. 63mm.   3.00

Hanley Egyptian Vase, inscribed: *Ancient Egyptian vase now in Hanley Museum*. No. 88. 63mm.   3.00

Herpes Jug, inscribed: *Jug from cemetary at Herpes, Charente*. No. 133. 45mm.   3.00

Horsham Jug, unnamed Foley model. No. 20. 65mm.   3.00

Indian wine vessel from Temple, Delhi. No. 303. 152mm.   3.00

Irish bronze pot. No. 109. 35mm.   3.00

Italian vase. 16th Century. No. 301. 100mm.   6.50

Italian vase. 16th Century. No. 309. 100mm.   6.50

(The) Kai. Ping vase, date about 2500 BC. No. 119. 63mm.   5.50

Kang Hi tea caddy. No. 144. 63mm.   6.50

Kang Hi vase, presented to George V. No. 305. 120mm.   5.00

Kent Roman Urn, inscribed: *Roman urn from warriors grave, Kent*. No. 211. 52mm.   3.50

Lesser Pyramid Vase, inscribed: *Vase taken from a tomb under the Lesser Pyramid about 3500 BC*. No. 117. 57mm.   4.50

Letchworth Celtic Urn, inscribed: *Celtic urn found in Letchworth*. No. 199. 80mm.   6.50

Lord Byron's Vase, inscribed: *Fine model of a Greek vase presented to the nation by Lord Byron. Now in South Kensington Museum*. No. 116. 57mm.   4.50

Loving Cup. 3 handled. Not found numbered. 40mm.   2.75

Malta Chatty. No. 89. 44mm.   5.50

Mayer Jug 1870, Model of. No. 326. 71mm.   14.50

Newbury Leather Bottle, inscribed: *Leather bottle found on battlefield of Newbury. 1644. Now in Museum*. No. 103. 60mm.   2.25

Notre Dame Candlestick, inscribed: *Altar candlestick in church of Notre Dame*. No. 306. 115mm.   9.50

Penmaenmawr Urn, inscribed: *Ancient urn found on Penmaenmawr*. No. 108. 48mm.   3.00

Persian cafeterre (fine), 15th Century. No. 302. 118mm.   10.50

Persian scent bottle 700 AD. No. 212. 55mm.   3.00

Persian Wallace vase. No. 82.   8.00

Persian wine server. 13th Century. No. 308. 105mm.   8.00

Phoenician vase, original in Stoke-on-Trent Museum. No. 86. 57mm.   4.00

Phoenician water jug. 1000 BC. No. 207. 65mm.   6.00

Pompeian vessel in Burslem Museum. No. 87. 60mm.   4.75

Pompeian Wine Bottle. No. 135. 54mm.   15.00

Potters vessel, found in Temple to Buda. No. 150. 54mm.   4.00

Puzzle Jug, with verse. No. 180. 65mm.   8.25

Roman money box, found at Lincoln AD 307. No. 131. 53mm.   5.00

Roman tear vase, 200 BC. No. 201. 63mm.   5.00

Roman wine vessel 500 BC. No. 142. 51mm.   6.00

Sacred vessel found in Bethlehem. No. 146. 68mm.   15.50

Salamis Lampshade, inscribed: *Lampshade found at Salamis*

ancient Cyprian pottery. No. 130.
60mm. — 7.00

Salonika Vase, inscribed: *Ancient Greek vase found at Salonika by the British troops when entrenching Jan 1916*. No. 170. 70mm. — 12.50

Scandinavian water bottle. No. 143.
83mm. — 4.00

Sevres vase, 18th Century. No. 300.
88mm. — 7.00

Sherborne Vase, inscribed: *Model of Roman Vase found in Sherborne*.
95mm. — 2.25

Silchester Urn, inscribed: *Roman urn, from Silchester in Reading Museum*. No. 107. 50mm. — 2.25

Silchester Vase, inscribed: *Vase from Silchester in Reading Museum*. No. 102. 51mm. — 2.25

Silver rose bowl. No. 147. 63mm. — 6.50

Sofia Cup, inscribed: *Very quaint cup found with silver belt, Sofia, Bulgaria*. No. 139. 42mm. — 5.00

Stafforshire cow cream jug. No. 317. — 16.50

Swindon Vase, inscribed: *Vase dug up near Swindon*. No. 105.
58mm. — 2.25

Tara vase, now in the Vatican, Rome.
No. 113. 50mm. — 5.50

Tibet Sacred Vase, inscribed: *Sacred vase from Temple in Tibet*.
No. 209. 60mm. — 3.00

Turkish scent jar S.K. No. 202.
66mm. — 5.00

Vatican Urn, inscribed: *Golden urn in the Vatican*. No. 145. 78mm. — 4.00

Vestal **Lamp,** inscribed: *Roman vestal lamp. 500 BC*. No. 149.
78mm. — 7.50
Has been found with a black boy's head popping out of lamp. — 30.00

Water Bottle, inscribed: *Ancient water bottle of rare form*. No. 136. — 4.00

Water bottle from tomb of Rameses II.
No. 210. — 10.00

Weymouth Vase, inscribed: *Roman vase found at Jordan Hill, Weymouth now in Dorset Museum*. No. 85. — 8.00

York Roman Ewer, inscribed: *Roman ewer from original in Hospitium, found in York*. No. 81.
63mm. — 3.00

Buildings – White

The Tower, Blackpool, Model of.
No. 322. 140mm. — 10.50

Blackpool Tower with buildings.
No. 412. 160mm. — 14.00

Burns cottage, Model of. No. 189.
68mm long. — 12.50

Forth Bridge. 130mm long. — 35.00

Manx Cottage, Model of (as Burns cottage above. No. 198 – with different inscription.
68mm long. — 15.25

Ross, Town Hall, with Clock Tower (not found numbered). 123mm. — 40.00

Skegness, clock tower, can also be found inscribed: *Monmouth clock tower*. No. 371. 155mm. — 10.00

Windsor round tower. No. 372.
88mm. — 10.00

Monuments

Douglas Isle of Man. Queen Victoria Jubilee Clock. 1887. — 45.50

King Alfred, Statue (not found numbered). 165mm. — 20.50

Southport Lifeboat Memorial.
No. 318. 140mm. — 12.50

Rock of Ages, with verse (not found numbered). 125mm. — 6.50

Rufus Stone, with lengthy inscriptions (not found numbered). 95mm. — 4.50

Historical/Folklore

Bunyan's Chair (also found inscribed: *The old armchair*).
No. 347. 90mm. — 12.50

Burn's Chair. No. 336. 86mm. — 8.50

Burn's Clock, Model of old Grandfather clock in Burns Cottage, Ayr. No. 307. 130mm. — 19.50

Ducking stool, Leominster.
120mm long. — 87.50

Mother Shipton with black hat and cat. With verse: *Near to the Knaresboro Dropping Well. I first drew breath as records tell*.
No. 409. 110mm. — 13.00

Sir Walter Scott's chair at Abbotsford, Model of. No. 325.
68mm. — 8.25

Traditional/National Souvenirs

Highland Mary. No. 411. — 26.00

Burns and Highland Mary on oval
base (not found numbered).
118mm. 20.00
Blackpool Ferris Wheel.
No. 373. 117mm. 10.50
Lancashire Clog. No. 162. 57mm. 6.00
Legs of Man, model of.
No. 351. 90mm. 15.25
Lincoln Imp, model of the.
No. 160. 122mm. 9.50
Ripon Horn Blower, model of
the, with inscription: *The old
time custom of sounding the horn
at 9pm each day is still observed*.
No. 158. 110mm. 13.00
M. ˄˅ Loving Cup, 3 handles as
legs of Man. 80mm (Foley mark
only). 11.00
Kathleen Mavourneen, standing
figure or Irish lady.
No. 405. 98mm. 56.50
Pat's Hat and Dudeen, model of.
(Irish Topper with pipe moul-
ded on top). No. 159. 53mm. 12.00
Thistle Vase, can be found
inscribed: *Just a wee deoch-an-
Doris*. No. 181. 2 sizes:
50mm. 4.75
65mm. 6.25
Welsh Lady, seated, inscribed:
Cymru-Am-Byth.
No. 404. 95mm (rare). 43.50
Welsh Hat, model of the. Can be
found with longest Welsh
place name round brim. (Very
occasionally the hat can be
found painted black with a red
hat band). No. 154. 35mm.
Plain 6.00
Welsh name 10.50
Coloured 14.50
Swiss Cattle Bell. No. 314. 95mm. 17.00

Seaside Souvenirs
Bathing Machine. No. 320. 70mm
long. 7.00
Lifebelt. No. 47. 100mm dia. 12.00
Lifeboatman, standing by Capstan, inscribed: *Lifesaver*. Some
colouring. No. 410. 112mm. 34.50
Lifeboat, with gold anchor.
No. 323. Can be found
inscribed: *Maud Pickup*.
115mm long. 10.50

Boat, almost canoe shaped on
two supports, with hole at top
possibly for candle.
160mm long (Foley mark only). 12.50
Motor Boat, model of. No. 353.
112mm long. 13.00
Paddle Steamer, model of.
No. 362. 160mm long. 43.50
Yacht in full sail. No. 401. 112mm. 14.00
Fisherman's Basket, inscribed: *A
good catch*. No. 186. 88mm long. 7.50
Beachy Head Lighthouse. No. 178.
100mm. 7.50
Pharos Lighthouse. No. 73. 98mm. 6.50
Scallop Shell.
No. 166. 78mm wide. 6.00
Whelk Shell, inscribed: *What are
the wild waves saying*.
No. 168. 70mm long. 7.00
Can also be found inscribed:
Sheringham Whelk. Add 5.00
Whelk Shell. No. 169.
70mm long. 7.00
Cabin Trunk. No. 167.
75mm long. 7.00
Valise, half open. No. 58.
73mm long. 4.75

Countryside
Pine Cone, closed, on its side.
90mm long. 3.00

Animals
Bear, walking. No. 67.
80mm long. 30.00
Camel, kneeling (1 hump). No.
64. 102mm long. 12.00
Cat, angry, inscribed: *Me backs up*.
2 sizes: No. 195. 90mm. 16.00
No. 198. 76mm. 21.75
Latter with no tail.
Cat, comical, and sitting with red
bow. No. 333. 132mm. 21.50
Cat, sitting. No. 68. 64mm long. 27.00
Cat, sitting, head slightly to one
side, tail curled around, ruffled
fur. No. 268. 96mm. 16.00
Cat, standing, with long body.
No. 381. 30.00
Cheshire Cat, model of the Real,
impressed: *Tim*.
No. 148. 82mm. 19.50
Cow, *Staffordshire cow cream jug*.
No. 317. 16.50

Bulldog, seated, inscribed:
Another Dreadnought. No. 233.
63mm.   17.00
Bulldog, black, in kennel,
inscribed: *Blackwatch*.   14.50
(Also found with Bulldog not
painted and no inscription).
No. 316. 95mm.   9.50
Bulldog, seated. No. 324.   21.75
Pup standing on hand mirror,
inscribed: *Some pup!* No. 382
(This number 382 is also found
on a large comical Pup,
inscribed: *some pup!* It has black
ears and spots. 116mm).   52.50
Dog, alert terrier. No. 377. 80mm.   34.50
Dog, Scottie, sitting. No. 505.
76mm.   21.75
Dog, Scottie, wearing tam
o'shanter. No. 506.   40.00
Dog, Scottie, wearing glengarry.
No. 506.   40.00
Dogs, 2 Scotties, sitting, one
wearing tam o'shanter and
other wearing Glengarry. Both
hats beautifully coloured. Can
be found inscribed: *Scots
Guards*. No. 386. 88mm.   55.00
Donkey. No. 376. 115mm.   23.00
Elephant, lying down. No. 70.
80mm long.   14.00
Elephant, standing. No. 363.   12.50
Fish Jug (tail forms handle).
No. 350. 105mm.   13.00
Fox, sitting. No. 62. 78mm.   47.50
Hare, looking round. 82mm long.   10.50
Lion. No. 369.   45.00
Monkey, sitting, can be found
inscribed: *Who hung the monkey?*
No. 61. 64mm.   10.50
Mouse, sitting with paws raised.
No. 65. 70mm.   32.50
Pig, standing with inscription:
*You can push, you can shuv but
I'm hanged if I'll be druv* or *Putney
on a Pig*. No. 74. 2 sizes: large
and small.   45.00
Pig, sitting, with folded arms,
found inscribed: *Very umble* or
Sussex Pig, won't be druv or
Putney on a pig. No. 60. 80mm.   24.50
Piglet, standing. No. 90.   10.50
Rabbit, sitting.
No. 66. 90mm long.   12.50

Toad. No. 71. 47mm.   12.50
Terrapin. No. 69. 85mm.   6.50

Birds
Duck, sitting. *A real prize
Aylesbury Duck*.
Reg. No. 582115. 85mm.   40.00
Goose, plump. No. 63. 93mm.   11.25
Penguin, with black beak, and
holding newspaper. No. 384.
100mm.   65.00
Swan, open wings, with
coloured beak. No. 321.
85mm long.   18.50
Swan Posy Holder.   4.50

Great War
Scottish soldier, standing figure,
inscribed: *Scotland for ever*.
No. 402. 114mm.   82.50
Soldier, playing concertina
outside tent, inscribed: *Blighty
is the place for Me-e-e*. No. 341.
108mm long.   65.00
Biplane, usually found with a
fixed prop, but can be found
with a movable one. No. 344.
150mm long.   65.00
Bleriot Warplane, model of.
Monoplane with fixed prop.
No. 311. 150mm long.   47.00
Zeppelin, model of.
No. 332. 154mm long.   65.00
Battleship, not found named.
No. 319. 125mm long.   17.00
Submarine, inscribed: *E9*.
No. 328. 150mm long.   25.75
Armoured Car, model of.
No. 329. 120mm long.   30.00
British Tank, model of, with
trailing steering wheels.
No. 400. 140mm.   13.00
Model of British Tank without
trailing wheels.
No. 400A. 115mm.   30.00
Tank Bank, as above but as money
box. No. 413. 140mm. Also
found numbered 511.   40.00
Red Cross Van, model of.
No. 330. 95mm long.   17.50
Howitzer. No. 340. 148mm long.   30.00
Field Gun. No. 331. 132mm long.   16.00
Trench Mortar, model of.
Inscribed: *For freedom*. No. 179
or No. 327. 63mm.   6.50

9.2mm Shell, model of.
No. 175. 90mm.   8.75
German Zeppelin Bomb, model
of. No. 177. 85mm.   6.50
Mills Hand Grenade, model of.
No. 334. 78mm.   11.25
Model of German Mine washed up on
the East Coast. Can be found
wrongly inscribed: Head of
German torpedo (Model of)   40.00
68mm.
Model of German Mine. No. 188.   40.00
German Torpedo. No. 187.   50.00
(Torpedo inscription being
rare)
Head of German Torpedo, Model of.
No. 187. 68mm.   82.50
Bandsman's Drum.
No. 57. 32mm.   4.75
Bugle. No.354. 112mm.   28.00
Fieldglasses. No. 343. 83mm.   14.00
Peaked Cap. No.54. 53mm dia.   5.50
Glengarry. No.176. 86mm long.   16.00
Anti Zeppelin Candlestick as used
during the Great War – souvenir.
No.348. 83mm.   43.50
Fireplace, inscribed: Keep the home
fires burning. No.338. 70mm.   13.00
Britannia, standing figure,
inscribed: Rule Britannia. Some
colouring.
No. 403. 108mm (rare).   82.50
Marianne, inscribed: Vive la
France. Some colouring.
No. 406. 108mm (rare).   105.00
Cenotaph, flags in relief. No.368.
2 sizes: 130mm.   17.50
             152mm.   21.50
Florence Nightingale, sitting
figure. No.408. 102mm (rare).   95.00
Matlock Bath War Memorial, not
found numbered. 180mm.   16.00

Home/Nostalgic

Anvil, inscribed: Every morning
sees some task to be done.
No. 183. 83mm long.   4.75
Armchair, inscribed: The old
armchair   5.50
(Also found inscribed Bunyan's
Chair.) No. 347. 90mm.   8.50
Baby's Cradle. (Often found not
numbered when marked Foley.)

Found No. 50 and No. 503.
(Shelley). 80mm long.   5.50
Bellows. No. 55. 95mm long.   10.50
Book. No.56. 63mm.   5.50
Clock, long case, inscribed: Model
of 14th Century clock in Wallace
collection. Can also be found
further inscribed: Wake up and
get to business, The moving finger
writes and having writ moves on,
or Burns clock. (see National
Souvenirs). No. 307. 130mm.   16.00
Desk, roll-topped. No. 380.
80mm long.   16.00
Lace iron. No. 504. 70mm.   10.00
Garden roller. No. 358.
104mm long.   7.50
Handbag. No. 184. 85mm.   12.50
Kennel. No. 49. 55mm.   5.50
Lantern, inscribed: Model of ye olde
lanterne and Ancient lights.
No. 346. 105mm.   7.50
Milk Can. No. 34. 70mm.   7.00
Milk Churn. No. 46. 71mm.   6.00
Shaving Mug. No. 164. 54mm.   6.50
Sundial, octagonal.
No. 359. 120mm.   11.00
Swing Mirror on stand. No. 376.
88mm.   10.50
Victorian Pillar Box, model of.
No. 157. 90mm.   17.00
Watering Can. No. 163. 63mm.   5.50
Water Pump. No. 51. 83mm.   6.50
Wheelbarrow.
No. 355. 110mm long.   7.50

Comic/Novelty

Black Boy in bath, inscribed: How
ink is made. Fully coloured.
No. 374. 108mm long.   40.00
Box of Matches, open to reveal
contents. Some colouring. No.
190. 74mm long.   15.25
Cigarette Case holding 6
gold-tipped cigarettes.
No. 349.   11.75
Coal Hod, inscribed: Coal rations,
Yours to a cinder or Your rations to
a cinder. No. 185.   6.00
Japanese Lady, inscribed: Yum,
Yum, some colouring.
No. 407. 123mm.   55.00

Tobacco Pouch, 2 crossed pipes
in relief on front.
No. 501. 98mm long.   6.50
Truck of black coal, inscribed:
Black diamonds from . . .
No. 389. 62mm long.   12.00

Alcohol
Beer barrel. No. 48. 63mm.   4.75
Beer barrel on stand.
No. 161. 65mm.   8.25
Bottle with cork, inscribed: *All
scotch*. No. 214. 90mm.   4.50
Soda Syphon. No. 502.   9.00
Toby Jug, with verse: *No tongue
can tell* etc. No. 335. 95mm.   8.00

Sport
Boxer, inscribed: *England's hope*.
Brown boxing gloves. No. 375.
100mm.   100.00
Golf Bag and Clubs. No. 197.
108mm.   13.50
Golf Ball. No. 210. 50mm.   5.50
Golf Ball on Tee. No. 215. 52mm.   5.50
Tennis Racquet with 3 Balls.
No. 194. 116mm long.   7.50

Musical Instruments
Banjo. No.72. 127mm long.   5.50
Piano, upright. No.345. 76mm.   16.00

Transport
Charabanc, inscribed: *The
Monarch*. No. 352. 125mm long.   40.00
Cycle Lamp, very rarely found
inscribed: *Model of cycle oil head
lamp*. No. 342. 83mm.   19.50
Locomotive. No. 365.
150mm long.   75.00
Motor Coupé. No. 360.
135mm long.   125.00
Open Motor Car. No. 361.
135mm long.   65.00
Single decker closed Motorbus 'K'
type. No. 370. 120mm long.   110.00
Steamroller. No. 364. 130mm long.   160.00

'Modern' Equipment
Flash Lamp, model of.
No. 191. 70mm.   5.50
Horn Gramophone.
No. 337. 95mm.   17.00

Miscellaneous
Bishop's Mitre. No. 58. 70mm.   4.50
Top Hat, found numbered 11 and
35. 60mm wide.   4.00
Trilby Hat, with black band. No.
500.   11.00
Bell, not found numbered. 63mm.   6.00
Dutch Sabot. No. 36. 84mm long.   6.50
Horseshoe. No. 182.   11.00
Horse's Hoof. No. 52 (often found
not numbered. 45mm.   4.00
Leather Highboot. No. 47. 69mm.   7.50
Shield on stand, not found
numbered. 52mm.   6.00

Miniature Domestic
Candleholder. No. 339.   8.25
Cheese Dish. No. 196. 50mm.   10.50
Tea Pot, inscribed: *Take a cup of
tea*. No. 38. *50mm*.   10.50

Numbered Ornamental Wares
No. 1. Pin Tray.   5.00
No. 2. Vase.   3.00
No. 3. Dish with ribbed sides.
120mm dia.   10.00
No. 4. 2 handled Loving Cup.
40mm.   3.00
No. 6. Bell shaped vase.   3.00
No. 7. Vase, 2 handled with
crinkle top. 56mm.   5.00
No. 18. Small Jug.   3.00
No. 21. Vase. 70mm.   8.25
No. 22. Vase, shaped. 38mm.   6.00
No. 24. Pot, with lid. 50mm dia.   7.00
No. 25. Vase, 2 handles, with
bulbous base. 60mm.   5.00
No. 26. Vase, 2 handles. 40mm.   5.00
No. 27. Vase, 2 handles, with
crinkle top. 85mm.   4.75
No. 28. Jug, square. 35mm.   3.00
No. 29. Two-Handled Mug.
64mm.   4.00
No. 30. Jug. 72mm.   3.00
No. 31. Cauldron, 2 handled.   4.00
No. 32. Jug, small. 38mm.   3.00
No. 33. Vase, 2 handles. 54mm.   10.50
No. 40. Cream Jug. 55mm.   4.00
No. 41. Jug. 63mm.   4.00
No. 42. Jug. 65mm.   3.00
No. 43. Vase, 2 handles. 54mm.   4.00
No. 44. Jug, 2 handles. 50mm.   6.00
No. 45. Vase, crinkle top. 52mm.   3.00
No. 106. Vase. 65mm.   4.00

No. 111. Urn.   3.00
No. 112. Taper Vase. 60mm.   6.50
No. 120. Box, heart-shaped.   7.00
No. 121. Pin box.   6.50
No. 123. Pin Box, square.   6.50
No. 124. Pin Box, crinkle edge.   6.50
No. 151. Bulbous Vase with 2
  handles and spout.   4.00
No. 165. Pen and ink stand.   21.75
No. 171. Salt Pot.   10.00

No. 173. Salt Pot, circular.
  100mm.   4.00
No. 174. Pepper Pot, circular.
  100mm.   4.00
No. 379. Pocket watch and
  matchbox holder. 100mm.   11.00

Signal Series

For mark see *Crested China*, p. 244.

Trademark used by an unknown manufacturer.

'Smalls' only found with this
  mark.   2.00

Skarab China

Snowdon China

For mark see *Crested China*, p. 244.

Trademark used for the Snowdon Mountain Tramroad and Hotels Co. Ltd, on china manufactured by Arkinstall & Sons Ltd, Arcadian Works, Stoke-on-Trent. (Usual trademark Arcadian).

Traditional/National Souvenirs

Welsh Harp. 80mm.	4.00
Welsh Hat, model of, with longest Welsh place name round brim. 52mm.	5.50

A mark used by J. Baker & Sons, Bristol.

Trademark used for J. Baker & Son, Bristol, by an unknown manufacturer.
   Only one small and one animal found with this mark.

Home/Nostalgic

Umbrella, open. 50mm dia.	7.50

Comic/Novelty

Bookmaker with greyhound and hare on ashtray. Some colouring. 90mm long.	37.50

Animal

Squirrel eating nut. 60mm.	13.00

'Modern' Equipment

Camera folding. 60mm.	22.50

Souvenir Series

S P Co Ltd

For mark see *Crested China*, p. 244.

Trademark used by an unknown manufacturer for a London wholesaler or retailer.

Traditional/National Souvenirs
Lancashire Clog. 85mm long.   4.00

Trademark used for a wholesaler or retailer in Manchester by an unknown manufacturer.

Only one pin tray 75mm long has been recorded with this mark.

Spencer Art China

Sphinx

For mark see *Crested China*, p. 245.

Trademark used for a retailer by a Fenton manufacturer.

Buildings – White
Osborne House. 150mm long.   62.50

Monuments
Arch Rock, Freshwater Bay.
   82mm.   19.50

Trademark used by a foreign (French or German) manufacturer for the Belgian souvenir market.

The only model found has crest of
   Bruxelles.

Historical/Folklore
Coach and Horses with 3 figures,
   coloured, on base. 100mm long.   25.00

SR

Stanley China

For mark see *Crested China*, p. 215.

For mark see *Crested China*, p. 245.

Trademark used by Samuel Radford (Ltd), High St, Fenton.

Trademark used by Charles Amison (& Co. Ltd), Stanley China Works, Wedgwood St, Longton.

Home/Nostalgic
Milk Churn. 70mm.   2.50

Miniature Domestic
Cheese dish and cover.
   64mm long.   4.00

Traditional/National Souvenirs
Lancashire Clog. 135mm long.   5.00

Great War
Battleship. 119mm long.   10.50

Home/Nostalgic
Pillar Box. 76mm.   5.50

Miscellaneous
Boot. 70mm.   7.00

Miniature Domestic
Cheese Dish and cover. 50mm.   4.00

Star Bazaar Art China

Strand China

For mark see *Crested China*, p. 245.

For mark see *Crested China*, p. 247.

Trademark used for the Star Bazaar, Douglas, Isle of Man, on china thought to have been manufactured by Hewitt & Leadbeater, Willow Potteries, Longton. (Usual trademark Willow Art).

Traditional/National Souvenir
Manx Man, John Bull with extra
leg at back. 126mm.   45.00

Animals
Manx cat with collar, not named.
63mm.   13.00

Home/Nostalgic
Anvil. 50mm.   4.75

Trademark used for a London retailer by Podmore China Co, Elm Street, Hanley. (Usual trademark Podmore).

Animals
Dog in kennel, inscribed: *Black
Watch* 67mm.   5.50

Birds
Woodpecker.   7.50

Great War
Cenotaph, inscribed.
2 sizes: 130mm.   4.75
        167mm.   5.50
Edith Cavell Memorial, London.
Inscribed: *Edith Cavell Brussels
dawn October 12th 1915.
Humanity sacrifice* 142mm.   12.00

Success (Art) China

Sussex China

For mark see *Crested China*, p. 247.

For mark see *Crested China*, p. 247.

Trademark used by an unknown manufacturer/s.

Parian/Unglazed
Bust of *John Peel* with details of
verse. 136mm.   16.00

Ancient Artefacts
Salisbury Leather Kettle. 61mm.   2.25

Seaside Souvenirs
Lighthouse, black band. 105mm.   4.00

Home/Nostalgic
Anvil. 58mm.   4.75
Grandfather Clock. 121mm.   8.75

Trademark used for an Eastbourne retailer
by Sampson Hancock (& Sons), Bridge
Works, Stoke. Pieces were sold with Sussex
coats-of-arms. (Usual trademark Corona).

Historical/Folklore
Ark. 90mm long.   2.25

Traditional/National Souvenirs
Laxey Wheel. 80mm.   30.00
Harp. 90mm.   4.00
Mother Shipton. 73mm.   4.00

Seaside Souvenirs
Lighthouse. 104mm.   3.00
Beachy Head Lighthouse, black
   band. 3 sizes: 102mm.   4.50
                        118mm.   4.50
                        150mm.   5.50

Animals
Staffordshire Bull Terrier. 79mm.   5.50
Teddy Bear, sitting. 85mm.   7.00

Great War
British Airship on base.
   128mm long.   13.00
Lusitania. 163mm long.   56.50
Submarine, inscribed: *E4*.
   102mm long.   8.75
Submarine, inscribed: *E5*.
   125mm long.   10.00

Home/Nostalgic
Cigarette case. 70mm long.   4.75
Hip bath. 95mm long.   7.00

Sussex China S.P. Co.

For mark see *Crested China*, p. 248.

Trademark used for a Sussex wholesaler by Arkinstall & Son Ltd, Arcadian Works, Stoke-on-Trent. (Usual trademark Arcadian).

Ancient Artefacts
Newbury Leather Bottle. 65mm.   2.25

Building – White
Cottage. 55mm.   4.00

Traditional/National Souvenirs
Welsh Hat. 35mm.   3.00

Seaside Souvenirs
Houseboat. 58mm.   2.25
Whelk Shell. 100mm long.   3.50

Countryside
Haystack, circular. 57mm.   3.50

Animals
Dog, Staffordshire bull terrier,
  sitting. 72mm.   7.50
Pig, sitting. 63mm long.   6.50
Rabbit, lying, ears along back.
  70mm long.   4.00
Tortoise. 70mm long.   4.00

Birds
Swan. 62mm. long.   3.00

Great War
British Airship found wrongly
  named *Model of Super Zeppelin*.
  128mm long.   13.00
Battleship, 3 funnels and tiny
  gun fore and aft. 120mm long.   13.00
Red Cross Van. 85mm long.   17.50
Howitzer. 140mm long.   13.00

Mills Hand Grenade, model of.
  62mm.   8.75
Bell Tent. 64mm dia.   5.50
Sandbag, model of. 73mm long.   8.75
Trench Dagger, model of.
  102mm long.   40.00

Home/Nostalgic
Old Armchair, not named.
  90mm.   4.00

Comic/Nostalgic
Pea pod, curved and split to
  reveal peas. 133mm long.   16.00
Policeman, no inscription.
  140mm.   16.00

Musical Instruments
Piano, upright. 70mm long.   8.75

Miscellaneous
Knight, chess piece. 63mm.   7.50
Pin box and lid – circular. 64mm
  dia.   2.00

Sussex Ware

No details of mark available.

Trademark used for Cheesman & Co, Brighton by Hewitt & Leadbeater, Willow Potteries, Longton. (Usual mark Willow Art).

A model of 'Ye Olde Sussex Pig' was reputedly made but so far has not been seen.   15.00

Swan China

For additional mark see *Crested China*, p. 249.

Trademark used by Charles Ford, Cannon St, Hanley, subsequently a branch of J.A. Robinson & Sons Ltd. (Usual trademark Arcadian).

Unglazed/Parian
These busts can be found with crests on their glazed bases, add £5.00 if the bust carries the correct Royal coat of arms.

Bust of King Edward VII on
    circular glazed base. 140mm.   30.00
Bust of Queen Alexandra, on
    circular glazed base. 140mm.   30.00
Bust of King George V, on circular
    glazed base. 135mm.   30.00
Bust of Queen Mary, can be found
    inscribed: *Queen Mary, born May
    26th 1867*. 135mm.   30.00
Bust of Sir John Jellicoe, on square
    glazed base. 175mm.   56.50
Bust of General Joffre, on square
    glazed base. 155mm.   45.00
Bust of Lloyd George, on circular
    glazed base. 135mm.   30.00
Bust of Burns. 80mm.   9.50
Bust of Wordsworth on glazed
    base. 118mm.   12.00

Ancient Artefacts

Butter Pot, old, of 17th Century.
45mm. 2.75

Canterbury Roman Ewer,
inscribed: *Roman Ewer found
near Canterbury original in
Canterbury Museum*.
No. 294. 64mm. 2.25

Canterbury Roman Vase. 65mm.
No.282 2.25

*Chinese Vase original in Hanley
Museum*. 58mm. 2.25

Devon Oak Pitcher. 60mm. No.
192 2.25

Eddystone Jug, inscribed: *old
Spanish jug dredged up near
Eddystone now in Atheneum,
Plymouth*. No. 585. 58mm. 2.25

Egyptian Vase, inscribed: *Ancient
Egyptian Vase 230BC*.
No. 155. 42mm. 2.25

Egyptian Water Bottle.
No. 156. 58mm long. 2.25

Fountains Abbey Cup. No. 709. 1.75

Glastonbury Vase. 50mm. 1.75

Highland Whisky Bowl.
134mm wide. 3.50

Kendal Jug. 75mm. No. 210. 2.25

Lincoln Jack from Original in
Museum. 62mm. No. 50. 2.25

Loving Cup originated by Henry
of Navarre, King of France.
3 handled
2 sizes: 40mm. 2.50
52mm. 2.50

Phoenician Vase, original in
Stoke-on-Trent Museum.
60mm. No. 217. 2.25

Puzzle Jug, original in South
Kensington Museum, with
verse: *Try how to drink and not to
spill*. 70mm. No. 147. 3.50

Salopian Roman Ewer inscribed:
*Roman Salopian Ewer found at
Uriconium now in Shrewsbury
Museum*. 70mm. 2.25

Shakespeare's Jug. 54mm. 3.00

Southwold Jar. 2.25

Toby Jug. 2 sizes: 61mm 5.75
75mm. 6.75

Upstones Jug, inscribed: *Ancient
jug found near Upstones, staffs*.
No. 221. 62mm. 2.25

Winchelsea Vase. 82mm. 1.75

Winchester Vase. 1.75
York Roman Ewer. 55mm. 1.75
York Roman Urn. 1.75

Buildings – Coloured

Shakespeare's House.
84mm long. 14.00

Building – White

Anne Hathaway's Cottage,
Shottery, near Stratford-on-
Avon. 83mm long. 6.50

First and Last Refreshment House
in England. 73mm long. 6.50

Highland Cottage, model of.
80mm. 10.50

Irish Round Tower. 106mm. 5.50

Marble Arch. 65mm. 5.50

Southampton Bargate. 66mm. 15.25

Tower Bridge, 93mm. 20.00

Welsh Cottage, Model of. (Same
model as Highland Cottage).
79mm long. 22.50

Monuments (including Crosses)

Barrow's Monument, Ulverston.
145mm. 52.50

Celtic Cross, not named. 125mm. 5.50

Iona Cross, not named. 120mm. 4.00

Historical/Folklore

Ancient Coaching Hat, model of.
65mm long. 7.50

Davey Safety Lamp 1836. 85mm. 10.50

Font, inscribed: *Model of ancient
font in Tideswell church dates back
to the 14th century*. 90mm. 8.25

Judge, bust, with inscription:
*Defend the children of the poor and
punish the wrong doer. Copy of
inscription of New Bailey Court,
London*. With inscription add £5.
2 sizes: 55mm. 6.50
70mm. 10.50

Mother Shipton, with verse: *Near
to Knaresboro dropping well*.
2 sizes: 76mm. 4.00
115mm. 7.50

Man in Stocks. 88mm. 10.50

Traditional/National Souvenirs

John Bull, bust, 66mm. 5.50

Lancashire Clog. 92mm long. 4.00

Luton Boater. 78mm dia. 5.50

Monmouth hat with verse.
54mm.   15.50
Melton Mowbray Pie, The. Pie with
moulded pastry adornments
and verse. 50mm.   12.50
Ripon Horn blower with
inscription. 130mm.   8.25
Welsh Lady, bust. 65mm.   7.50
Welsh Leek, can be found with
inscription: *King Henry V. The
Welshmen did goot servace (at
Crecy) in a garden where leeks did
grow. Shakespeare.* 98mm.   2.50

Seaside Souvenirs
Bathing Machine with '32' above
the door. 85mm.   4.75
Bell Rock lighthouse. 141mm.   18.50
Lifeboat with blue band and
yellow rigging. Sometimes
found named *Elizabeth Simpson,
John Birch* or *Nancy Lucy* and
£7.00 premium should be
added for any name printed on
the bow. 118mm.   4.75
Novel Collecting Box for the
Royal National Lifeboat
Institution Robin Hoods Bay,
model of fish standing on
square base inscribed: *My diet is
£.s.d.* 128mm.   40.00
Lifeboatman bust. 85mm.   12.50
Rowing Boat, with coloured
rope. 115mm long.   4.75
Fishing Basket, found inscribed:
A good catch. 50mm.   3.50
Beachy Head Lighthouse,
2 sizes: 102mm.   4.00
        140mm.   5.50
Eddystone Lighthouse
2 sizes: 105mm.   3.00
        140mm.   4.75
Pharos Lighthouse, Fleetwood,
model of. 88mm.   5.50
(Lighthouse also found not
named 127mm.)   4.00
Scallop Shell. 70mm. dia.   1.75
Scallop Shell Menu Holder.
62mm.   7.50
Shell Ink Well, one open shell
inverted on another inscribed:
*We are always glad to hear from
you.* 105mm.   6.00
Whelk Shell, inscribed: *Listen to
the sea.* 85mm long.   2.50

Punch, bust, not named, same
colouring. 83mm.   9.00

Countryside
Beehive on Table. 78mm.   4.00
Haystack, circular. 58mm.   4.00
Haystack, rectangular. 50mm.   4.00
Pinecone. 90mm long.   3.00

Animals
Cat, angry, standing with arched
back and green eyes.
63mm long.   8.75
Cat, Cheshire. 100mm.   8.50
Cat, climbing in boot, chasing
mouse (peeping out of toe).
105mm long.   16.00
Cat, long necked and sitting.
Inscribed: *My word if you're not
off.* 108mm.   6.50
Cat, sitting, and smiling
(grotesque, rather similar to
Cheshire Cat). 75mm.   5.50
Cat, sitting, with bow round
neck. 56mm.   10.00
Black Cat, sitting in octagonal
dish. 100mm wide.   24.50
Three black cats on sledge.
118mm long.   56.50
Bulldog, ferocious. 129mm long.   10.50
Dog, Collie, lying down,
inscribed: *Shetland Collie.* 78mm
long.   10.50
Dog, lying, with cross paws.
108mm long.   14.00
Dog, King Charles Spaniel,
begging on cushion.
2 sizes: 68mm.   5.50
        95mm.   11.00
Dog, Pup, with one ear raised.
68mm.   4.50
Dog, pug, sitting. 78mm.   5.50
Dog, puppy, sitting, inscribed: *Daddy
wouldn't buy me a bow-bow.* 75mm.   12.00
Dog, Scottish Terrier. 66mm long.   5.50
Donkey, inscribed: *Hee Haw.*
120mm.   16.00
Elephant, African (big ears).
58mm.   6.50
Elephant, trunk modelled free
from body, inscribed: *Baby
Jumbo.* 50mm.   8.50
Fish, open-mouthed.
108mm long.   2.25

Frog, open-mouthed and green
eyes. 80mm long. — 5.50

Hare. 73mm long. — 7.50

Lion, walking. 110mm. — 8.75

Monkey, sitting, hand to mouth.
65mm. — 10.50

Otter with fish in mouth. 125mm. — 40.00

Pig, lying down, alert ears.
78mm long. — 6.50

Pig, lying down, inscribed: *I wunt
be druv*. 90mm long. — 7.50

Pig, sitting and fat. No.587, can be
found inscribed *My word if
you're not off*. 90mm long. — 14.50

Pig, standing, with drooping
ears. 90mm long. No. 300. — 10.50

Sussex Pig, model of, standing
thin pig, inscribed: *You can push
or you can shuv but I'm hanged if
I'll be druv*. 78mm long. No. 148. — 13.00

Piglet, standing, with erect ears.
73mm long. No. 277. — 6.50

Polar Bear.
2 sizes: 100mm. — 40.00
136mm long. — 47.50

Rabbit, crouching. 70mm long. — 4.00

Teddy Bear.
2 sizes: 68mm. — 7.00
87mm. — 9.00
Large size can be inscribed with
verse: *Come and be my Teddy
Bear*.

Tortoise. 72mm long. — 4.00

Welsh Goat, model of, inscribed:
Yr Afr Cymreig. 100mm long. — 30.00

Birds (including Eggs)

Chick breaking out of egg. 63mm
long. — 4.00

Egg, with flattened base. 44mm. — 2.25

Cock, standing, legs modelled
separately, inscribed: *Cock o'th
North*. Some colouring to head.
100mm. — 8.25

Hen, roosting. 54mm. — 3.00

Norwich canary
2 sizes: 90mm. — 6.50
125mm. — 21.50

Owl, baby. 40mm. — 5.25

Owl, long eared. 95mm. — 7.50

Swan. 70mm long. — 3.00

Swan, No. 295. 55mm long. — 5.00

Great War

'Arry, bust of airman. 83mm. — 52.50

British Soldier, model of, on oval
domed base. 135mm. — 65.00

Despatch Rider, model of, on
motorbike. 120mm long. — 40.00

Nurse and Wounded Tommy,
model of. 108mm long. — 75.00

Nurse, inscribed: *Soldier's friend*.
Red Cross on chest. 132mm. — 40.00

Russian Cossack, model of, on
horseback. 122mm. — 117.50

Sailor, bust, found with hatband
impressed: *HMS Dreadnought*
or *HMS Queen Elizabeth*.
Inscribed: *The handyman*.
92mm. — 25.75

Sailor, bust, inscribed: *Sailor
beware* and with verse *Hearts of
Oak*. 95mm. — 25.75

Sailor, standing with hands on
hips. 132mm. — 56.50

Sailor, winding Capstan, model
of. 105mm. — 75.00

Scotch Soldier, model of, on
domed oval base. 135mm. — 87.50

Soldier, bust, inscribed: *Tommy
Atkins* with verse: *Soldiers of the
King*. Some colouring. 90mm. — 21.75
with verse — 26.00

Soldier with respirator, bust,
inscribed: *Model of new gas mask*.
95mm. — 170.00

Tommy Driving a Steam Roller
over the Kaiser, inscribed: *To
Berlin*. 120mm long.
(Very Rare). — 400.00

Tommy in Bayonet Attack, model
of. 130mm. — 95.00

Tommy and his Machine Gun.
100mm long. — 26.00

Tommy on Sentry Duty, model
of. 110mm. — 40.00

Tommy Throwing his Grenade,
model of. 130mm. — 87.50

New Aeroplane, model of.
Biplane with fixed prop, and
roundels in relief. 120mm long. — 75.00

New Aeroplane, model of, with
revolving prop. 153mm long. — 30.00

British Airship on stand. 128mm
long. — 13.00

Observer or Sausage Balloon,
model of. 84mm. — 30.00

Super Zeppelin, model of.
127mm long. — 17.50

Battleship, inscribed: *HMS Queen Elizabeth*. 115mm long.	10.50
Battleship, 3 funnels. 120mm long.	13.00
Torpedo Boat Destroyer, model of. 126mm long.	16.00
Submarine, inscribed: *E4*. 95mm long.	8.75
Submarine, inscribed *E5*. 126mm long.	13.00
Armoured car, model of. 95mm long.	22.50
Red Cross Van, red cross on each side and rear. 'EH 139' printed on radiator. 85mm long.	17.50
Tank model of. 160mm long.	21.75
Tank, model of, with inset steering wheels. 115mm long.	10.50
Tank, model of, with trailing steering wheels. Can be found inscribed: *Original made in Lincoln* with Lincoln crest and £10 should be added for this. 144mm long.	13.00
Field Gun. 140mm long.	11.00
Field Gun with screen. 100mm long.	13.00
German Howitzer. 140mm. long.	13.00
Trench Mortar, model of. 70mm long.	8.75
Anti Aircraft Shell, model of. 98mm.	8.75
Cannon Shell. 2 sizes: 70mm.	2.25
90mm.	3.00
The 90mm size is often inscribed: *Jack Johnson*.	4.50
or *Hartlepools Bombardment Dec 16th 1914*.	6.00
Clip of Bullets, model of. 57mm.	10.50
Bomb dropped on Bury St Edmunds. 75mm.	5.50
Bomb which killed a chicken at Southend, Model of. 75mm.	25.75
Bomb dropped from Zeppelin, model of. 75mm.	4.75
British Aerial Bomb. 75mm.	21.75
Canister Bomb, model of. 60mm.	8.75
Plum Pudding Bomb, Model of. 72mm long.	75.00
German Aerial Torpedo. 88mm long.	21.75
Mills Hand Grenade, Model of. 62mm.	8.75

Bandsman's Drum. 53mm.	4.75
Bell Tent, open base and flap. 60mm.	6.00
Capstan. 56mm.	4.00
Ghurka Knife, model of. 110mm long.	13.00
Pair of Field Glasses, model of. 78mm long.	10.00
Sandbag. 70mm long.	8.75
Tommy's Hut, model of. 105mm long.	40.00
Trench Dagger. 102mm long.	40.00
Trench Lamp. 70mm.	8.75
Waterbottle, model of. 65mm.	8.75
Colonal Hat, model of. 88mm wide.	5.50
Glengarry. 90mm long.	11.25
Officer's Peaked Cap, with coloured badge and hatband. 65mm dia.	8.75
Fireplace, inscribed: *We've kept the home fires burning*. 90mm.	8.75

Home/Nostalgic

Anvil. 66mm.	4.75
Bellows. 95mm long.	4.00
Chair, highbacked. 90mm.	4.00
Firebucket. 55mm.	3.00
Grandfather Clock, model of a usually found inscribed: *Make use of time let not advantage slip. Shakespeare* Can be found inscribed: *The time of day*. 110mm.	10.50
Milkchurn. 63mm.	3.00
Pillar Box, inscribed: *GRV* and *If you haven't time to post a line here's the pillar box*. 63mm.	8.25
Stool, 3 legged. 40mm.	3.00
Table, square. 39mm.	3.50
Water Pump. 90mm.	4.00
Wicker Basket, twisted handle, inscribed *Fruit Basket*. 63mm.	5.50

Comic/Novelty

Billiken. 65mm.	
Clown, bust, inscribed: *Put me amongst the girls*, some colouring. 80mm.	16.50
Golliwog, fully coloured, verse to near.	65.00
Invalid carriage. 55mm.	10.00

Jester, double faced, happy and
sad, and eyes open and closed.
Can be found inscribed: *Ye jester
awake, ye jester asleep*. 65mm.   4.00
                            Inscribed   7.50
Policeman on duty, with verse.
148mm.   16.50
Suffragette handbell, double-
faced. Front, sour old lady,
inscribed: *Votes for women*. Back
pretty young girl, inscribed:
This one shall have the vote. Some
colouring. 98mm.   19.50

Cartoon/Comedy Characters
Harry Lauder, bust, not named.
Inscribed: *Stop ye're tickling Jock*.
83mm.   15.25
Mrs Gummidge, standing figure,
with inscription: *A lone lorn
creetur and everything goes
contrairy with her*. 112mm.   9.50

Alcohol
Beer Barrel, on stand. 40mm.   3.00
Monk, jovial and holding glass,
with verse: *A jovial Monk am I*.
2 sizes: 70mm.   8.75
           112mm.   10.50
Soda Syphon. 100mm.   7.50
Thimble, inscribed: *Take a
thimblefull*. 40mm.   8.75
Toby Jug. 62mm.   5.50

Sport
Cricket Bag. 80mm long.   6.50
Football. 50mm dia.   4.50
Golf Ball, inscribed: *The game of
golf was first played in the year
1448*. 42mm.   4.75
Tennis Racquet. 90mm long.   5.50

Musical Instruments
Banjo. 154mm long.   4.75
Guitar. 153mm long.   6.50
Piano, Upright. 70mm long.   8.25
Tambourine. 70mm dia.   7.50

Transport
Car, Saloon, inscribed: *EH 139*.
76mm long.   21.75
Open Sports Car, inscribed
EH 139. 110mm long.   20.00

Can of Petrol, impressed: *Motor
spirit*. 55mm.   8.75

Modern Equipment
Gramophone with horn. 112mm.   17.00

Miscellaneous
Fireman's Helmet. 82mm long.   22.00
Mortar Board. 66mm long.   16.00
Handbell, no clapper. 53mm.   3.00
Knight chess piece. 62mm.   7.50
Rook, chess piece. 55mm.   2.50
Oriental shoe. No. 302.
           102mm long.   6.50
Ankle boot. 83mm long.   4.00

Miniature Domestic
Cheese dish, one piece. 50mm.   5.00
Cheese dish and cover. 50mm.   5.00
Teapot and Lid. No.145. 40mm.   5.25

Sylvan China

See mark in *Crested China*, p. 254.

Trademark used by Dura Porcelain Co. Ltd,
Empress Pottery, Hanley.

Historical/Folklore

Burns Chair, model of.	6.50
Mary Queen of Scots Chair,	
Edinburgh Castle, Model of.	
76mm.	4.75

Traditional/National Souvenirs

Welsh Hat. 55mm.	3.00

Animals

Cat sitting on circular pouffe, inscribed: *Luck* in orange. 80mm.	8.75
Scottie Dog, black, looking out of Kennel. Inscribed : *Black Watch*. Green bow. 68mm.	4.00
Scottie Dog, sitting wearing Tam O'Shanter. 76mm.	4.50
Scottie Dog, standing. 90mm long.	7.00

Birds

Cockerel. 65mm.	6.50

Great War

Lady of the Lamp, Florence Nightingale. 1820–1910.	12.50

Home/Nostalgic

Fireplace, inscribed: *East or West home is best, Home Sweet Home.* Some colouring. 95mm long.	8.25

Comic/Novelty

Billiken sitting on throne, inscribed: *the God of things as they ought to be.* 100mm.	4.00

Cartoon/Comedy Characters

Mr Pussyfoot, all water!! We don't think. 97mm.	22.50

Alcohol

Toby Jug with verse. 88mm.	6.00

Sport

Golf Ball, inscribed: *The ancient game of golf was first played in 1448.* 48mm.	4.75

Miscellaneous

Hand holding tulip. 90mm.	2.25

Miniature Domestic

Cheese dish and cover. 45mm.	4.00

Syren China

Talbot China

For mark see *Crested China*, p. 255.

For mark see *Crested China*, p. 255.

Trademark used by Wiltshaw & Robinson Ltd, Carlton Works, Stoke-on-Trent, (Usual trademark Carlton).

Birds
Comic Duck on green base.
108mm.   18.50

Sport
Sports Trophy, 132mm.   6.50

Trademark used for a retailer by Sampson Hancock (and Sons), Bridge Works, Stoke. (Usual trademark Corona).

Animals
Fish Vase. 60mm.   2.00

Miscellaneous
King, Chess Piece. 115mm.   17.00
Queen, Chess Piece. 112mm.   15.00

'Modern' Equipment
Gas Cooker. 70mm.   6.50

Taylor and Kent

Mark found on model exported to Australia.

For additional mark see *Crested China*, p. 156.

Trademark used by Taylor and Kent (Ltd), Florence Works, Longton. (Usual trademark Florentine).

Buildings – Coloured
Ann Hathaway's Cottage.
3 sizes: 50mm.		11.50
70mm.		14.00
115mm long.		26.00

Shakespeare's House.
2 sizes: 70mm.		14.00
115mm long.		26.00

Home/Nostalgic
Baby in hipbath. 100mm long.	6.50

Temple Porcelain

For mark see *Crested China*, p. 256.

Trademark used by an unknown manufacturer.

Ancient Artefacts
Loving Cup. Three handled. 39mm.	2.25

Home/Nostalgic
Bellows.	3.50
Bucket with upright handle. 70mm.	2.50
Coat scuttle, shell shaped, on two ball feet.	3.00
Cradle. 62mm long.	5.50
Milk Churn. 15mm.	4.00

Sport
Curling Stone.	13.00

Miniature Domestic
Cheese dish and cover. 50mm.	4.00

Miscellaneous
Oriental Slipper. 98mm long.	5.50

Thistle China

T.M.W. and Co Ltd/and S Ltd.

For mark see *Crested China*, p. 236.

For mark see *Crested China*, p. 257.

Trademark used for L.M. Mack, Ayr, by Hewitt & Leadbeater, Willow Potteries, Longton. (Usual trademark Willow Art).

Trademark used for a wholesaler by an unknown manufacturer.

Parian/Unglazed
Bust of *Burns*. 150mm (with
Ayr crest). 16.00

Buildings – coloured
Model of Burns cottage, inscribed:
Robert Burns The Ayrshire Bard
was born at Alloway, Near Ayr on
Jan 25th 1759. He died on 21st July
1796 at Dumfries where he was
buried. 107mm long. 30.00

Monuments
Burns, statue. 2 sizes: 108mm 16.00
177mm. 16.00

Great War
Monoplane with fixed prop.
146mm long. 30.00
New field gun with screen and
sight groove. 109mm long. 13.00

Home/Nostalgic
Bucket, 76mm. 2.50

Historical/Folklore
Mother Shipton. 105mm. 4.75

Animals
Bulldog. 55mm. 6.50
Scottie dog, wearing blue, red
and black Glengarry. 60mm. 6.50

Birds
Chick. 65mm. 4.00

Alcohol
Barrel. 33mm. 2.50

Tourist Art China

Towy China

For mark see *Crested China*, p. 257.

For mark see *Crested China*, p. 257.

Trademark used for Frank Duncan Ltd, Auckland, New Zealand, by Hewitt & Leadbeater Ltd, Willow Potteries, Longton. (Usual trademark Willow Art).

NB: All models have New
   Zealand crests.

Seaside Souvenirs
Lighthouse. 110mm.   5.00

Birds
Kiwi. 66mm.   24.75

Home/Nostalgic
Wheelbarrow. 110mm long.   6.00

Alcohol
Barrel on stand. No.35. 58mm.   4.00

Trademark used for a Welsh retailer by Hewitt and Leadbeater Ltd, Willow Potteries, Longton. (Usual trademark Willow Art).

Traditional/National Souvenirs
Welsh Hat. No. 75. 57mm.   3.00

Tre-Pol-Pen Series

Triood

TRE-POL-PEN SERIES

For mark see *Crested China*, p. 259.

Trademark used for an unknown manufacturer.

Only one model recorded.

National Souvenir
Cornish Pastie, inscribed: *Will ye ave a piece of my pasty*.
95mm long.   4.50

Trademark used by Hoods Ltd, International Works, Fenton.

Buildings – white
Micklegate Bar, York. 110mm.   15.25

Traditional/National Souvenirs
Lancashire Clog.   4.00

Seaside Souvenirs
Lighthouse. 108mm.   3.50

Animals
Collie Dog, sitting.   7.50
Rabbit, ears raised. 62mm long.   4.00

Great War
Airship on base. 130mm long.   13.00
Battleship. 120mm long.   10.50
Submarine, impressed *E4*.
   104mm long.   8.75
Red Cross Van. 100mm long.   17.50
Tank, with inset steering wheels.
   102mm long.   10.50
Field Gun. 130mm.   13.00
Bell Tent, with open flaps.   5.50
Picklehaube. No. 58. 52mm.   13.00

Home/Nostalgic
Grandfather Clock. 125mm.   9.50
Jardiniere on stand, fixed. 80mm.   2.50

Musical Instruments
Upright Piano. 62mm.   7.50

Modern Equipment
Gas cooker. 70mm.   6.50

Miscellaneous
Ladies shoe. 90mm long.   7.50

Miniature Domestic
Cheese dish, one piece. 58mm.   4.00
Cheese dish, two piece.
   82mm long.   4.25

Tudor Arms China

Tuscan China

For mark see *Crested China*, p. 259.

For mark see *Crested China*, p. 259.

Trademark used for a wholesaler by Hewitt & Leadbeater Ltd, Willow Potteries, Longton. (Usual trademark Willow Art).

Trademark used by R.H. and S.L. Plant (Ltd), Tuscan Works, Longton.

Ancient Artefacts

Loving Cup, 3 handled. No. 82. 39mm.	2.25
Nose of Brasenose. 95mm long.	5.50

Buildings – White

Lloyd George's Home. 102mm long.	30.00

Buildings – White

Newquay Look-out-house, some colouring. 100mm.	30.00
Tower of Refuge, Isle of Man. 93mm.	25.00

Historical/Folklore

Model of Burns chair. 88mm.	6.50

Historical/Folklore

Coronation Chair. 80mm.	7.50
The Chertsey Abbey or *Curfew Bell*, cast circa 1370. With clapper. 88mm.	11.00

Traditional/National Souvenirs

Welsh Hat, with blue ribbon and longest place name around brim. No.75. 57mm.	5.00

National Souvenirs

Welsh Hat. 47mm.	3.00

Seaside Souvenirs

Bathing Machine. 65mm.	4.75

Seaside Souvenirs

Lighthouse, not named. 90mm.	3.00
Withernsea Lighthouse, with details. 110mm.	11.00
Crab. 88mm long.	6.50
Seashell. 118mm long.	2.50
Seashell, No.36. 84mm long.	2.50

Animals

Bulldog, standing. 125mm long.	8.75
Elephant, walking. 52mm.	6.50

Great War

Tank with trailing wheels. 125mm long.	10.50
Kit Bag with verse: *Pack up your troubles in your old kit bag*. 74mm.	10.50
Church Bell, inscribed: *Curfew must not ring tonight*. 70mm.	5.50

Animals

Camel with two humps, kneeling. 125mm long.	16.00
Cat, Cheshire with one bead eye. 91mm.	6.50
Cat, winking.	5.00
Dog, Bulldog. 72mm long.	8.75
Dog, Hound, running. 200mm long.	21.75
Dog, Spaniel, sitting. 53mm.	7.50
Donkey, lying down, yellow bead eyes. 125mm long.	23.00
Elephant, sitting and comical, with yellow bead eyes. 80mm.	19.50
Fish, curled. 105mm long.	3.50

Home/Nostalgic

Coal Scuttle, helmet shaped. 53mm.	3.00

Miscellaneous

Boot. 112mm long.	7.50

Fish, open mouthed with green
glass eyes. 120mm.   8.25
Pig, running, red bead eyes.
87mm.   12.00
Polar bear on tree trunk, bead
eyes. 110mm long.   32.50
Rabbit.
Terrapin. 95mm long.   8.50
Tortoise/Turtle, standing with
bead eyes. 108mm long.   8.50

Birds/Eggs
Egg, cracked open and lying on
side. 65mm long.   2.00
Chicken, plump. 55mm.   4.50

Great War
Kit bag, with no inscription.
63mm.   10.50

Home/Nostalgic
Baby, naked, lying on tummy.
105mm long.   21.75
Bellows. 106mm long.   4.00
Grandfather Clock, inscribed
Time for tea 5 o'clock. 128mm.   10.50
Loaf of Bread. 62mm.   20.50
Milk Churn.   3.00

Comic/Novelty
Boy Scout, saluting. 140mm.   26.00
Girl dressed as clown on square
base. 130mm.   24.00
Lemon, open top. 75mm long.   4.00
Man in nightshirt and nightcap.
Could be Wee Willie Winkie.
2 sizes: 60mm.   8.25
        90mm.   10.50
Sun with face. 100mm.   40.00
Tomato with green leaves. 60mm
dia.   9.50

Cartoon/Comedy
Snooker or the Kitten Cat, cat sitting
on square base putting on
crown. Can be found coloured
and unglazed. (Daily Sketch
Cartoon Character). 130mm.   56.50

Alcohol
Carboy. No.11. 70mm.   2.00

Miscellaneous
Bamboo Vase. 100mm.   2.00
Top Hat Matchstriker. 45mm.   4.00

Miniature Domestic
Cheese dish and cover. 2 pieces.
50mm.   5.50
Shaving Mug. 57mm. No.180.   5.00

Numbered 'smalls'
No.5. Vase. 65mm.   1.75
No.6. Vase. 60mm.   1.75
No.10. Ewer. 70mm.   1.75
No.21. Vase.   1.75
No.22. Vase. 30mm.   1.75
No.24. Jug. 45mm.   1.75
No.42. Crinkle top vase. 42mm.   1.75
No.57. Ewer. 58mm.   1.75
No.58. Ewer.   1.75
No.59. Vase. 43mm.   1.75
No.71. Vase. 63mm.   1.75
No.72. Jug. 63mm.   1.75
No.89. Vase. 55mm.   1.75
No.100. Urn. 65mm.   1.75
No.101. Ewer.   1.75
No.110. Jug. 51mm.   1.75

Tuskar Rock China

Trademark used for a Wexford retailer by an
unknown manufacturer.

Only one 'small' and the model
below bound with a Wexford
Crest.

Novelty
Girl with ostrich feathers on her
hat, inscribed: *Harriet*.
Reg No.448566 70mm.   43.50

Union K

For mark see *Crested China*, p. 261.

Trademark used by the German firm
Klösterle (near Carlsbad), the former
Gräflich Thun'sche Porzellanfabric.

Domestic ware only.

Strand. 'Black Watch'

Tuscan. Newquay Look Out House

Tuscan. Wee Willie Winkie

Vectis. Donkey in Well

Vectis models. Old Village Shanklin white and coloured

German. Hot Air Balloon

German. Boy and Girl on Donkey

German. Boy and Girl with flags

Matching Pair. German boy and girl bell hops with globes

German. Flat Iron

German. Flapper with Scottie dog

German. Girl in canoe

Unity China

Universal Series

For mark see *Crested China*, p. 261.

For mark see *Crested China*, p. 261.

Trademark used by the German firm of Max Emanuel and Co, Mitterteich. (Bavaria). (Usual trademark Mosanic).

Trademark used by an unknown manufacturer.

Miniature Domestic
Cheese Dish. 50mm.   4.00

Great War
Bandsman's Drum. 57mm dia.   4.75

Vale China

Venetia China

For mark see *Crested China*, p. 263.

Trademark used by an unknown manufacturer. No example of mark recorded. Only one small recorded with a Southport crest.

Trademark used by Charles Waine (and Co), Derby Works, Longton.

Ancient Artefacts
Loving Cup. 3 handles. 40mm.   2.25

Seaside Souvenirs
Lighthouse on rocky base.
    114mm.   3.00

Birds
Swan Posy Bowl. 80mm.   2.25

Home/Nostalgic
Coal Scuttle. No.35. 80mm.   3.00

Miniature Domestic
Cheese Dish and cover. 55mm.   4.00
Teapot and lid. 58mm.   4.00

Vectis/Victis Models

Victoria Arms China

For mark see *Crested China*, p. 263.

Trademark used for Nigh, a fancy goods dealer in the Isle of Wight by J.A. Robinson and Sons, subsequently Cauldon Ltd. (Usual trademark Arcadian).

Parian/Unglazed
Osborne House, Isle of Wight.
140mm long.   82.50
Sleep of innocence. Osborne House.
Cowes. I.O.W. Two babies lying
on a couch. 96mm long.   45.00

Ancient Artefacts
Cadogan teapot, not named.
50mm.   5.00

Buildings – Coloured
The old village, Shanklin, I.O.W.
100mm long.   90.00

Buildings – White
Carisbrooke Castle, Isle of Wight,
80mm long.   86.00
Old Church, Bonchurch.
105mm long.   44.50
The old village, Shanklin, I.W.
100mm long.   44.50
Osborne House, Cowes, Isle of
Wight. 48mm.   82.50

Monuments
Arch Rock, Freshwater Bay,
I.O.W. 80mm.   19.50

Traditional/National Souvenirs
Donkey in wheel, donkey coloured,
Carisbrooke Castle. 90mm.   26.00
Map of Isle of Wight. A coloured
map standing upright on an
oval ashtray. 106mm long.   24.00

Seaside Souvenirs
Needles Rock and Lighthouse.
125mm long.   24.50

Animals
Calf 100mm long.   13.00
Lion, walking. 145mm long.   18.00

S. BENNION

Trademark used by an unknown manufacturer.

Great War
Tank with trailing wheels,
inscribed: *Model of British Tank.*
130mm long.   10.50
(This looks like a Willow tank).

Victoria China

For mark see *Crested China*, p. 363–4.

Trademark thought to have been used on crested wares by James Reeves, Victoria Works, Fenton.

Ancient Artefacts

Carlisle Salt Pot. 70mm.	2.25
Chester Roman Vase, named. 58mm.	2.25
Fountains Abbey Cup. 50mm.	1.75
Puzzle Jug. 67mm.	3.50
Tyg. 1 handle. 70mm.	1.75

Building – White

Blackpool Tower, with buildings. 142mm.	7.50
Old Pete's Cottage, I.O.M. 75mm long.	15.00

Monuments (including Crosses)

Iona Cross. 108mm.	4.00
Wallace Monument, Stirling. 120mm.	17.50

Historical/Folklore

Man in pillory. 101mm.	12.00
Miner's Lamp. 84mm.	10.50
Mother Shipton. 70mm.	4.50
Suffragette handbell. 72mm.	10.50

Traditional/National Souvenirs

Blackpool Ferris wheel. 108mm.	8.75
Laxey wheel, Isle of Man. 95mm.	30.00
Legs of Man, inside life belt. 90mm.	18.50

Ripon Horn. 90mm.	13.00
Ripon Hornblower. 90mm.	10.50
Bust of Scotsman wearing Tam O'Shanter and plaid. 63mm.	10.50
Welsh Bardic Chair. 86mm (identical to Old Arm Chair.)	16.00
Welsh Harp. 90mm.	4.00
Welsh Hat with thin blue ribbon band. 48mm and 58mm.	3.00
Welsh Hat, two different moulds one with twisted cord band, and the other with blue band with gold tassels. Can be found with Llanfair . . . etc. around brim. 62mm.	3.00
Inscribed	5.50

Seaside Souvenirs

Baby seated on rock. 109mm.	8.25
Bathing Machine. 65mm long.	4.75
Canoe. 102mm.	4.50
Houseboat, rectangular. 90mm long.	2.50
Fisherman's bust. 87mm.	12.00
Fisherwoman bust. 87mm.	12.00
Lifebelt, legs of man	18.00
Lighthouse. 97mm.	3.00
Lighthouse, un-named Flamborough. 110mm.	4.00
Whelk Shell, inscribed: *Listen to the sea*. 95mm long.	2.50
Gladstone Bag. 45mm.	2.25
Portmanteau. 55mm.	2.25

Animals

Cat, with long neck. 115mm.	5.50
Cat, The Cheshire. Inscribed: *Always smiling*. 80mm.	5.50
Cat, *Manx*. 80mm long.	13.00
Bulldog in kennel. 70mm long.	5.50
Dog, King Charles Spaniel, begging on cushion.	6.50
Dogs, two King Charles Spaniels in Top Hat. 70mm.	10.50
Fish, inscribed: *Caught at . . .* 102mm long.	3.00
Frog. 39mm.	5.50
Monkey, crouching, hands to mouth. 88mm.	8.25
Pig, sitting. 39mm.	6.50
Pig, standing. 88mm long.	8.25
Rabbit with upright ears. 70mm long.	4.00
Seal with ball. 73mm.	13.00
Teddy Bear, sitting. 98mm.	7.00

Birds

Hen, roosting. 92mm long.	3.00
Kingfisher cream jug. 58mm.	4.00
Kingfisher, with long beak, 80mm.	7.50
Owl. 2 sizes: 70mm.	6.50
100mm.	8.25
Parrot. 76mm.	5.50
Pelican Jug. 63mm.	4.00
Swan. 2 sizes: 70mm 3.00	
90mm long. 4.00	
Swan Posy Bowl. 80mm long.	2.25

Great War

Bust of Sailor. 90mm.	19.50
Airship on base. 128mm long.	13.00
Zeppelin. 132mm long.	17.50
Monoplane with roundels and movable prop. 165mm long.	30.00
Battleship. 120mm long.	13.00
Lusitania, 165mm long.	56.50
Torpedo Boat Destroyer. 110mm long.	16.00
Submarine, inscribed *E4*.	8.75
Submarine, inscribed *E9*. 147mm long.	13.00
Red Cross Van. 102mm long.	17.50
Renault Tank. 82mm long.	55.00
Tank, with inset steering wheels. 100mm long.	10.50
Tank, with large side turrets. 120mm long.	10.50
Field Gun. 127mm long.	12.50
Trench Mortar. 65mm long.	8.75
Torpedo, fixed prop. 155mm long.	40.00
Colonial Soldier's Hat. 73mm long.	5.50
Field Glasses. 80mm long.	8.75
Ghurka Knife, 143mm long.	13.00
Grandfather Clock, usual model but with clock transfer at 3.25. With inscription: *World War 1914–1919. Peace signed 3.25pm June 28 1919.* 110mm.	47.50
Bell Tent, hexagonal, open flap. 89mm.	5.50
Sandbag. 74mm long.	8.75
Cenotaph. 135mm.	4.00
Matlock Bath War Memorial. 178mm.	16.00
Ripon War Memorial. 118mm.	30.00

Home/Nostalgic

Baby in bath. 100mm long.	6.50
Broom Head. 105mm long.	12.00
Cradle. 80mm long.	4.00
Garden roller. 85mm long.	4.50
Lady in Bonnet, salt pot. 93mm.	7.00
Lamp. 70mm.	3.50
Lantern. 86mm.	4.00
Milk Churn.	2.50
The old armchair, with inscription. 83mm.	4.75
Pillar Box, inscribed: *I cant get a letter from you, so send you the box*. 70mm.	8.00
Sundial on large square base, inscribed *Tempus fugit*. 109mm.	8.75
Tobacco Pouch, 72mm long.	5.00
Watering Can. 70mm.	4.75

Comic/Novelty

Boy's face, smiling on cream jug. 73mm.	4.00
Boy on Scooter. 106mm.	13.00
Jack in the Box. 95mm.	10.50
Pierrot playing banjo, some colouring. 120mm.	18.50
Screw, inscribed: *You could do with a big fat screw*. 76mm.	21.75
Suffragette Handbell, two sided. One side ugly old lady, inscribed: *Votes for women*. Reverse, a pretty young girl, inscribed: *This one shall have a vote*. 108mm.	19.50

Cartoon/Comedy Characters

Ally Sloper bust, not named. 83 mm.	12.50
Harry Lauder, bust. 63mm.	7.50

Alcohol

Champagne Bottle in ice bucket inscribed: *Something good – a bottle of the boy*. 83mm.	6.50
Whisky Bottle.	4.00

Sport

Cricket Bag. 115mm long.	6.50

Musical Instruments

Grand Piano, with closed lid. 80mm long.	14.50
Tambourine. 68mm dia.	3.00

Transport
Charabanc, with driver.
  115mm long.   19.50
Motor Horn, inscribed: *Pip Pip*.
  90mm long.   13.00
Saloon Car. 80mm.   21.75

'Modern' Equipment
Gramophone, square without
  horn. 58mm.   12.50
Radio Horn. 95mm.   13.00

Miscellaneous
Carboy. 72mm.   2.00
ChessPawn. 60mm.   10.00
Ladies 18th Century Shoe.
  92mm long.   7.50
Oriental Shoe with pointed
  turned-up toe. 95mm long.   7.50

Miniature Domestic
Cheese dish, 2 pieces. 50mm.   4.00
Coffee Pot. 69mm.   3.00
Shaving Mug. 50mm.   4.00
Tea Pot. 60mm.   4.00

Victoria (China)

For additional mark see *Crested China*, p. 265.

Trademark used by two Geman manufacturers, Schmidt and Co, Carlsbad (Bohemia), and Moschendorf, Hof, Bavaria.

Birds
Hen, pepper pot, red comb &
  beak. 70mm.   2.50
Swan Posy Bowl. 58mm.   2.25

Miscellaneous
Sabot. 84mm long.   4.50

Miniature Domestic
Cauldron. 58mm.   1.75
Cheese dish and cover. 30mm.   4.00
Cup and saucer with lithograph
  of Blarney Castle. 60mm.   15.00

Victorian Porcelain

Vignaud

For mark see *Crested China*, p. 265.

Trademark used by Robinson and Leadbeater, Wolfe St, Stoke-on-Trent. (Usual
trademark R & L).

Ancient Artefacts
Loving Cup, 2 and 3 handled.
39mm.   2.25
Oxford Jug. 83mm.   1.75
Scarboro jug, inscribed: *Jug about
600 years old found in ancient moat
Scarboro (sic)*. No. 180. 42mm.   2.25

Birds
Swan Posy Holder, yellow beak &
feet. 75mm long.   2.25

Home/Nostalgic
Bellows. 110mm long.   3.50

$FRANCE$
VIGNAUD
$LIMOGES$

Trademark used by a French china manufacturer, Vignaud, Limoges, France for the
French souvenir market.

Only 60mm vase with a Paris crest
recorded.   1.75

W

Wade

For marks see *Crested China*, p. 267.

No details of mark available except that marks incorporate 'Wades'.

Trademark used by H.M. Williams and Sons, Bridge Pottery, Longton.

Ancient Artefacts

Loving Cup, 3 handles. 55mm.	2.25
Salisbury Kettle. 102mm.	1.75

Seaside Souvenirs

Portmanteau. 80mm long.	2.25

Animals

Cat, long necked. 112mm.	5.50
Frog cream jug. 60mm.	4.00
Pig, standing. 100mm long.	7.50
Seal.	8.50

Birds

Kingfisher Cream Jug, 58mm.	4.00
Swan Posy Bowl. 80mm long.	2.25

Home/Nostalgic

Oil Lamp. 58mm.	2.25
Old Lantern. 71mm.	3.50
Shaving Mug. 55mm.	4.00
Watering Can. 55mm.	4.75

Trademark used by Wade & Co, Union Pottery, Burslem, subsequently Wade, Heath & Co. (Ltd).

A small range of earthernware domestic wares was produced.

Warwick China

For mark see *Crested China*, p. 267.

Trademark used for W.H. Smith and Sons
by Arkinstall and Son Ltd, Arcadian Works,
Stoke-on-Trent. (Usual trademark Arcadia).

Ancient Artefacts

Ancient Tyg. model of. 70mm.	2.25
Cambridge Roman Jug. 58mm.	2.25
Canterbury Roman Urn, inscribed: *Roman Urn found near Canterbury, original in Canterbury Museum.* 70mm.	2.25
Chester Roman Vase 60mm.	2.25
Egyptian Vase, about 230BC. 41mm.	2.25
Lincoln Jack, from original in Museum. 62mm.	2.25
Newbury Leather Bottle. 65mm.	1.75
Winchelsea Roman Cup, inscribed: *Roman cup found near Winchelsea* 51mm.	2.25

Buildings – White

Rowton Tower, with inscription:
*King Charles I stood on this tower
Sept 24th 1645 and saw his army
defeated on Rowton Moor.*
105mm.   30.00

Historical/Folklore

Yorick's Skull, inscribed: *Alas poor
Yorick.* 57mm.   6.50

Traditional/National Souvenirs

Prime Cheddar Cheese, with slice
out. 60mm.   4.50

Seaside Souvenirs

Fishing Basket, inscribed: *A good
catch* 70mm long.   4.00

Animals

Dog, Collie. 95mm.	8.25
Otter, holding fish in mouth. 120mm long.	40.00
Polar Bear, 96mm.	40.00

Pony, Shetland. 105mm long.	19.50
Teddy Bear, sitting. 90mm.	7.00

Birds

Chick breaking out of egg. 63mm long.	4.00
Hen, roosting. 54mm.	3.00
Egg shaped salt pot, inscribed: *s* 56mm.	1.75
Egg shaped pepper pot, inscribed: *p* 56mm.	1.75

Great War

British Airship on stand. 128mm long.	13.00
Red Cross Van, red cross on each side and rear. *'EH 139'* inscribed on radiator. 85mm long.	17.50
Field Glasses. 78mm.	10.00

Miscellaneous

Rook, Chess Piece. 55mm.	3.00

Miniature Domestic

Cheese Dish and cover. 50mm.	4.00
Three-legged stool. 42mm.	4.00

Waterfall Heraldic China

For mark see *Crested China*, p. 268.

Trademark used for a Northern wholesaler by Hewitt and Leadbeater, Willow Potteries, Longton. (Usual trademark Willow Art).

Ancient Artefacts

Lincoln Jack, not named. No. 44. 60mm.	1.75

Buildings – White

Grimsby Hydraulic Tower. 165mm.	21.75

Monuments (including Crosses)

Hull fishermans memorial, with inscription. 2 sizes: 135mm.	13.00
160mm.	16.00
Hull South African War Memorial, with inscription. 165mm.	16.00
Kilnsea Cross, Hedon with inscription: *Erected at Ravenspurne 1339 by King Henry IV. Re-erected at Hedon*. 134mm.	40.00
Sir William de la Pole, Statue of, with long inscription. 160mm.	16.00

Historical/Folklore

James V Chair, Stirling Castle, Model of. No. 200. 100mm.	6.00
Mary Queen of Scots Chair. 82mm.	5.50
Skull. 60mm long.	6.50

Traditional/National Souvenirs

Bagpipes, with turquoise ribbon. 118mm long.	13.00

Seaside Souvenirs

Grimsby fisherman, bust. 83mm.	10.50
Lighthouse, not named. 115mm.	3.00
Spurn lighthouse, with inscription. 130mm.	13.00
Withernsea Lighthouse, with inscription. 105mm & 130mm.	10.50

Animals

Cat, Chesire inscribed: *Still smiling*. 95mm.	5.50
Cat, sitting impressed box. No. 62. 75mm.	10.50
Cat with arched back. 65mm.	8.75
Dog, Bull Terrier, standing. 60mm.	6.00
Elephant, walking. 52mm.	6.50
Fish with open mouth. 103mm long.	2.00
Teddy Bear, sitting. 76mm.	7.00

Great War

Monoplane, with revolving prop. 150mm long.	30.00
Battleship, impressed: *HMS Lion*. 140mm long.	13.00
Submarine impressed: *E4*. 116mm long.	8.75
Red Cross Van. Red cross on side. 84mm long.	17.50
British Tank, Model of. 92mm long.	8.75
British Tank, Model of with trailing wheels. 130mm long.	10.50
Field Gun. 120mm long.	8.75
Field Gun, with screen. 115mm long.	13.00
Howitzer. 115mm long.	13.00
Glengarry, some colouring. 83mm long.	13.00
Fireplace with cooking pot, inscribed: *Keep the Home Fires*. No. 199. 80mm long.	6.50

Home/Nostalgic

Milk can with lid. 60mm.	3.00
Watering Can. 75mm.	4.75

Comic/Novelty

Billiken, not named. 73mm.	3.00
Dutch Boy. 80mm.	8.25

Alcohol

Beer Barrel on stand. 58mm.	2.50

Miscellaneous

Ladies Shoe with blue bow. 114mm long.	13.00
Mortar Board. 65mm long.	15.25

Waterloo Ware

Trademark probably used by a retailer for items thought to be produced by Sampson, Hancock & Sons, Stoke. (Usual trademark CORONA).

The only item to be found has a
  Sunderland Crest.

Buildings – White

Bottle Oven, inside of. 84mm.   8.75

Waverley China

For mark see *Crested China*, p. 269.

Trademark used for Wyman & Sons Ltd, by Arkinsall & Son, Ltd, Arcadian Works, Stoke-on-Trent. (Usual trademark Arcadian).

Ancient Artefacts
Glastonbury Bronze Bowl.
  2 models: No. 74. 40mm. No.
    100. 41mm.   2.25
Hastings Kettle. 62mm. No. 237   2.25
St Davids vase, inscribed: *vase
found at St Davids.* 69mm.   2.25

WCG

Wedgwood

For marks see *Crested China*, p. 269.

Trademark used by Josiah Wedgwood (and Sons Ltd), Etruria.

The famous firm of Wedgwood made a few small vases with crests at the turn of the century.   4.00

Trademark used by an unknown manufacturer.

Domestic ware only.   1.00–5.00

Wembley China

For mark see *Crested China*, p. 269.

Trademark used on china for sale at the British Empire Exhibition of 1924 and 1925 by the Cauldon Group of Companies. (Usual trademark Arcadian).

Parian/Unglazed

George V statue on glazed plinth inscribed: *A souvenir from Wembley*, with inscription: *King George V – Born June 3rd 1865 – Ascended the throne May 6th 1910*. 2 sizes: 125mm & 140mm.	35.00
Prince of Wales, (Edward VIII) bust on glazed plinth, with inscription: *HRH The Prince of Wales, Born June 23rd 1894*. 135mm.	35.00

Historical/Folklore

Miner's Lamp. 70mm.	8.50
Mother Shipton. 115mm.	8.50
Man in Stocks. 88mm.	12.50

Traditional/National Souvenirs

Thistle Vase. 70mm.	4.00
Welsh Hat. 52mm.	6.00
Welsh Teaparty group. 98mm.	25.00

Seaside Souvenirs

Bathing Machine. 65mm.	5.50
Yacht. 125mm.	10.50
Lighthouse, not named. 2 sizes: 110mm.	4.00
140mm.	6.00

Countryside

Beehive on table. 78mm.	6.50
Haystack, circular. 55mm.	3.50

Animals

Cat with long neck, sitting. 108mm.	8.25
Black Cat, sitting on armchair. 55mm.	24.50

Fawn. 50mm.	30.00
Frog, with open mouth. 62mm.	5.50
Monkey sitting. 69mm.	12.00
Pig, sitting and smiling. 63mm long.	7.50

Great War

Nurse and Wounded Tommy. 108mm long.	75.00
Sailor winding capstan, Model of. 105mm.	75.00
Soldier Bust, unnamed Tommy Atkins. Some colouring. 90mm.	21.75
Biplane, in lustre. 120mm long.	77.50
Armoured car, model of. 95mm long.	22.50
Tank, Model of. 115mm long.	9.50
Trench dagger. 105mm long.	40.00
Capstan. 56mm.	6.50
Pair of field glasses, Model of. 78mm long.	10.00
Officer's Peaked Cap. 65mm dia.	8.75
Cavell Memorial, inscribed: *Nurse Cavell*. 160mm.	12.50

Home/Nostalgic

Fireplace, no inscription but much colouring. 90mm.	9.50
Grandfather Clock. 108mm.	11.50
Kennel. 50mm.	4.50
Lantern, horn. 85mm.	5.25

Comic/Novelty

Hand holding pig's trotter. 110mm long.	5.50
Policeman on duty. 145mm.	15.00

Sport

Curling Stone. 49mm.	13.00

Transport

Car, open tourer, (2 seater). 110mm long.	23.75

Miscellaneous

Boy Scout's Hat. 73mm dia.	7.50

White Horse China

The White House

For mark see *Crested China*, p. 270.

Trademark used for a Manchester retailer by an unknown manufacturer.

Only one small recorded.   2.00

Trademark used for the Royal Mail Steam Packet Company by an unknown manufacturer.

All pieces known display transfer prints of ships.

Historical/Folklore
Coaching Hat, not named.
   No. 124. 39mm.   6.00

W.H.H. and S

For mark see *Crested China*, p. 270.

Trademark used by a German manufacturer, Wilhelm Kutzscher & Co. Schwarzenberger Porzellanfabrik, Schwarzenberg, Saxony (Now in East Germany).

Buildings – White
Clock Tower, not named. 125mm.   6.00

Monuments
Sir Francis Drake, statue.
   Plymouth. 163mm.   8.75

Animals
Dog, spaniel. Sitting. 60mm.   4.25
Elephants, two on a sledge or
   slope. 76mm.   18.50

Sport
Cricket Cap. 70mm long.   19.50

Wilco Series

For mark see *Crested China*, p. 270.

Trademark used for a retailer probably by Hewitt and Leadbeater. Willow Potteries. Longton. (Usual trademark Willow Art).

Animals
Rabbit, crouching with alert ears.
   No. 97. 60mm long.   4.00

Miniature Domestic
Cheesedish and cover. 50mm.   5.00

Williamsons

Willow Art and Willow China

For mark see *Crested China*, p. 293.

For mark see *Crested China*, p. 271.

Trademark used by H.M. Williamson and Sons, Bridge Pottery, Longton.

A range of crested domestic ware.

Ancient Artefacts
Guernsey Milk Can, with lid. 105mm. (Found with a Guernsey crest).   3.00

Trademark used by Hewitt and Leadbeater, Willow Potteries, Longton, subsequently, Hewitt Bros, and eventually Willow Potteries Ltd, a branch of Cauldon Ltd.

Models can be found marked Willow or Willow Art.

Parian/Unglazed
All the busts can be found impressed H. and L. (Hewitt and Leadbeater). The known busts form an odd group and one suspects that there are more to be recorded.

Busts

Bust of Albert King of the Belgians, not named on square glazed base. 170mm.	56.50
Bust of French, not named, on square glazed base. 170mm.	47.50
Bust of Burns impressed *Burns* and impressed on the reverse *H. Bros* on square unglazed base with a crest. 150mm.	16.00
Bust of Burns, not named, on circular glazed base. 140mm.	17.50
Bust of Sir Walter Scott, not named, on circular glazed base. 130mm.	14.00
Bust of Gladstone, not named, on circular glazed base. Can be found with crest of W.E. Gladstone on glazed base when £5 should be added. 160mm.	17.50
Bust of Shakespeare, on circular base. 120mm.	12.50

Ancient Artefacts

Beccles Ringers Jug, with full inscription. 67mm.	6.50

Chester Roman Jug, not named.
55mm.   1.75
Loving Cup. 2 and 3 handled.   2.25
Phoenician Water Jug, not
named. 66mm.   1.75
Puzzle Jug with verse: Try how to
drink. 70mm.   3.50

Buildings – Coloured
Coloured Buildings can be found
glazed or unglazed. Some of
these models can also be found
white.
Ann Hathaway's Cottage. 2 sizes:
60mm   14.00
105mm.   25.00
Battle Abbey Gateway.
139mm long.   40.00
Bell Hotel, Abel Fletcher's House in
John Halifax Gentleman. 3 sizes:
55mm   40.00
84mm   55.00
124mm.   65.00
John Bunyan's cottage. 75mm long.   65.00
Burns Cottage, Model of.
105mm long.   30.00
Burns House, inscribed: The poet
occupied this house from 1793
until his death 21st July 1796.
85mm.   40.00
Cat and Fiddle. 92mm.   110.00
Feathers Hotel, Ludlow.   110.00
Godalming Old Town Hall. 100mm.   110.00
Knox' House, inscribed: Model of
the house in Edinburgh where John
Knox the Scottish reformer died
24th Nov 1572. 102mm.   110.00
Old Blacksmiths shop and marriage
room, Gretna Green. 85mm long.   30.00
Old Chapel, Lantern Hill,
Ilfracombe. 76mm long.   45.00
Old Curiosity Shop. No. 14,
Portsmouth Street. 80mm long.   65.00
Old Maids Cottage, Lee near
Ilfracombe. 59mm long.   47.50
Old Ostrich Inn, Colnbrook. 80mm.   110.00
Historical, Old Mint House,
Pevensey 1342 AD. 120mm long.   130.00
The Olde Trip to Jerusalem Inn, 1199
AD, inscribed: Home Brewed
Ales. 106mm long.   110.00
St. Bernards Monastery, Coalville.
102mm long.   110.00

St. Ann's Well, Gt. Malvern.
167mm long. Rare.   105.00
St. Nicholas Church, Great
Yarmouth. 140mm long. Also
found unglazed.   41.50
Shakespeare's House. 4 sizes:
65mm   12.00
110mm   32.50
125mm   36.50
135mm long.   39.50
Tan House, Little Stretton. 120mm
long.   110.00
Upleatham Church. 90mm.   80.00
Whittington Inn, with inscription.
100mm long.   85.00
Wilberforce Museum with
inscription. Coloured grey.
115mm long.   85.00

Buildings – White
Bath Abbey, West Front. 110mm.   18.50
Bell Hotel, Abel Fletchers House in
John Halifax Gentleman. 2 sizes:
84mm & 124mm long.   21.75
Bell Hotel, Abel Fletchers House in
John Halifax Gentleman, on
ashtray base. Some colouring.
75mm long.   18.50
Big Ben. 146mm.   16.00
Blackpool Tower. 125mm.   9.50
Blackpool Tower, with buildings.
150mm.   7.50
Blackpool Tower, with buildings,
impressed: Variety, Dancing,
Concert. 165mm.   11.00
Bourne Abbey, West Font. 108mm.   30.00
John Bunyan's Cottage, Model of.
75mm long.   16.00
Burns Cottage, Model of, with
inscription. 105mm.   10.50
Burns Mausoleum, Dumfries.
95mm.   45.00
Bury St. Edmunds, Abbey Gate.
80mm.   30.00
Canterbury Cathedral, West Front.
125mm.   19.50
Canterbury, West Gate. 90mm.   16.00
Carillon Tower. 159mm.   20.00
Carnegie's Birthplace, inscribed:
The birthplace of Andrew
Carnegie. 85mm long.   30.00
Castle Hill Tower, Huddersfield.
115mm.   30.00

Chantry Front, Model of.	
95mm long.	30.00
Chatham, Town Hall, Model of.	
146mm.	32.50
Chesterfield Parish Church, Model of	
found with inscription.	
125mm.	24.50
Citadal Gateway, Plymouth.	
110mm.	19.50
Clifton Suspension Bridge, Model of,	
with long inscription.	
120mm long.	30.00
Conisborough Castle. The Keep.	
95mm.	75.00
Cottage, inscribed: *Built in a day*	
4th June 1819. 43mm long.	21.75
Crofter's Cottage. 55mm long.	13.00
Fair Maids House, Perth.	
78mm long.	40.00
First and last house in England.	
83mm long. With greendoor.	10.50
First and last house in England, with	
annexe. 95mm long.	21.50
Grimsby Hydraulic Tower.	
165mm.	21.75
Hampton Court Palace, flat frontage	
on ashtray base. 108mm long.	25.75
Hamsfell Hospice. Grange over	
Sands. (Often found not	
named). 72mm.	26.00
An odd square building with	
outside stairs and flat roof, and	
with impressed Greek	
inscription over door.	
Hasting Castle Ruins. 100mm.	22.00
Hastings Clock Tower. 165mm.	10.50
Hay Castle. 94mm.	41.50
Hop Pole Inn, flat frontage on	
ashtray base, with long	
quotation referring to the inn	
from Chapter 50 'The Pickwick	
Papers' by Charles Dickens, on	
ashtray. 60mm long.	35.00
Lancaster, Castle Gateway.	
90mm.	30.00
Leicester Clock Tower. 175mm.	13.00
Lincoln Cathedral, West Front.	
118mm.	18.50
Lincoln, Stonebrow. 104mm long.	19.50
Lloyd George's Home, inscribed.	
102mm long.	40.00
Loch Leven Castle, Kinross. 75mm.	45.00
Old London Bridge on ashtray base,	
small. 105mm long.	18.50

Mickelgate Bar, York. 116mm.	18.50
Monnow Bridge, Monmouth.	
92mm.	17.50
Monument, The. 160mm.	40.00
Morpeth Castle, Model of. 78mm.	45.00
Nottingham Castle, Model of.	
92mm long.	40.00
Old Bridge House, Ambleside.	
88mm.	43.00
Old Nottingham Inn. Ye Olde Trip to	
Jerusalem, 1199 AD, Model of.	
95mm.	48.00
Old Ostrich Inn, Colnbrook. 80mm.	30.00
Park Tower, Barnsley. 137mm.	35.00
Peterborough Cathedral, West Front.	
80mm long.	30.00
Peveril Castle. 115mm long.	35.00
Pump Room, Harrogate. 75mm.	40.00
St. Albans Clock Tower.	37.50
St. Ann's well, Buxton. 120mm.	27.50
St. Ann's Well, Great Malvern.	
102mm long.	56.50
St. Benet's Abbey, Norfolk Broads,	
castle ruins on ashtray base.	
70mm long.	45.00
St. Botolph's Church, Boston.	
112mm.	20.50
St. Denny's Church, Sleaford.	
2 sizes: 95mm & 134mm.	45.00
St. Nicholas' Church, Great	
Yarmouth. 143mm long.	45.00
Saville Fountain, Saville Gardens,	
Windsor. No. 730. 140mm.	43.50
Saxon Church, Bradford on Avon.	
74mm.	37.50
Shakespeare's House. 2 sizes:	
120mm.	16.50
160mm long.	17.50
Skegness, Clock Tower. 2 sizes:	
125mm.	12.50
165mm.	14.50
Skegness, Pier Entrance.	
85mm long.	35.00
Solomon's Temple, Grinlow Tower,	
inscribed: *Erected on site of a*	
prehistoric barrow. Buxton.	
88mm.	35.00
Temple Bar, Waltham Cross.	
100mm long.	25.00
Tennysons House, Mablethorpe.	
85mm long.	35.00
Tudor Gabled House, Taunton AD	
1878. 100mm.	24.50
Upleatham Church. 88mm.	17.50

Uttoxeter Market Place, Conduit,
Scene of Dr. Johnson's Penance.
123mm.   40.00
Wainhouse Tower, Halifax.
130mm.   24.50
Wallingford, Town Hall. 84mm.   56.50
West Malling, Abbey Tower. 94mm.   40.00
Whittington Inn with inscription.
100mm long.   37.50
Wilberforce House, Hull. 86mm.   35.00
Windsor Castle. 125mm long.   17.50
Windsor Castle. Round Tower.
76mm.   13.00
Worcester Cathedral. 144mm long.   40.00
Worksop, Priory Gate House,
88mm.   40.00

Monuments (including Crosses)
Ancient Runic Cross, Bakewell.
110mm.   16.00
Arwenack Monument, erected by
Martin Killigrew. AD 1787.
132mm.   11.00
Banbury Cross. 140mm.   13.00
The Blackwatch Memorial.
Edinburgh. 127mm. This
monument is the form of a
Scottish soldier on a square
base and is often not named.   47.50
Bruce statue, Stirling. 160mm.   40.00
Burns statue, on square base.
170mm.   16.00
Burns and Highland Mary.
2 sizes: 117mm   18.50
130mm   18.50
Bunyan statue. 165mm.   11.50
Burmah Cross, Taunton,
inscribed: *Burmah 1885–6–7* and
Somerset Light Infantry. 118mm. 56.50
Burton statue, inscribed: *Michael*
Arthur, first Baron Burton.
128mm.   16.00
Caister-on-Sea Lifeboat Memorial.
Moulded in relief: 1903 and
Caister Lifeboat on lifebelt.
162mm.   16.00
Carnegie Andrew statue. 150mm. 23.00
Cleethorpes Fishermans'
Memorial, with inscription:
Erected by Public Subscription to
the memory of George Henry
Smith (skipper) and William
Richard Leggatt (Third Hand) etc.
unveiled August 30th 1908.
155mm.   21.75

Old Cornish Cross, Model of,
100mm.   8.75
Drake, Statue, Plymouth. 160mm.   8.75
Druids Well, Sutton Park, Sutton
Coldfield. 45mm.   25.00
Flodden Cross, inscribed: *Flodden*
1513, to the brave of both nations.
136mm.   15.25
General Sir Redvers Buller's Cross at
Crediton, model of. 100mm.   35.00
Gibbet Cross, Hindhead,
inscribed: *Post Tenebras Lux In*
Luce Spes In Obrtu Pax Post
Obitum Salus. 136mm.   10.50
Gladstone Statue, Blackburn.
130mm.   26.50
Hector Macdonald Memorial,
Dingwall. 112mm.   55.00
Highland Mary Statue, Dunoon,
on plinth. 150mm.   21.75
Huddersfield, Market Cross.
150mm.   24.50
Tom Hughes Monument Rugby
School. 140mm.   30.00
Hull Fisherman's Memorial.
2 sizes: 135mm.   13.00
160mm.   16.00
Hull South African War
Memorial, with inscription:
Erected to the memory of the men of
Hull who fell in the late South
African War. 165mm.   16.00
Keppels Column 1778. 140mm.   37.50
King George Statue, Kingstown.
135mm.   40.00
Laceby, The Monument.
2 sizes: 120mm   19.50
150mm   21.75
Lord Myton of Holderness.
155mm.   35.00
Lowestoft Fisherman's Memorial.
130mm.   23.00
Maiwand Memorial Forbury
Gardens Reading. Lion
sometimes coloured black.
98mm.   13.50
Black lion.   21.00
Margate Surf Boat Monument,
with usual lengthy inscription.
130mm.   14.50
Nelson's Column. 160mm.   40.00
Isaac Newton, statue. 165mm.   15.25
Peter Pan, statue. 140mm.   47.50
Queen Victoria's Statue,
Wakefield. 115mm.   30.00

Saxon Soldier, statue on square
base. 125mm. 30.00
Sir William de la Pole, Statue of, with
long inscription of its
presentation and the history of
Sir William. 160mm. 16.00
Richmond Market Cross. 137mm. 12.50
Rock of Ages, usual verse &
inscription. 80mm. 6.50
C.S. Rolls Memorial, inscribed:
Memorial to the late Honourable
C.S. Rolls. 128mm. 28.00
Rufus Stone. 110mm. 4.00
Ruskin Memorial, Friars Crag.
180mm. 18.00
Sailor's Stone, Hindhead. 95mm. 8.75
St. Alban, Statue of. 146mm. 65.00
Scone, The Cross. 142mm. 23.00
Toad Rock, Tunbridge Wells.
83mm. 12.50

Historical/Folklore

Archbishops Chair, Canterbury
Cathedral. 100mm. 10.50
inscribed. 12.50
Bangor Abbey Bell, inscribed:
Model of the old bell, Bangor
Abbey, Co. Down. 85mm. 13.50
Bill Sykes and his dog, standing
figure on base. Coloured beige,
no crest. 128mm. 40.00
Bishop's Jester, Wells Cathedral.
Fully coloured. No crest.
2 sizes: 110mm 40.00
125mm 65.00
Bunyan's Chair, Model of. 90mm. 8.00
Bunyan's Cushion, Model of.
105mm long. 13.00
Burns Chair, Dumfries.
85mm. 6.50
Daniel Lambert, sitting on chair.
With long inscription.
118mm. 40.00
Devil looking over Lincoln. 115mm. 16.00
The Ducking Stool, with
inscription as Arcadian.
120mm. 87.50
Father Christmas carrying sack of
toys. 110mm. 50.00
Font, not named. 87mm. 6.00
James V Chair, Stirling Castle.
100mm. 6.50
Lady Godiva. 80mm. 24.50

Man in the Moon. 55mm. 12.50
Mary Queen of Scots Chair.
Edinburgh Castle, Model of.
75mm. 5.50
Mermaid, seated on rock,
combing hair. 105mm. 15.25
Mons Meg, Edinburgh Castle.
130mm long. 7.50
Mother Shipton.
2 sizes: 80mm. 4.00
105mm. 7.50
Peeping Tom, bust. 130mm. 16.00
Ripon Hornblower. 120mm. 8.25
A rubbing stone for asses, a 17th
century puzzle printed on a
brick wall. 100mm long. 35.00
Shakespeare's Font on hexagonal
plinth, inscribed: Model of Font
in which Shakespeare was
baptised. 128mm. 20.00
Sir Walter scots Chair, Abbotsford,
Model of. 80mm. 6.50
Skull, can be inscribed: Alas poor
Yorick. 60mm long. 7.50
Sundial, Tideswell Church, Model
of. 110mm. 8.75
Trusty Servant, with verse on
both sides, fully coloured.
132mm. 65.00

Traditional/National Souvenirs

John Bull, standing. 120mm. 21.75
Banbury cake. 105mm wide. 19.50
Bolton Trotter. 4.50
Blackpool Big Wheel.
2 sizes: 88mm 4.50
100mm. 10.50
Blackpool Big Wheel, rectangular
base. 120mm. 12.50
Cheddar Cheese, slice out.
70mm dia. 4.50
Cornish Pasty. 100mm long. 4.50
Chester Imp, The. 80mm. 30.00
Englishman, bust, wearing Black
coat. 76mm. 19.00
Lancashire Clog. 88mm long. 4.00
Leaking boot. Grimsby. 22.50
Lincoln Imp. 63mm. 4.00
Lincoln Imp, on pedestal. 102mm. 5.50
Manx Man, John Bull as above but
with an extra leg added at rear.
Same colouring. 120mm. 50.00
Melton Mowbray Pie with verse.
55mm. 12.50

Reading Biscuit, with verse: *Than Reading biscuits there are no finer, Here's a good one reproduced in china*. Coloured fawn. 85mm long. 30.00

can also be found on stand. 32.50

River Thames pleasure punt, 175mm long. 45.00

with coloured cushions add £20.

Yarmouth bloater. 121mm. 2.50

Irish Harp. 105mm. 5.00

Irishman, bust, No. 115. Wearing Black hat. 78mm. 19.00

Bagpipes. 118mm long. 13.00

Blacksmiths Anvil, Gretna Green, often found not named, with inscription. 76mm. 4.75

Burns and Highland Mary, impressed and inscribed. 115mm. 19.50

Jimmy Strength, with inscription: *A well known Border character whose name was James Stuart a descendant of the Royal Family of that name. He was famous for his age and great strength and died in his 123rd year*: Figure on square plinth. 114mm. 72.50

Scotsman, bust. No. 116. Wearing Tam o'Shanter. 80mm. 19.00

Scotsman matches holder. Comic fully coloured figure. Inscribed: *Matches*. 90mm. 14.00

Souter Johnny, sitting figure, with verse. 130mm. 21.75

Tam O'Shanter, sitting figure, with verse. Can be found with some colouring. 135mm. 21.75

Thistle Vase. 50mm. 2.00

Welsh Hat, Model of, with longest place name. 52mm. (Arcadian mould). 5.50

Welsh Hat, can have blue hat band. Can be found with longest Welsh place name printed round brim. 57mm. inscribed. 3.00 / 4.75

Welsh Harp, very delicate. 90mm. 5.00

Welsh Lady, bust, with black hat. No. 117. 110mm. 18.50

Welsh Leek. 55mm. 2.25

Welsh tea party, a figure group, some colouring. 50mm. 15.25

Seaside Souvenirs

Bathing Machine, inscribed: *A morning dip*.
2 sizes: 65mm. 4.75
80mm. 6.50

Lifeboat, coloured ropes if found inscribed: *A.E. Davies* add £7.00. 118mm long. 4.75

Motorboat, with driver, at sea. 115mm long. 13.00

Paddlesteamer. 154mm long (rare). 40.00

Rowing boat on rocks, can be found inscribed: *The City of Glasgow*. 11.75

Yacht in full sail. 122mm. 8.25

Lifeboatman, standing on plinth (hand raised to hat). 19.50

Fisherman's Basket with handle. 77mm long. 3.50

A Yarmouth fish swill, basket. 40mm. 6.50

Lighthouse, not named. 100mm. 3.00

Lighthouse on rocks with brown rowing boat. 133mm. 14.00

Beachy Head lighthouse, with black band. 136mm. 5.50

Flamborough Lighthouse. 110mm. 16.00

North Foreland Lighthouse. 135mm. 19.50

Scarborough Lighthouse, with inscription. 132mm. 47.50

Scarborough Lighthouse, with rectangular buildings. 110mm. 66.50

Spurn Lighthouse, with details of size and power. 125mm. 13.50

Withernsea Lighthouse, with details of size and power. 127mm. 10.50

Crab. 83mm long. 7.50

Shell menu holder on coral base. No. 360. 90mm. 6.50

Scallop Shell flower holder, on rocky base. 92mm. 3.50

Whelk shell, inscribed: *Listen to the sea*. 110mm. 2.50

Open bag with four feet. 4.00

Stick of Rock, pink stick with resort printed (very realistic) so far *Great Yarmouth* and *Southsea* have been recorded. *Bexhill-on-Sea* has been found as a Pepper pot, white, glazed. 75mm.
White 35.00
Pink 70.00

Truck of Sand, same model as
truck of coal but with coal
painted yellow, can be
inscribed: *sand for the kiddies
from . . . .* or *A truck of sand from
. . . .* 90mm long.   30.00

Countryside

Pinecone. 90mm.   3.00
Treetrunk vase, four necks.
80mm.   3.50

Animals

Bear, sitting. No. 112. 70mm.   15.00
Boar, standing on rocky base.
102mm long. Two varieties of
base may be found.   35.00
Bulldog, sitting, feet moulded
separately. Black Collar and
red mouth. 55mm.   13.00
Bulldog, sitting, feet internally
moulded. 50mm.   12.50
Bulldog, black, emerging from
kennel inscribed: *The Black
Watch*. 70mm long.   7.50
Cat, angry, with tail in the air.
Blue bow. 80mm long.   8.75
Cat, in Boot. 88mm long.   11.00
Cat, *Cheshire*, with coloured face.
Inscribed: *Always smiling*.
95mm.   6.50
Cat's head on base. 60mm.   16.00
Cat, sitting, bow round neck.
80mm.   6.50
Cat, sitting, blue bow. 60mm   7.50
Cat, sitting. Large red bow, and
red and green eyes. 70mm.   8.25
Cat, sitting, detailed thick coat,
and tail around paws. 57mm.   10.00
Cat, standing, chubby. 70mm.   8.25
Cat, standing (long back), green
eyes and red tongue.
117mm long.   30.00

Black Cats

See 'Crested China' page 281 for
details of Willow Black Cats.
Black Cat on Curling Stone.
60mm.   35.00
Black Cat on Cushion. 100mm.   17.50
Black Cat on Diamond Ashtray,
inscribed: *Ashtray* and *Good
Luck*. 120mm long.   16.00
Black Cat on Pouffe, inscribed:
Good luck. Can be found with
blue bow. 85mm. Impressed.
No. 539. 95mm.   19.50

Smaller Arcadian type Black Cats

Black Cat, playing Bagpipes.
60mm.   56.50
Black Cat with bottle. 70mm (Arc.
Mould).   30.00
Black Cat, wearing kilt and sitting
on a curling stone.   60.00
Black Cat, playing Bagpipes,
and wearing kilt, standing on
thistle ashtray. 88mm long.   56.50
Black Cat on golf ball. 70mm.   60.00
Black Cat, standing beside thistle
vase. 57mm.   56.50
Black Cat, playing Harp. 60mm.   65.00
Black Cat, wearing a Welsh Hat,
standing beside a Leek. 67mm.   65.00
Black Cat, climbing into cup,
inscribed: *May your cup of Good
Luck brim over*. 90mm. *Willow*.   56.50

Cow. 105mm long.   21.75
Deer, sitting. 2 sizes: 64mm   25.00
                        115mm long.   30.00
Dog, Bulldog, sitting, feet
moulded separately. Black
collar and red mouth. 55mm.   13.00
Dog, Bulldog, sitting, feet
integrally moulded. 50mm.   12.50
Dog, Bulldog, black, emerging
from kennel, inscribed: *The
Black Watch*. 70mm long.   7.50
Dog, Bull Terrier, standing.
60mm.   7.50
Dog, Collie, sitting. 78mm.   6.50
Dog, Collie, standing. 85mm.   8.25
Dog, Dachshund, sitting, long
ears and rather comic. 75mm.   40.00
Dog, foxhound, 69mm.   15.25
Dog, The Manx three legged,
often found not named.
Inscribed: *Prince Toby Orry*.
70mm.   30.00
Dog, rather like St. Bernard. No.
116. 50mm.   20.50
Dog, Scottie, wearing a glengarry.
2 sizes: 60mm.   5.50
        100mm.   7.50
Dog, Scottie, wearing a tam o'
shanter. 60mm.   6.50
Dog, Scottish Terrier, standing.
90mm long.   7.00
Donkey in harness.
No. 294. 110mm long.   12.50
Elephant, with trunk in the air.
80mm long.   7.50
Elephant, walking.
No. 113. 52mm.   6.50
Elephant Jug. 70mm.   4.00

Fish Ashtray, in shape of plaice. 78mm long.	4.00
Fish, curved. 75mm long.	4.50
Fish, straight. 130mm long.	3.00
Fish, straight, with open mouth. 115mm long.	2.50
Fox. 100mm.	40.00
Hare. 77mm long.	7.00
Highland Bull, inscribed: *King of the Herd*. 115mm long.	43.50
Kangaroo. 115mm.	46.50
Lion, crouching. Red open mouth. 82mm long.	16.00
Lion, crouching, red open mouth on base, roaring at a tiny mouse on a green apple, inscribed: *Much ado about nothing*. 110mm.	37.00
Lion, walking. 105mm long & 160mm long.	15.00
Lion with mane and 'furry' legs. 164mm long. (Pair with Arcadian Lioness).	10.50
Monkey, holding coconut. 85mm.	7.50
Three Monkeys on diamond shaped ashtray. Monkeys inscribed: *See not evil speak not evil, hear not evil*. 130mm long.	13.00
Mouse. 62mm.	12.50
Pig, sitting on haunches can be found inscribed: *You may push* etc. 60mm.	11.00
Pig, standing, Very fat, with double chin. 96mm long.	12.50
Pig, fat, ears pointing forward. 82mm long.	10.00
Polar Bear. 96mm.	30.00
Polar Bear, sitting. 83mm.	30.00
Pony, inscribed: *A Native of Shetland*. 108mm long.	19.50
Rabbit, lying down. 54mm long.	4.00
Rabbit, sitting, alert ears. 60mm long.	4.00
Ram, with curly horns. 90mm long.	23.00
Rhinoceros, standing. 87mm long.	40.00
Stag, lying down. 115mm long.	35.00
Teddy Bear, sitting. 65mm and 75mm.	7.00
Toad, grotesque. 80mm long.	19.50
Tortoise. 88mm long.	4.00
Isnt this rabbit a duck: On its base a rabbit, turned on its side, a duck. 75mm.	17.00

Birds (including eggs)

Bird (reputedly a tit). 77mm long.	7.50
Bird on plinth. 103mm.	6.50
Bird Posy Holder. 104mm long.	2.50
Canary on rock, can be found coloured yellow on green base, 98mm. White	6.50
Coloured	13.00
Chicken, very fluffy. 65mm.	4.50
Chicken-Pepper Pot. 70mm.	2.50
Chicken, emerging from egg, inscribed: *Every little helps mother will be pleased*. 50mm. Willow.	12.50
Cock. 100mm.	8.25
Goose, some colouring. 155mm.	28.00
Pelican, with inscription: *A wonderful bird is the pelican, his beak will hold more than his belican*. 75mm.	21.75
Swan, with yellow beak. 60mm.	3.50
Swan, with head on breast. 58mm.	3.50
Swan Posy Holder. 2 sizes: 65mm.	2.25
93mm long.	2.25
Turkey. 57mm.	10.50
Wise Owl with verse: *An aged owl sat in an oak etc*. 98mm.	7.50

Great War

Airman, standing to attention. 140mm.	157.50
Air Force Officer, a hero holding medal. 140mm.	157.50
Can rarely be found coloured.	220.00
Nurse, inscribed: *A friend in need*. 130mm.	25.75
Sailor, at attention, inscribed: *Our brave defender*. 130mm.	25.75
N.B. 170mm size not now thought to exist.	
Soldier, with rifle, inscribed: *Our brave defender*. 132mm.	21.75
Monoplane, with fixed prop. 164mm long.	30.00
Monoplane with revolving prop. no colourings. No. 67. 150mm long.	30.00
Monoplane with revolving prop., coloured roundels on wings, and stripes on tail. 150mm long.	47.50
Aeroplane Propeller. 150mm long.	13.00

Airship (Observation Balloon), inscribed: *Beta*. 80mm long. — 30.00

Battleship. 4 funnels. 127mm long. — 13.00

Battleship, impressed: *HMS Lion*. 140mm long. A rare variety with black mast and red striped funnels has been seen. — 17.00

Troop Carrier, Liner converted. No. 213. 140mm long. — 90.00

Submarine, impressed: *E5*. 116mm long. — 13.00

Submarine, inscribed: *E4*. 95mm long. — 8.75

Red Cross Van, red cross on side. 84mm long. — 17.50

British Tank, Model of. 92mm long. — 10.00

British Tank, Model of. With trailing wheels. 130mm long. — 13.00

Field Gun. 120mm long. — 11.00

Field Gun, with screen. 115mm long. — 13.00

Howitzer. 115mm long. — 13.00

Cannon shell. 70mm long. — 2.25

Bandsman's Drum, with cording. 60mm. — 4.75

Bugle. No. 379. 2 sizes: l70mm — 7.50
115mm long. — 12.50

Field Glasses. 83mm. — 10.00

Forage Cap. 83mm long. — 16.00

Glengarry. Some colouring. 83mm long. — 13.00

Kit Bag with verse: *Pack up your troubles in your old kit bag*. No. 220. 74mm. — 10.50

Officer's Peaked Cap. 70mm dia. — 5.50

Pickelhaube (German Spiked Helmet). 50mm. — 13.00

Tent, cone shaped with open flaps on base. 70mm. — 10.50

Tommy's Steel Helmet. 76mm long. — 16.00

Trench Lamp. 70mm. — 8.75

Fireplace, inscribed:*Keep the home fires burning*. Some colouring. 100mm long. — 8.75

Kitchen range, with pot on fire, inscribed: *Keep the home fires burning*. Some colouring. 78mm long. — 6.50

Edith Cavell. Statue, London, inscribed:*Brussels dawn Oct 12th 1915. Sacrifice, Humanity*. 2 sizes: 110mm — 7.50
150mm. — 11.50

Edith Cavell, Nurse. Patriot and martyr, memorial statue. Norwich. 2 sizes: 155mm. — 17.00
175mm. — 17.00

Cenotaph, inscribed: *The Glorious Dead MCMXIV-MCMXIX* with green wreaths. 3 sizes: 70mm. — 4.00
145mm. — 4.00
184mm. — 7.50

Chatham *Naval War Memorial*. 160mm. — 41.50

Coalville War Memorial. 135mm. — 65.00

Dumfries War Memorial, inscribed: *Black Watch*. 130mm. — 65.00

Florence Nightingale Statue, Model of. Can be found inscribed: *Florence Nightingale 1825—1910*. 2 sizes: 120mm. — 10.00
160mm. — 13.50

Great Yarmouth War Memorial. With inscription. 166mm. — 21.75

Ilkeston War Memorial, with inscription. — 65.00

Loughborough War Memorial. 155mm. — 60.00

Matlock Bath *War Memorial*, inscribed 182mm. — 19.50

Southsea. *Royal Naval War Memorial*. 160mm. (Chatham, Plymouth and Southsea War Memorials are identical in design and value.) — 41.50

Worthing War Memorial, inscribed: *Duty nobly done 1914–1918*. 170mm. — 55.00

Home/Nostalgic

Ali Baba Storage Basket, very detailed. 75mm. — 2.00

Anvil on base, can be found inscribed:*A Sussex Legend*, with verse. 35mm. — 4.75

Basket, oval with handle. 70mm long. — 1.75

Bell, inscribed: *Curfew must not ring tonight*. No. 107. 65mm. — 4.50

Book, Model of. 57mm.	3.50
Child smiling, bust. 60mm.	10.00
Chinese Lantern. 80mm.	8.25
Coal Scuttle, helmet shaped. 53mm.	2.75
Dressing table mirror, with one drawer. 87mm.	10.00
Fireplace, inscribed: *There's no place like home.* 70mm.	13.00
Flat Iron. 64mm.	4.75
Flat Iron on stand. (2 pieces). 66mm.	7.50
Garden Roller. 51mm.	5.50
Garden Trug. 75mm long.	1.75
Grandfather Clock, found inscribed: *Make use of time let not advantage slip. Shakespeare,* or more rarely: *nae man can tetha time or tide. Burns.* 2 sizes: 112mm and 128mm.	11.50
Hand mirror with reflective silvering. 150mm long.	13.00
Milk Can with lid. 60mm.	3.00
Old Armchair with verse. 88mm.	4.00
Pail, with moulded rope handle. 63mm.	3.00
Pillar box, impressed G.R., inscribed: *If you haven't got time to post a line here's the pillar box.* 78mm.	6.50
Pillar Box, impressed GR. 90mm.	14.50
Pipe. 93mm long.	12.50
Shaving Mug. No. 125. 2 sizes: 55mm.	5.00
70mm.	5.50
Sundial, circular with round base, with inscription: *I mark not the hours.* 118mm.	7.50
Sundial, circular on square base, with inscription: *I mark not the hours.* 98mm.	5.50
Umbrella. 50mm.	8.75
Watering Can. 75mm.	4.75
Wheelbarrow. 105mm long.	6.00

Comic/Novelty

Basket of Milk, six bottles with brown tops. 64mm.	9.50
Biliken, The god of luck, often found unnamed. 73mm.	3.00
Billiken, The God of luck, sitting on high backed chair. 100mm.	3.50
Boy on Pigs back, boy fully coloured. 94mm long.	75.00

Broadbean pod splitting open, inscribed: *Good old bean.* 130mm long.	16.00
Dutch Boy. 80mm. Can be found fully coloured when £10.00 should be added.	6.50
Dutch Girl. 80mm. Can be found fully coloured when £10.00 should be added. (A pair to the Dutch Boy.)	6.50
Fat Lady on weighing scales, scale registers 20 stone, inscribed: *Adding weight.* Blue Bonnet. 90mm.	25.75
Policeman, very jolly. 80mm. *Willow* version found fully coloured.	16.00
Sack of Meal with Mouse, inscribed: *May the mouse ne'er leave yer meal-poke wi' a tear-drop'n its e'e.* 63mm.	8.75
With brown mouse.	10.50
A truck of coal from . . . Wagon of black coal, also found with coal painted grey and inscribed: *A truck of iron ore from . . .* 90mm long.	14.00

Black Boys

All of these boys are fully coloured but sit on white boxes etc. All uncommon.

Black Boy, playing drum. 70mm.	66.50
Black Boy, in bath of ink, inscribed: *How ink is made.* 110mm.	65.50
Black Boy, in bed with spider, inscribed: *A little study in black and fright.* Boy can be have red or blue pyjamas. 70mm long.	40.00
Black boy in bed, face coloured, inscribed: *Just a little Study in black and white.* 62mm long.	40.00
Black Boy, eating slice of melon, sitting on soap box. 80mm.	75.00
Black boy with pumpkin. 80mm.	85.00
Black Boy, at table eating a boiled egg which has a chicken popping out. 70mm.	75.50

Two Black Boys, heads popping out of box, inscribed: *Box of chocolates.* Can be found with boys painted as white children, yellow hair and blue eyes and is

often found not coloured at all.
60mm.
Coloured 30.00
White 13.00
Black Boy, holding container for
matches. 100mm. 56.50

Little Birds
From Arcadian moulds. Head
fully coloured, eggs white.
Flapper's head hatching from
egg, inscribed: *A little bird from
. . .* 50mm long. 12.50
Black Boy's head hatching from
egg, inscribed: *A blackbird from
. . .* 50mm long. 21.75

Comic Ashtrays
Scotsman, really grotesque,
sitting on white bench on white
ashtray. 95mm. 18.50
Scotsman can be found coloured. ... 32.50

Cartoon/Comedy Characters
Baby, with arms outstretched,
inscribed: *Cheerio.* Some
colouring on face. 125mm. 16.00
Baby, saluting, inscribed: *One of
the b'hoys.* Can be found with
A.W.W.H. on chest. Some
colouring on face. 2 sizes
125mm & 150mm. 30.00
Harry Lauder, bust. Brown Hat
with thistle. 80mm. 9.50
Can be found named. 17.50
Dr. Beetle (impressed). 142mm. ... 40.00
Teddytail, impressed. 142mm. ... 40.00
Two Cartoon Characters sitting in
Armchair. 90mm. (Thought to
be Dr. Beetle and Sunny Jim!) ... 50.00
Winkie, not named, inscribed:
Glad Eyes on beak. 60mm. 6.50

Alcohol
Barrel. 50mm. 2.25
Barrel on stand. No. 35. 58mm. ... 3.00
Barrel with opening on one side.
54mm long. 3.50
Beer bottle with red hand. 98mm. ... 8.75
Beer Bottle and Tankard on
horseshoe ashtray, with
inscription: *The more we are
together the merrier we'll be.*
Silver Tankard. 85mm. 7.50

Bottle. No. 104. 90mm. 4.00
Drunks, two on ashtray,
inscribed: *Another little drink
wouldn't do us any harm.* 92mm. ... 22.50
Hand, holding beaker, inscribed:
Good health. 50mm. 4.75
Monk holding tankard. 155mm. ... 9.00
Stud, lapel with miniature bottle
attached, inscribed *The More We
are together. The Merrier we will
be at Yarmouth* (Great). 31mm.
Rare. 30.00
Tankard, foaming. 58mm. 4.00
Thimble, inscribed: *Just a
thimbleful.* 50mm. 8.75
Thistle Vase, with verse: *A wee
Deoch an Doris.* 56mm. 3.00
Toby Jug. 78mm. 7.50
Whisky Bottle, inscribed: *One
special scotch.* 63mm. 4.00
Whisky Bottle, with cork,
inscribed: *One special scotch.*
88mm. 4.50
Whisky Bottle and Soda Syphon
on Tray, inscribed: *Scotch and
soda.* 88mm dia. 7.50
Whisky Bottle, Soda Syphon on
Tumbler on horseshoe ashtray.
With inscription: *The more we
are together, the merrier we will be*
or *Scotch and Soda.* Some
colouring. 2 sizes: 87mm long ... 7.50
　　　　　　　　　 115mm long. ... 8.75

Sport
Golfer's Caddie holding golf bag,
figure coloured. 110mm. 65.00
Golf clubs in bag. 108mm. 22.50
Football. 50mm dia. 4.00
Jockey on Racehorse on base
found in different coloured
silks. Can be found coloured
but unglazed. 2 sizes 104mm &
112mm. 87.50
Racehorse, impressed. 102mm. ... 75.00

Musical Instruments
Banjo. 160mm long. 4.75
Guitar. 163mm long. 5.50

Transport
Car, open 4 seater. 2 sizes 114mm
& 140mm long. 21.75
Car, open 2 seater. 116mm long. ... 21.75

Tram, double decker, open top.
Inscribed: *Life on the ocean wave*.
No. 333. 108mm long.   75.00
Can of Petrol, impressed: *Motor*
spirit. 55mm.   8.75

'Modern' Equipment
Camera, folding. 60mm.   19.50
Horn Gramophone, square.
95mm.   17.00
Horn Gramophone on round
base. 60mm.   22.50
Radio Horn, inscribed: *Hello* . . .
(name of town) *calling*. 70mm.   13.00

Miscellaneous
Book. No. 71. 60mm.   3.50
Boot. 112mm long.   7.50
Cauldron, 2 handles. 36mm.   2.00
Cauldron, on three feet. 60mm.   2.50
Ladies' Riding Shoe, square toe
and blue tie. 115mm long.   13.00
Sabot. No. 334. 75mm long.   4.00
Edwardian Shoe, blue bow.
110mm long.   7.50
Slipper Wall Pocket, blue bow.
178mm long.   12.50
Bell. 60mm.   3.00
Hammer Head, Matchholder,
inscribed: *My speciality is*
striking or *Matches*. 80mm long.   9.00
Hand holding a tulip.
No. 74. 80mm.   2.25
Horse shoe ashtray. 80mm.   2.00
Pipe. 76mm long.   13.00
Wedding ring, gold, in open box.
60mm.   13.00

Miniature Domestic
Cheesedish, one piece. 45mm.   5.00
Cheese dish and cover. 45mm.   5.00
Coffee Pot with lid. 70mm.   3.00
Teapot with lid. 60mm.   4.00

Interesting Domestic Items with
Crests
Bridge Trump indicator.
Coloured suit symbols on
circular base, spinning cover
allowing only one suit to be
seen. Very ornate. 104mm dia.   18.00
Diamond, Trump indicator.
65mm.   6.00
Hairpins, box. 105mm.   3.00

Hat Pins, curved fluted holder.
125mm.   5.50
Pin Box, horseshoe shaped.
62mm.   3.00
Pin Box, oval, with safety pin in
relief on lid. 90mm long.   6.00
Playing cards, box. 154mm long.   4.00

Trinket Box, oval on eight collar
stud feet with moulded
cufflinks placed between each
stud. Border of moulded
cufflinks and tie pin in relief on
lid. 90mm long.   6.50

Willper Heraldic China

Wilton China

For mark see *Crested China*, p. 293.

For mark see *Crested China*, p. 293.

Trademark used by an unknown Hanley manufacturer.

Only two 'smalls' have been seen
to date. Each: 2.00

N.B. The second mark given on that page should be dated 1932–1934.

Trademark used by A.G. Harley Jones at Wilton Pottery, Fenton.

Ancient Artefacts

Ancient Tyg, 1 handle. 70mm.	1.75
Bronze Pot, not named. 35mm.	1.75
Loving Cup, 3 handles. 39mm.	2.25

Buildings – Coloured
These can be found with crests
Feathers Hotel. 1600. Ludlow.
80mm long.   56.50
Shakespeare's House. 53mm long.   12.00

Buildings – White
Ann Hathaway's Cottage, on
ashtray base in lustre.   8.25
Ann Hathaway's Night light in
pearl lustre, 106mm long.   9.50
Blackpool Tower, found in lustre.
92mm.   5.00
Blackpool Tower and buildings.
175mm.   6.50
Christchurch Priory. 108mm.   19.50
Cottage, Thatched. (Probably
unnamed Anne Hathaway's
Cottage.) 56mm long.   6.00
Shakespeare's House. 53mm long.   6.00

Monuments
Liberty Statue. 175mm.   26.00
Toad Rock near Hathersage. 95mm
long.   26.00

Historical/Folklore
Dick Whittington and cat on
ashtray base, inscribed: *IV miles
to London* on milestone and
Turn again Whittington on
ashtray. 110mm.   65.00

Traditional/National Souvenirs

Blackpool Big Wheel. 105mm.
Found with the Felix transfer
and Pathe trademark,
inscribed: *Felix the cat comes to
Blackpool*.   13.00
Irish Harp, with green
shamrocks. 105mm.   5.00
Welsh Hat. 2 sizes:
35mm.   8.50
70mm.   7.00

Seaside

Bathing Machine with girl in
doorway. Can be found with
some colouring, lustre or
inscribed: *Morning Dip' 7 a.m.!*
100mm.   8.50
Fisherman's creel, fish on lid,
inscribed: *A good catch*.
88mm long.   3.50
Sailing Yacht, inscribed: *Saucy
Sue*. 125mm.   16.00
Lighthouse, inscribed: *Sailor
beware*. Found in lustre.
155mm.   5.50

Animals

Cat on pouffe, outpressed *Luck*.
62mm.   19.50
Cat, sitting, red bow. 60mm.   8.50
Cat, sitting, inscribed: *Luck*. Red
tongue. 102mm.   5.50
Black cat on lid of fishing creel,
inscribed: *I'm here just for luck*.
80mm.   24.50
Black cat on cheese, mouse at
base. 80mm.   27.50
Terrier Dog, sitting, lustre.
85mm.   10.50
Dog, begging. 72mm.   7.00
Dog, Pug. 57mm.   6.00
Pig, inscribed: *You may push*.   9.00

Birds

Cock. 70mm long.   8.25
Duck, sitting. Found in lustre.
50mm.   4.25
Turkey. 55mm.   8.25

Great War

Sailor, kneeling, and holding
submarine. Blue cap band.   30.00
75mm coloured.   40.00

Battleship, tall top mast and no
forward guns. 115mm long.   13.00
Fieldglasses. 83mm.   8.75
Folkestone War Memorial,
inscribed: *Road of Remembrance*.
78mm.   56.50
St. Anne's *War Memorial*. 152mm.   60.00
Thetford *War Memorial*. 150mm.   82.50
Walsall War Memorial.   75.00

Home/Nostalgic

Book with clasp. 65mm.   3.00
Grandfather Clock, inscribed:
*Make use of time let not advantage
slip*. 128mm.   8.00
Sundial, inscribed: *What o'clock
and Serene I stand among the
flowers and only count life's sunny
hours*. 146mm.   9.50

Comic/Novelty

Bookmaker, standing figure,
inscribed: *6 to 4 the field*. 80mm.   65.00
Broke to the wide, man standing
with head and shoulders
bowed. 82mm.   60.00
Open Razor Ashtray, inscribed:
Got me through many a scrape.
95mm long.   28.00
Tramp holding glass of beer,
sitting by milestone, inscribed:
*Its better to be alive with eighteen
pence than dead with a thousand
pounds*. 76mm.   47.50
Truck of Coal, inscribed: *Black
Diamonds*. Black coal,
sometimes found unpainted.
Found in lustre. 98mm long.   10.50

Cartoon/Comedy Characters

Bonzo Dog. Lustre. 48mm.   21.75
Can also be found sitting on a
lustre ashtray base.
110mm long.   16.00
Comedian, standing figure
wearing brown Oxford bags,
black jacket, blue tie, brown
trilby hat and black shoes.
96mm (rare).   56.50
Mutt and Jeff, on rectangular
base. 105mm long.   52.50

Alcohol

Barrel of Beer, on stand. 55mm.   3.00
Whiskey Bottle. 98mm.   4.00

'Modern' Equipment

Horn gramophone, inscribed: *His Master's Voice*. 104mm.	22.75
Radio operator, inscribed: *Listening in*. Some colouring. Found lustre. 80mm.	30.00
Telephone, upright. 105mm.	8.75

Miscellaneous

Bishop, Chess Piece. 70mm.	12.50
Cigarettes, octagonal holder. 64mm.	3.00
Pastry cutter, clover shaped. 90mm long.	6.00
Thimble. 43mm.	8.75

Miniature Domestic

Cheese dish, 1 piece. 50mm.	5.00
Cheese dish and cover, horseshoe shaped. 45mm.	10.00

Wil-Wat China

For mark see *Crested China*, p. 297.

Trademark used for a retailer by Alfred B. Jones and Sons Ltd, Grafton China Works, Longton. (Usual trademark Grafton).

Monuments

The Monument, Laceby. 150mm.	16.00

Traditional/National Souvenirs

Leaking boot, Cleethorps. (Statue of boy, boot joined to hand by string). 156mm.	27.00

Animals

Fish, straight, with open mouth. 100mm long.	3.00

W and R

W.R & S.

For mark see *Crested China*, p. 297.

For mark see *Crested China*, p. 298.

Trademark used for a London wholesaler by Hewitt and Leadbeater, Willow Potteries, Longton. (Usual trademark Willow Art).

Trademark used by William Ritchie and Co. Ltd, 24, 26 and 28 Elder Street, Edinburgh. (Usual trademark Porcelle).

Seaside Souvenirs
Lighthouse, not named. 110mm.   3.00

Seaside Souvenirs
Whelk Shell. 100mm.   2.50

Animals
Cat, sitting, badge on chest.
  72mm.   6.50
Pig, standing. 85mm long.   8.75

Great War
Nurse. *A Friend in Need*.   25.75
Bell Tent. 74mm.   5.50

Great War
Soldier, with rifle, inscribed: *Our
  brave defender*. 132mm.   25.75
Battleship, impressed: *HMS
  Lion*. 140mm long.   13.00

Miscellaneous
Top Hat. 45mm.   2.50

Comic/Novelty
Billiken, not named. 73mm.   3.00

Transport
Car, open 4 seater. 114mm long.   21.75

Miscellanous
Hand holding a tulip. 80mm.   2.25

Wy Not? Crest China

For mark see *Crested China*, p. 298.
Mark can also be found as Wy Knot.

Trademark used for a wholesaler by Hewitt
and Leadbeater, Willow Potteries, Longton.
(Usual trademark Willow Art).

Ancient Artefacts
Loving Cup, 3 handles. 39mm.   2.25

Historical/Folklore
Bunyan's Chair. 90mm.   8.25
Bunyan's Cushion. 100mm long.   13.00
Burn's Chair, Dumfries. 83mm.   6.50
James Vth Chair at Stirling Castle,
  Model of. 102mm.   6.50
Mary Queen of Scots Chair,
  Edinburgh Castle Model of.
  75mm.   6.50
Sir Walter Scotts Chair, Abbotsford,
  Model of. 85mm.   6.50
Skull, inscribed: *A Prehistoric*
  Skull. No. 171. 60mm.   7.50

Traditional/National Souvenirs
Lancashire Clog, with yellow
  buckle. 88mm long.   5.25
Welsh Hat. 57mm.   3.00

Animals
Cat, sitting, blue bow. No. 62.
  2 sizes: 60mm.   7.50
          75mm.   8.50
Dog, sitting, badge on chest.
  80mm.   6.50
Dog, Collie, standing. 85mm.   8.25
Elephant, walking. 52mm.   6.50
Mouse (very fat, often described
  as a guinea pig). 62mm.   12.50

Great War
Nurse, inscribed: *A friend in need.*
  130mm.   25.75
Sailor, inscribed: *Our brave*
  defender, and carrying a flag on
  his chest instead of a crest. The
  flag transfer is inscribed: *Good*
  Luck. The boys in blue. 130mm.   37.50

Battleship, 4 funnels.
  127mm long.   30.00
Red Cross Van, red crosses on
  side. 84mm long.   17.50
Field Gun. 120mm long.   11.00
Field Gun with screen. 115mm.   13.00
Kit Bag. 74mm.   10.50
Tommy's Steel Helmet. 76mm long.   16.00

Comic/Novelty
Billiken. 70mm.   3.00

Miscellaneous
Book. 58mm.   3.00
Hand holding a tulip. 81mm.   2.25

Miniature Domestic
Cheese dish and cover. 50mm.   5.50

Unmarked Models

Many models found unmarked are recognisably pieces from the major firms which for some reason escaped from the pottery without the trademark. (Some, but by no means all, of these pieces can be substandard or seconds and collectors would rather have a marked model). Perfect models especially if they have no crest and are unglazed could well be travellers samples. These unmarked models of known origin are not listed below. (Many models in the original listings in earlier publications have turned out to be Savoy).

There are however quantities of unmarked crested china which cannot be attributed to any one manufacturer. This china could have been made by several firms known to have made crested wares but do not appear to have used a trademark. These firms include:

George Proctor and Co., High Street, Longton.
Barkers and Kent Ltd, The Foley Pottery. Fenton.
Biltons (1912) Ltd, London Road Works, Stoke-on-Trent.
C.J. Bisson and Co, 82 Liverpool Road, Stoke-on-Trent.

As these firms were earthenware manufacturers the models would tend to be reasonably heavy.

Many German firms also manufactured crested china for the English souvenir market and chose not to use a trademark, especially after the Great War. German wares tend to be somewhat greyer and of poorer quality than British made wares. These include:

Max Emanuel, The Mosanic Pottery, Mitterteich. (Usual trademark Mosanic).
Moschendorf, Hof, Bayern (Usual trademark PM and Rex).
Hutschenreuther, Probstzella, Thuringia (Trademark P).
Klösterle, Carlsbad (Usual trademark Union K).

However many of the models listed below are known to have been produced by Wilhelm Kutzscher and Co., Schwarzenberger, Porzellanfabrik, Schwarzenberg, Saxony, now in East Germany (Usual trademark, St George China, Impero and Princess).

Generally, pieces with neither factory mark nor inscription are less desirable than those which do and are worth slightly less. This is not as important with rare items or with medium range wares.

Values for pieces with firing defects and therefore not finished off, i.e. mis-shapen, having no crest, colouring, gilding or factory mark are about half to three-quarters of the full value.

Parian/Unglazed
St Pauls, stone coloured.
87mm long (Probably Savoy)　30.00

Ancient Artefacts
Winchester Bushel. 102mm dia.　5.75

Buildings – Coloured
Craigwell House, Bognor.
115mm long.　70.00
Dan Winter's Cottage, where the first Orange Lodge was formed in Co. Armagh, Ireland. A money box.
128mm long.　75.00
Old Falcon Tavern. Bidford-on-Avon. 115mm.　65.00
The Feathers Hotel Ludlow. 112mm.　65.00
Plas Newyd House, impressed: *The House of the Ladies of Llangollen.* 115mm long.　65.00
Pump room and baths, Trefriw Wells, plus long inscription.
95mm long.　70.00

Buildings – White
Archway, wooden door, large iron hinges, steps up to door.
105mm.　8.25
Beverly, North Bar. 90mm. (Kutzscher).　8.50
Birmingham Town Hall.
95mm long.　13.00
British Government Pavilion B.E.E. Wembley 1924–5. 60mm.　24.50
Guildford, The Castle. 100mm.　27.50
Mickelgate Bar, York. 98mm.　14.00
Windmill on stilts on square base, fixed sails, in form of scent bottle.
78mm.　13.00

Monuments

Ashington Boer War Memorial. 138mm.	13.00
Bradlaugh's Monument, North-ampton. 2 sizes: 110mm.	30.00
140mm.	30.00
Clock Tower, not named. 127mm.	00.00
Hall Cross, Doncaster. 185mm.	25.00
Larg's Tower, inscribed: Battle of Largs Memorial. 166mm.	14.00
The Metal Man, Tramore.	50.00
Pannells Memorial 165mm.	45.00
Swanage Globe, some colouring. 65mm.	9.50

Historical/Folklore

Bass Rock. In relief on square plaque. 125mm long.	20.00
Baby in wraps, perhaps Moses in bullrushes. 66mm long.	10.50
Burns Cottage, interior of, in relief on square plaque. 125mm long.	20.00
Bust of General Booth, can be found inscribed: Salvation Army. 75mm.	19.50
Charles Dickens, bust. 110mm.	16.00
Edwardian Lady carrying black cat and basket. 106mm.	24.50
Giant's Causeway, Wishing Chair. 105mm.	40.00
Jacobean Font at Newport I.W., Model of. 70mm.	7.50
John Bull. 75mm.	6.50
Knaresborough Dropping Well. 77mm.	16.50
Knight's Helmet and Visor, with reclining animal on top. 80mm.	17.50
Mary Bull, witch, holding black cat. 108mm	22.50
Sanctuary Chair, Beverley Minster. 68mm.	11.00
Scold's Bridle, bust of old woman wearing bridle, with story of gossiping women. Can be found coloured. 64mm.	21.75
Ulphus Horn, Original in York Minster, Model of. 110mm long.	12.50

Traditional/National Souvenirs

Bolton Trotter. 132mm long.	5.00
Bolton Trotters, two joined as a pair. 107mm long.	15.00

Cheddar Cheese, Model of, with inscription: This famous cheese has been made in and around cheddar for centuries, and to this day no country in the world has been able to equal it. 60mm dia.	7.00
Two lady grape treaders with skirts rolled up standing in barrel of grapes. 105mm	30.00
Jersey Milkmaid. 80mm.	23.00
Melton Mowbray Pie, A, with pastry rose and leaves. With verse. 55mm.	10.50
Plate o'Bolton Trotters, A. Three pigs' trotters on a plate.	11.00
Gretna Priest, inscribed: The famous Gretna Priest from the celebrated Blacksmiths shop, Gretna Green (Kutzscher). 118mm.	14.00
Dutch Girl, bust, flowers in relief on base.	14.00
Welsh Lady in chair. 100mm.	10.50

Seaside Souvenirs

Beachy Head Lighthouse. 124mm.	3.50
Cabin Trunk. 60mm long.	4.50
Un-named rock, original could be off the Devon coast. 40mm.	12.50
Mermaid with baby. 84mm.	15.25
Waves, group of. 95mm long.	8.00

Countryside

Axe in tree stump. 75mm.	10.50
Four bar gate with stile and mile-stone. 96mm long.	4.00
Tree Trunk spill holder, with 2 sheep in front. 50mm.	13.00
Tree Trunk spill holder, with 2 sheep and lady with sickle. 75mm.	13.50

Animals

Bear, playing a mandolin. (German).	9.50
Butterfly with open wings. 90mm long.	14.50
Camel kneeling on rectangular base. 122mm long.	13.00
Cat, in holdall, can be inscribed: Good Morning. 55mm long.	22.50
Cat, with toothache, bandage round jaw. 95mm.	16.00
Cat, singing from long sheet of music. 65mm.	24.50

Cat, singing, holding book. 74mm.	22.50
Cat, Egyptian, with long ears. 90mm long.	26.00
Cat, long necked. 115mm.	4.50
Cat, Posy Bowl.	9.00
Cat and Rabbit, in high boot, inscribed: *A jolly place for a jolly couple*. 83mm.	16.00
Cat, furry kitten with open mouth. 90mm.	7.50
Cat and kitten either side of posy bowl. 105mm long.	8.25
Cat standing drinking from jug, inscribed: *Mothers favourite*. 70mm long (Kutzscher).	10.50
Cat, Manx, standing drinking from jug, sometimes inscribed: *Mothers favourite*. 70mm long. (Kutzscher).	12.00
Cat with mouse. 77mm.	24.50
Cat, standing, hands on hips, tail forming third leg. 86mm.	15.50
Cat scent bottle, two-piece. 90mm.	16.00
Cow lying down, with gold horns, inscribed: *The Jersey Cow*. 108mm long.	9.50
Cow standing, gold horns, inscribed: *The Jersey Cow*. 108mm long. (Pair with above).	7.50
Cow Cream Jug. 125mm long.	13.50
Dinosaur jug. 85mm long.	2.50
Dog wearing dress and overcoat, green colouring on hat. 92mm.	27.50
Dogs, two Bulldogs, one seated and the other two standing. 57mm (Kutzscher).	18.50
Dogs, two Pharos Hounds, on oblong base. 76mm long. (Kutzscher).	24.50
Dog, Pug, lying down. 96mm long.	9.25
Dog, Spaniel with droopy ears. 60mm.	7.50
Dog, King Charles spaniel, wearing ribbon, lying on cushion. 82mm long.	12.00
Dog, sitting Labrador puppy. 70mm.	9.50
Donkey, inscribed: *A Malvern Donkey*. 95mm long.	9.50
Elephant, circus, with front feet on stool. 102mm.	26.50
Elephant heads, 2 on vase as handles. 76mm.	4.00

Two Elephants on toboggan going downhill. 70mm.	24.50
Elephant with one foot on ball. 57mm.	15.00
Elephant with hunter and two Indian bearers. 95mm.	20.00
Elephant, kneeling. 85mm long.	8.75
Giant Frog with huge open mouth, sitting. 80mm (rare).	35.00
Fish with open back for pin cushion. 118mm long.	4.50
Kangaroo. 95mm.	30.00
Lion, full mane. 145mm.	16.50
Lion, on rectangular base. 116mm long.	8.50
Lion wearing coat and trousers, holding telescope. 132mm.	29.50
Pig, wearing barristers wig and glasses, muzzle pink. (*Gemma*). 85mm.	55.00
Pig, sitting, wearing monocle and bowler hat, muzzle pink. (*Gemma*). 82mm.	55.00
Piglet, gold in colour, clambering up the side of a pot. 70mm.	8.50
Rabbits, 2 on sledge or slope. (Futzscher).	18.50
Rhino, grotesque. 155mm long.	30.00
Squirrel, large, in shape of milk jug. 90mm.	9.50
Tortoise pin box and lid. 80mm long.	3.50

Birds

Blackbird on perch. 118mm long.	8.75
Duck ashtray, some colouring. 95mm long.	4.00
Duck pepper pot. 77mm.	5.50
Ducks, 2 with coloured beaks and feet on an oval stand. 185mm (an enormous model).	40.00
Duckling, airing wings. 69mm.	8.25
Duck, circular base, some colouring. 95mm.	14.00
Eagle on rock, colour on beak and feet.. 130mm.	13.50
Fledgling birds, 2 sitting on base sharing one open beak.	6.50
Hen and Cockerel on circular base. 82mm.	14.00
Kingfisher. 60mm.	7.50
Parakeet, fully coloured on plinth. 215mm.	25.00
Pelican. 100mm.	12.00
Stork, nesting beside chimney pot with baby in nest. 100mm.	21.75

Unmarked. Housekeeper

Unmarked. Burns Statue

Unmarked. Statue of Baron Burton

Unmarked. Tom O'Shanter

Unmarked. The Famous Gretna Priest

Unmarked. Lady carrying case and bottle

Unmarked. John Bull

Unmarked. Dutch Girl bust

Unmarked. Bust Welsh Lady

Unmarked. The Metal Man Tramore

Unmarked. Man with earphones and beer mug

Unmarked. Cherub in window, spill holder

Swan, head back. 72mm.   4.50
Wagtail on rock, black edging to
wings. 109mm.   8.75

Great War
Jack Ashore, boy sailor on round
base, coloured face. 153mm.   37.00
Tank, forward guns only.
110mm long.   8.75
Llandudno War Memorial, not
named. 183mm.   35.00

Home Nostalgic
Armchair, padded and three-
legged. 66mm.   9.50
Corner seat. 80mm.   6.50
Armchair, padded with blue
forget-me-nots around back
rest. 62mm.   9.50
Armchair, upholstered. 85mm.   12.50
Folded Blankets. 56mm long.   27.50
Girl in nightdress standing on
square base inscribed: *Morning*.
125mm.   19.50
Hip bath. 90mm long.   4.00
Housemaid, standing figure,
hands on hips, keys at waist,
mob cap. 118mm.   20.00
Ring. 64mm dia.   6.50
Pair of Staffordshire Flatbacks
comprising sheep and
shepherds. 75mm. Each.   9.50
Umbrella. 38mm.   8.50
Wall plaque, buildings and trees
scene. 127mm.   25.00

Comic/Novelty
Artist's easel on stand.   1.75
Boy bathing dog in tub.   25.00
Cook, holding wooden spoon.
115mm.   22.50
Girl, sitting on horse by tree
trunk. 110mm.   30.00
Monk, carrying lantern and
basket. 135mm.   17.00
Pillar Box, miniature. 58mm.   13.00
Tomato Pepper Pot on leaf base.
42mm.   6.50
Vaulting Horse, square looking
bulldog with legs joined by
poles. 80mm long.
(Kutzscher).   7.50
Washer Woman, holding a basket
of washing. 118mm.   25.00
Womans Head on Turtle trinket
box. 80mm long.   5.50

Womans Head tea pot, some
colouring. 66mm.   9.00
Woman carrying case and bottle.   19.50

Cartoon/Comedy Characters
Crested faced man white or fully
coloured. (*Carlton*). 80mm.   20.00
                        coloured   30.00
Felix, standing cat on oval base,
no colouring. 87mm. (This is a
really nice Felix.)   65.00
The Sprinter. Comic figure with
cork-screw legs – wound up for
action. 100mm.   75.00
Sunny Jim, bust. 85mm.   19.50

Alcohol
Bust of man holding beer mug
and wearing ear phones.
60mm.   8.00

Sport
Footballer, with ball, no
colouring. 130mm.   62.50
(Savoy range advertised a
coloured version of this model)
Golf ball, pepper pot on circular
base. 50mm dia.   3.00
Rugby ball. 74mm long.   6.00
Tennis Court Liner in form of a
wheelbarrow. 90mm long.   13.00

Musical Instruments
Drum set with cymbals and
drumsticks. 65mm.   8.50
Harp. 93mm.   6.00

Transport
Aeroplane with pilot, size varies
usually 100mm long. (Almost
certainly German.)   15.00
Bust of Bleriot, inscribed: *Messieur
Bleriot. 1st man to cross the
Channel in an Aeroplane. June
25th 1909*. 90mm.   24.50
Car, vintage, with open top and
hood folded back. 90mm long.   20.50
Car with chauffeur. 85mm long.   20.50
Hot Air Balloon, square basket.
65mm. (Kutzscher).   7.50
Sleigh, ornate. 105mm long.   30.00

Modern Equipment
Cash Register. 44mm.   8.25
Typewriter inscribed: *My little
typewriter*. 44mm.   7.50

Miscellaneous

Boater, straw, unglazed. 107mm long.	8.75
Clog, Lancs. 112mm long.	6.00
Ladies heeled shoe, lace frill. 107mm.	7.00
Ladies shoe, gilded heel and toe. 150mm long.	8.50
Ladies shoe, frilled tongue and edge. 145mm long.	12.50
Ladies boot, pierced eyelets. 83mm.	14.50
Top Hat (very wide brim).	3.00
Top Hat, with antlers across brim. 65mm.	5.00
Top Hat, with umbrella across brim. 65mm.	7.50
Peaked Cap. 126mm across.	10.50
Gourd. 70mm.	9.25
Knight's helmet forming pin box. 80mm.	16.00
Loaf of Bread.	10.50
Loving Cups, 3 handled, with lithoplanes of King Edward, Queen Alexandra, King George or Queen Mary. 39mm.	22.50
Lithophane match holder/striker with lithophane of King Edward VII. 43mm.	16.00
Shoe, walking with pierced eyelets. 94mm long.	7.00
Spade trump. 60mm.	3.00
Trilby. 96mm long.	10.50

Miniature Domestic

Dressing table set comprising: two scent bottles and stoppers, three rouge pots and lids, ring tree, all on tray. 155mm long.	Set 25.00
Miniature coffee set comprising: coffee pot and lid, sugar basin, milk jug, two cups and saucers on rectangular tray. 155mm long.	25.00
Miniature tea set comprising: teapot and lid, sugar basin, milk jug, two cups and saucers on rectangular or circular tray.	25.00

Country of origin

For marks see *Crested China*, p. 299.

British Manufacture

Some models are most often found with a simple British Manufacture stamp, than marked. These include arks, anvils, cottages, footballs, grandfather clocks, lighthouses, petrol cans, parian straw boaters, pillar boxes, propellers, puzzle jugs and top hats. These all often have transfer views rather than crests. They were probably manufactured by the British firms listed in the unmarked section.

The pieces listed below are thought to have been produced in Great Britain.

Historical/Folklore

Mary Queen of Scots' chair. 74mm.	3.50
Ye Olde Chertsey Bell, with coloured wooden clapper. 88mm.	6.00

Traditional/National Souvenirs

Cheddar Cheese, inscribed: *Prime Cheddar Cheese*, coloured yellow. 52mm.	5.00
Cheddar Cheese, model of, with verse and flowers. 60mm dia.	5.00

Seaside Souvenirs

Whelk Shell. 84mm long.	2.25

Animals

Bull's head cream jug. 78mm.	5.00
Fish, gilded tail. 112mm long.	2.50

Home/Nostalgic

Basket with coloured fruit. 85mm.	10.50

Comic/Novelty

Jack in the box with open lid. 92mm.	7.50

Transport

Petrol can impressed: *Motor Spirit*. 67mm.	8.25

Miniature Domestic

Kettle and lid. 80mm.	3.00
Cheese dish and cover.	
64mm long.	4.00
Cheese dish and fixed cover.	
64mm long.	4.00
Shaving Mug. 37mm.	3.50
Shaving Mug, angular handle.	
44mm.	4.00

German or Foreign

For marks see *Crested China*, p. 304.

Austria and Czechoslovakia can also be found.

These marks were used by the German firms listed under unmarked wares. The models with impressed numbers would appear to be made by Max Emanuel. (Usual trademark Mosanic), as he was the only German manufacturer to be known to use stock numbers and registered numbers. Foreign, Austria or Czechoslovakia would be used after the Great War. Nearly all of these models can be found in various shades of lustre, mostly yellow/brown.

Ancient Artefacts

Southwold Jug. No.4687. 40mm	
(lustre).	1.25

Buildings

Bandstand.	
2 sizes: No.3921. 75mm.	7.50
No.3972. 90mm (lustre).	8.75
Birmingham Town Hall.	12.50
Blackpool Tower. No.3484.	
130mm.	2.50
Clock Tower. No.7727.	6.00
Cottage. No.7208. 65mm long	
(lustre).	4.50
Dunster Yarn Market. 24932.	
95mm long.	14.50
Margate Clock Tower. No.3797.	
153mm.	6.50
Scarborough Clock Tower.	
No.3560. 138mm.	7.50

St. Winifred's Well, Holywell.	
60mm.	16.00
Windmill, fixed sails. No.7223.	
90mm.	10.50
Windmill, Fixed sails, with hoist	
and rope. 110mm.	10.50

Monuments

Banbury Cross.	
2 sizes: No.6895. 135mm.	7.50
No.3295. 150mm.	8.50

Historical/Folklore

Cinderella's Coach. 96mm.	24.50

Traditional/National Souvenirs

Blackpool Big wheel.	
2 sizes: No.7534. 80mm.	6.50
No.3561. 90mm.	7.50
Coronation Chair. 97mm.	3.00
Mussolini bust in uniform on	
rectangular base. 130mm. Rare.	50.00

Seaside Souvenirs

Bathing Hut with girl peeping	
out. No.4421. 104mm.	6.50
Bathing Hut with bather sitting	
outside. No.5668. 70mm long.	7.50
Canoe, flag at back and girl inside.	
No.5174. 140mm long.	7.50
Canoe, Indian. 104mm long.	3.00
Liner on back of oval ashtray.	
80mm.	6.50
Rowing Boat with rudder.	
130mm long.	7.00
Yacht. No.3482. 103mm.	4.00
Yacht with waves. No.4422.	
105mm.	5.00
Yacht, full sail on waves. no.4438.	
85mm.	8.75
Fisherman on Plinth. No.3562.	7.50
Fisherman with rope. No.6528.	
118mm.	7.50
Lifeboatman. No.6528. 115mm.	7.50
Lifeboatman, statue.	
2 sizes: No.3562. 128mm.	5.00
No.7200. 122mm.	5.00
Lighthouse. No.11223. 110mm.	2.00
Beachy Head Lighthouse, black	
band. 100mm.	3.00
Corbiere Jersey Lighthouse.	
No.751. 100mm.	7.50
Shell dish, black edging. 145mm	
long.	2.50

Boy on Lobster. No.4426. 100mm
long.   16.00
Boy in trunks on diving board.
No.5799. 110mm long.   12.00
Girl in rubber duck in sea.
No.5179. 85mm.   8.25
Girl wearing a hat on a donkey.
No.4170. 110mm.   10.50
Girl riding a donkey. No.4840.
115mm.   10.50
Boy riding a donkey. No.4840.
115mm. Pair with above.   10.50
Mermaid on a shell. No. 4430.
100mm long.   14.50

**For Bathing Beauties see under
Comic/Novelty.**

Countryside
Milkmaid holding churn. 124mm.   16.00
Shepherd and Lamb by hollow
Tree Trunk. No.846A. 75mm.   17.50
Shepherdess and Lamb by
Hollow Tree Trunk No.846B.
75mm.   17.50
Stile with hearts and initials.   4.00
Stile with milestone.   4.00

Animals
Cat with arched back. No.8922.
65mm.   7.00
Cat in bandages, sitting.   16.00
Cat, black on ashtray. No.5002.
92mm long.   13.00
Cat, Cheshire. No.6622. 70mm.   5.50
Cat, standing on hind legs,
comical. 85mm.   14.50
Cat on Trinket Box. No.5678.
88mm long.   12.00
Cats, one large and one small
either side of a cauldron.
105mm long.   16.50
Cat with paw or rat.   18.50
Dog, pointer with metal coiled
tail. 135mm long.   15.00
Dog in bandages, sitting.   16.00
Dog, Scottie, wearing Tam
O'Shanter. 74mm.   4.00
Dog, Terrier, standing. No.6630.
74mm long.   6.50
Dog's head spill holder. 46mm.   5.00
Dog with dead hare in mouth, on
rocky base, plaque. 140mm.   18.50
Donkey, ears laid back, standing
on oval base, in harness. 88mm
long.   9.50

Donkey and tree stump.
No.3486. 90mm.   9.50
Donkey, standing inscribed
Carisbrooke Donkey. 88mm long. 19.50
Fox, standing, wearing dress.
85mm.   15.25
Frog on shell, the frog is usually
green on a lustre shell.
No.4450. 110mm long.   4.50
Horse's head and horse shoe,
ashtray. No.3925. 44mm.   1.75
Jaguar, open mouthed,
crouching on oval base.
No.934. 125mm long.   40.00
Lion on base. No.4166. 90mm
long.   7.50
Lion on a plinth. No. 4155.
115mm.   7.50
Pig, standing. No. 3566. 95mm.   7.50
Pig, standing, posy holder. Pink.
135mm long.   9.00
Polar Bear. No.4439. 90mm.   30.00
Rabbit in clothes on slope.
90mm long (Kutzscher).   21.75
Seal on rectangular base.
127mm long.   5.50
Shetland Pony. 100mm long.   10.50
Snail No.5178. 112mm long.   7.00
Tortoise Trinket box. No.6625.
85mm long.   4.50

Birds
Chickens, two and flowers on
vase. No.5806. 120mm.   4.00
Cock and two chickens on slope.
No.5807. Some colouring.
95mm long.   13.50
Fledgling, blue with orange beak
on ashtray base.   10.00
Owl on three books. No.937.
100mm.   8.25
Parrot. No.6626. 75mm long.   5.50
Penguin Pepper pot. 82mm.   5.50
Seagull Posy Holder. No.4445.
120mm long.   4.00
Swan Posy Bowl, yellow beak.
93mm.   2.25
Swan Posy Bowl. No.3486. 81mm
long.   2.25

Great War
Monoplane with pilot. No.7207.
100mm long.   10.50
Zeppelin posy holder. 130mm
long.   8.25

French Soldier's Cap. 60mm. long.	20.00
Cenotaph with inscription.	
2 sizes: No.6725. 110mm.	3.00
No.6726. 148mm.	3.50
Clacton on Sea War Memorial. No.6999.	13.00
Great Yarmouth War Memorial. 110mm.	19.50
Matlock Bath War Memorial	
3 sizes: No.6655. 120mm.	13.50
No.4194. 140mm.	15.00
No.3924. 160mm.	16.00
Southsea War Memorial. No.6660. 120mm.	14.50
Worthing War Memorial. No details of size.	12.50

Home/Nostalgic

Armchair, upholstered. 74mm.	4.00
Box Iron. No.5671. 90mm long.	6.50
Bucket. No.5185. 62mm.	2.50
Carpet bag, open top. 86mm.	4.50
Coffee table, central stem. 60mm.	2.00
Chair, ornate. No.3567. 105mm.	10.50
Fireplace, *There's No Place Like Home*. No.2275. 65mm.	8.25
Grandfather Clock, inscription. *Make use of Time*. No.3401. 140mm.	8.50
Policeman's lamp. 70mm.	3.00
Mantle Clock. No.4810. 100mm long.	4.00
Milk Pail. No.5185.	2.00
Pedestal. No.6905. 83mm.	1.75
Post Box. No.6496. 75mm.	4.50
Post Box, oval, inscribed: *Letters*. 88mm.	8.75
Sack of Meal. No.1645. 80mm.	8.00
Sewing machine, treadle. 72mm.	8.50
Sofa, ornate. 70mm. lag.	6.00
Stool, blue lustre. 53mm.	3.50

Comic/Novelty

Boy Scout and dog. 100mm.	9.50
Bride and groom in large shell. No.5795. 105mm.	10.50
Boy or cherub with wings (Peter Pan?) standing inside window on spill holder. 90mm.	9.50
Child on swing (probably boy). No.5809. Some colouring. 110mm.	14.50

Boy, Tennis player match holder. 80mm.	16.00
Girl Guide with cat. 103mm.	9.50
Girl, Tennis player match holder. 80mm (pair).	16.00
Boy with flag. No.5798.	9.50
Girl with flag. No.5798 (pair).	
Boy and girl on a donkey.	9.50
Boy dressed as Bell Hop with Globe. No.5197. 98mm.	8.75
Girl dressed as Bell Hop with Globe. No. 5194. 98mm (pair).	8.75
Girl dressed as Bell Hop sitting on suitcase. No.5804. 75mm long.	8.75
Girl with pigtails sitting on side of oval wooden tub, holding two kittens. Cat on other side. 85mm.	12.00
Dutch boy with wheel barrow. No.5803. 95mm.	14.00
Dutch girl with wheel barrow. No.5803. 95mm (pair).	14.00
Dutch girl, fully coloured. No.7062.	35.00
Two children skiing on downhill slope. No.5805. 95mm.	17.50
Two children on sledge on slope. No.5802. 95mm.	17.50
Two children with a wheel barrow on slope. No.6381. 90mm.	14.50
Pierrot standing by open bag. No.3315. 90mm.	8.50
Pierette standing by open bag. No.3315. 90mm (pair).	8.50
Pierrot on Trinket box. No.3498. 110mm.	8.50
Sultan sitting on bowl. No.4834. 100mm.	9.25

Twenties Flappers

Found decorated in two styles – white ware with clothes edged in rust brown and the face and hair coloured, or yellow/rust or other shaded lustre. Value the same.

Bathing Beauty on ashtray. No.4424. 95mm long (lustre).	8.50
Bathing Beauty on square ashtray. 110mm long.	8.50
Bathing Beauty on Oyster ashtray. No.4172. 75mm (lustre).	8.50

Bathing Beauty on lustre shell,
figure coloured. No.4174.
70mm. 8.50
Bathing Beauty on shell. No.4173.
90mm long. (lustre). 8.50
Bathing Beauty on slope.
No.5801. 102mm. (lustre). 8.50
Bathing Beauty on Turtle.
No.4451. 100mm long (lustre). 8.50
Flapper on stool with Scottie
dog. No.5672. 108mm (lustre). 11.00
Girl in Basket chair, 115mm.
(White ware and lustre). 12.50
Girl in Basket Chair. No.8902.
74mm (lustre). 14.50
Girl with parasol in Basket chair.
2 sizes:
No.4165. 120mm. 17.50
No.4074. 104mm (white ware) 17.50
Girl in slacks on Beach Ball.
115mm. 12.50
Girl in sleeveless dress on sea
shell. No.4430. 85mm (lustre). 7.50

Alcohol
Toby Jug. No.6608. 63mm. 5.50

Musical Instruments
Grand Piano. No.4168.
85mm long. 7.50
Horn, gramophone, beige
coloured with lucky white
heather. 42mm. 11.25

Transport
Girl in Car. No.5774. 100mm long
(lustre) 10.50
Hot Air Balloon, square basket.
90mm. 7.50
Motor Car. No.3917. 75mm long
(lustre). 9.50
Motor car, open tourer.
92mm long. 9.50
Passenger Plane, Monoplane.
85mm wide. 12.50
Petrol can, impressed: *Motor
Spirit*. No.7214. 67mm. 6.50

'Modern' Equipment
Binoculars. No.5187. 75mm. 5.00
Camera. No.5182. 75mm. 8.75

Flat Iron. 4.00
Gramophone. No.3563. 70mm
long. 10.50
Treadle sewing machine.
No.5439. 73mm. 7.50

Miscellaneous
Ankle boot, open top. 8.75
Artist's easel and brushes.
No.4841. 65mm. 1.75
Club, card suit indicator. no.3919.
80mm. 6.00
Dutch clog. No.2079. 70mm long. 4.00
Ladies slipper. 150mm long. 8.50

Miniature Domestic
Coffee Pot. 65mm. 3.00
Cheese dish and cover, flat
sloping top. 70mm long. 6.50
Shaving Mug. 40mm. 3.50
Teapot, wide base. 45mm. 7.50

Saxony

See *Crested China*, p. 304 for mark.

Country of origin mark used by Wilhelm Kutzscher and Co, Schwarzenberger Porzellanfabrik, Schwarzenberg, Saxony.

Ancient Artefacts

Old Roman Salt Pot, 14th century, found near Carlisle by Permission of Tullie House Committee. 63mm.	2.25
Puzzle Jug with verse. 66mm.	3.50

Buildings

Hall Cross, Doncaster. 158mm.	27.50
Iona Cathedral. 50mm.	20.00
Skegness Clock Tower. 123mm.	7.50
Weymouth Clock Tower. 124mm.	8.50

Monuments

Captain Scott Memorial. 148mm.	17.50

Traditional/National Souvenirs

Welsh Hat, with longest place name round brim. 44mm.	5.50
Welsh Lady, seated. 102mm.	20.00

Seaside Souvenirs

Beach chair, whicker. 70mm.	12.50
Fisherwoman with bundle. 117mm.	17.50
Needles Lighthouse. 125mm.	19.50

Animals

Cat holding music. 66mm.	22.50
Cat, singing, holding book. 74mm.	22.50
Cat with mandolin. 74mm.	22.50
Cat in Gladstone bag, right paw raised. Can be found inscribed: *Good Morning*. 55mm long.	22.50
Cat in Gladstone bag, left paw raised. 55mm long (pair)	2.50
Frog under tulip, candleholder. 100mm.	13.50
Hare, sitting. 95mm long	8.50

Three puppies in a basket. 65mm.	17.50
Two puppies and a kitten in a basket. 65mm.	17.50
Tortoise dish with shell lid. 75mm long.	6.50

Birds

Duck, airing wings, some colouring. 88mm.	8.50
Duck on round base, brown beak and feet. 98mm.	6.50
Seagull on rock, black edging on wings. 109mm.	12.50
Seagull on rock, huge spread wings. 130mm.	14.50
Seagull on posy holder. 114mm.	5.00
Egg, imprisoning a rabbit (he looks through barred window). A large hare in tail coat standing beside it. 67mm.	27.50
Swan, open wings. 80mm.	2.25

Great War

Clacton War Memorial, with inscription. 140mm.	13.00
Folkestone War Memorial. 160mm.	16.50
Great Yarmouth War Memorial. 130mm.	16.50
Matlock Bath War Memorial. 150mm.	15.00

Musical Instruments

Harp with wide base. 90mm.	4.50

Transport

Steam Locomotive, inscribed: R.H. and D.R. (Romney Hythe and Dymchurch Railway). 115mm long.	47.50

'Modern' Equipment

Gramophone. 60mm.	12.50

Miscellaneous

Ladies shoe. 115mm long.	13.00

CRESTED CHINA
By Sandy Andrews

This title, first published in 1980, is the first serious and comprehensive reference work ever attempted – although written in a readable light-hearted style.

A large, lavish production with hard cover and coloured dust jacket, it contains 304 pages. Over 750 illustrations – 90 in full colour – are included, depicting over 1000 pieces from all factories and showing items from every possible theme with special emphasis on animals, buildings and Great War crested china.

Particulars of well over 4000 pieces are given with their dimensions and relevant details where thought to be of interest. This is the first attempt at a complete listing of all the pieces made by every factory. The history of and all known information about over 220 factories is provided, and a mass of other exciting facts answer all the questions that collectors have been asking for years such as 'Why does the same piece appear with a different factory mark?' 'Why to some pieces have no crest, factory mark or name?' 'Why are some pieces numbered?'; etc. etc.

In addition to all this information, over 270 line drawings of factory marks are shown to aid identification, the majority of which are not in any of the usual 'mark books'.

The story of crested china, how the trade expanded, and some of the colourful characters involved in it is told for the first time. A chapter on the W.H. Goss factory with illustrations of pieces from all periods of that factory's life, throws important new light on the later period and what happened during the Goss England era about which there is often confusion.

The book is not a price guide, although indications of rare items are given, but a lasting, profusely illustrated reference work which is recommended to all crested china enthusiasts.

303mm × 220mm. 304 pages. Cased. 753 illustrations. £14.95

Available from bookshops everywhere or by post direct from Milestone Publications. Descriptive leaflets on this and all other titles connected with Goss and crested china sent on request.

The 1984 Price Guide to Goss China
Nicholas Pine

This is a completely revised edition of the original price guide, published in 1981.

This latest guide has much fresh information including numerous new pieces, many announced for the first time. A well illustrated domestic section clarifies this area of the factory's wares and improved layout and explanations make this chapter easier to understand and pieces easier to locate.

The dimensions of every piece are now given and the models section contains the correct matching arms for each piece – all separately priced. Prices have moved considerably since the publication of the earlier guide, a few down but most up – some as much as 200–500%. The very latest revised prices are given right through the book which is also a now virtually complete descriptive listing of every piece of Goss ever produced.

The guide is the standard work on Goss china and is used by the leading dealers and auctioneers.

The prices given form the base prices of pieces to which the values for particular arms or decorations should be added.

The work is well illustrated and is superbly bound in hardcover with colour jacket. It is a pair with **The 1985 Price Guide to Crested China** and the sequel to **Goss China Arms Decorations and Their Values** by the same author.

The Major Features of the 1984 Price Guide to Goss China include:

- Every chapter revised and updated incorporating hundreds of vital amendments.
- 1100 illustrations – a 40% increase including many rare items shown for the first time.
- Every model now illustrated – even the rare Haamoga Amaui from Tonga.

- Goss England Chapter radically revised with over 50 new pieces listed and a further 80+ photographs including 30 of Flower Girls alone.
- Domestic Ware chapter re-designed and better laid out with more illustrations.
- Every correct matching arms recorded and priced.
- Dimensions given in virtually every case.
- Over 100 new pieces listed.
- A complete chapter on factory marks with 24 photographs encompassing every known mark – with dates.
- An informative history of W.H. Goss and Goss China containing really exciting new information, some of which will surprise you!
- Additional chapters on Goss Postcards, Goss Cabinets, The Goss Records and The League of Goss Collectors.

155mm × 214mm. 1100 Illustrations. 256pp. 903852 41 1

Goss China Arms, Decorations and their Values
Nicholas Pine

Goss China collecting was a craze during late Victorian and Edwardian times. Tens of thousands of pieces of Goss Heraldic Porcelain were sold throughout the country as souvenirs to bring home for the family what-not or mantlepiece. This fascinating book, written by the leading author-ity on the subject, lists, describes and values all the different coats-of-arms and decorations which appear on Goss models – over 7000 of them.

A fully revised and updated version of the original book, first published in 1978, this new edition includes over 400 new additions and countless detail improvements, amendments and corrections, making it a truly definitive listing of virtually every known decoration.

In addition, up-to-date market values are given throughout the book showing the premium to be added to a piece for a crest or decoration.

Its 13 chapters include: U.K. and overseas arms, Royal, Nobility, Educa-tional, Ecclesiastical, Commemorative, Transfer printed, Regimental, Flora & Fauna, Flags, Welsh, Masonic and late decorations. These are further sub-divided into 55 easy-to-use sections – **With prices.**

The book contains 415 illustrations in 120 packed pages and is sewn and strongly case bound with a full colour jacket.

The book has been designed for use in conjunction with **The Price Guide to Goss China** by the same author. Collectors and dealers who possess a copy of the price guide are strongly advised to acquire this new book so that accurate up-to-date values may be obtained for each piece, for, as often as not, the decoration on a particular piece is worth much more than the piece itself.

245mm × 213mm. 120 pages. 415 illustrations. £9.95.

Goss & Crested China Ltd. are the leading dealers in Heraldic China

We have been buying and selling for over fifteen years and our experienced staff led by Nicholas Pine will be able to answer your questions and assist you whether you are a novice or an experienced collector.

We have a constantly changing attractively priced stock of some 5000 pieces at our Horndean showrooms including Goss cottages, fonts, crosses, shoes, lighthouses, models etc. and the full range of crested ware including military, animals, buildings etc. covering all the other manufacturers.

Visitors are welcome to call during business hours of 9.00–5.30 any day except Sunday. Those travelling long distances are advised to telephone for an appointment so that they may be sure to receive personal attention upon arrival.

Most of our business is by mail order and we publish **Goss & Crested China**, a monthly 24–28 page illustrated catalogue containing hundreds of pieces for sale from every theme and in every price range. The catalogue is available by annual subscription; please send for details.

In addition, if you specialise, we will be pleased to offer you particular pieces or crests from time to time as suitable items become available. Please let us know your wants as with our ever changing stock we will probably have something to suit.

Our service is personal and friendly and all orders and correspondence are dealt with by return. You will find us fair and straightforward to deal with, as we really care about crested china and we hope that this is reflected in our service.

Finally, we are just as keen to buy as we are to sell and offers of individual items or whole collections are always welcome. These will be dealt with by return and the very highest offers will be made.

Milestone Publications
Goss & Crested China Ltd.
62 Murray Road,
Horndean,
Hampshire
PO8 9JL.
Telephone: Horndean (0705) 597440

Other titles available from
Milestone Publications

Please send for full catalogue

Crested China. The History of Heraldic Souvenir Ware
Sandy Andrews

The 1984 Price Guide to Goss China
Nicholas Pine

Goss China: Arms Decorations and their values (1982)
Nicholas Pine

Take Me Back To Dear Old Blighty
The Great War through the eyes of the Heraldic China Manufacturers
Robert Southall

Goss and Other Crested China
Nicholas Pine

Arcadian Arms China Catalogue (reprinted)

The Goss Record 8th Edition (1914) (reprinted)

The Goss Record War Edition (1916) (reprinted)

Goss for Collectors – The Literature
John Magee

Let's Collect Goss China
Alf Hedges

A Handbook of Goss China
John Galpin

Goss & Crested China. Illustrated monthly catalogues. Available by Annual Subscription. Details upon request.